The Attributes of God

The Attributes
of God

Arthur W. Pink

BAKER BOOK HOUSE
Grand Rapids, Michigan 49516

Copyright © 1975 by Baker Books
a division of Baker Book House Company
P.O. Box 6287, Grand Rapids, MI 49516-6287

ISBN: 0-8010-6989-0

Twenty-ninth printing, June 1998

Printed in the United States of America

For information about academic books, resources for
Christian leaders, and all new releases available from
Baker Book House, visit our web site:
http://www.bakerbooks.com/

CONTENTS

PREFACE

"Acquaint now thyself with Him, and be at peace: thereby good shall come unto thee" (Job 22:21). "Thus saith the Lord, Let not the wise man glory in his wisdom, neither let the mighty glory in his might, let not the rich glory in his riches: But let him that glorieth glory in this, that he understandeth, and *knoweth Me,* that I am the Lord" (Jer. 9:23, 24). A spiritual and saving knowledge of God is the greatest need of every human creature.

The foundation of all true knowledge of God must be a clear mental apprehension of His perfections as revealed in Holy Scripture. An unknown God can neither be trusted, served, nor worshipped. In this book an effort has been made to set forth some of the principal perfections of the Divine character. If the reader is to truly profit from his perusal of the pages that follow, he needs to definitely and earnestly beseech God to bless them to him, to *apply* His Truth to the conscience and heart, so that his life will be transformed thereby.

Something more than a theoretical knowledge of God is needed by us. God is only truly *known* in the soul as we yield ourselves to Him, submit to His authority, and regulate all the details of our lives by His holy precepts and commandments. "Then shall we know, if we follow on (in the path of obedience) to *know* the Lord" (Hosea 6:3). "If any man will *do His will,* he shall know" (John 7:17). "The people that do *know* their God shall be strong" (Dan. 11:32).

—ARTHUR W. PINK

1

THE SOLITARINESS OF GOD

The title of this article is perhaps not sufficiently explicit to indicate its theme. This is partly due to the fact that so few today are accustomed to meditate upon the personal perfections of God. Comparatively few of those who occasionally read the Bible are aware of the awe-inspiring and worship-provoking grandeur of the Divine character. That God is great in wisdom, wondrous in power, yet full of mercy, is assumed by many to be almost common knowledge; but, to entertain anything approaching an adequate conception of His being, His nature, His attributes, as these are revealed in Holy Scripture, is something which very, very few people in these degenerate times have attained unto. God is solitary in His excellency. "Who is like unto Thee, O Lord, among the gods? Who is like Thee, glorious in holiness, fearful in praises, doing wonders?" (Ex. 15:11).

"In the beginning, God" (Gen. 1:1). There was a time, if "time" it could be called, when God, in the unity of His nature (though subsisting equally in three Divine Persons), dwelt all alone. "In the beginning, God." There was no heaven, where His glory is now particularly manifested. There was no earth to engage His attention. There were no angels to hymn His praises; no universe to be upheld by the word of His power. There was nothing, no one, but God; and *that,* not for a day, a year, or an age, but "from everlasting." During a past eternity, God was alone: self-contained, self-sufficient, self-satisfied; in need of nothing. Had a universe, had angels, had human beings been necessary to Him in any way, they also had been called into existence from all eternity. The creating of them when He did, added nothing to God essentially. He changes not (Mal. 3:6), therefore His essential glory can be neither augmented nor diminished.

God was under no constraint, no obligation, no necessity to

create. That He chose to do so was purely a sovereign act on His part, caused by nothing outside Himself, determined by nothing but His own mere good pleasure; for He "worketh all things after the counsel of His own will" (Eph. 1:11). That He did create was simply for His *manifestative* glory. Do some of our readers imagine that we have gone beyond what Scripture warrants? Then our appeal shall be to the Law and the Testimony: "Stand up and bless the Lord your God forever and ever: and blessed be Thy glorious name, which is exalted *above all blessing* and praise" (Neh. 9:5). God is no gainer even from our worship. He was in no need of that external glory of His grace which arises from His redeemed, for He is glorious enough in Himself without that. What was it that moved Him to predestinate His elect to the praise of the glory of His grace? It was, as Eph. 1:5 tells us, "according to the good pleasure of His will."

We are well aware that the high ground we are here treading is new and strange to almost all of our readers; for that reason it is well to move slowly. Let our appeal again be to the Scriptures. At the end of Rom. 11, where the Apostle brings to a close his long argument on salvation by pure and sovereign grace, he asks, "For who hath known the mind of the Lord? Or who hath been His counsellor? Or who hath first given to Him, and it shall be recompensed to him again?" (vv. 34, 35). The force of this is, it is impossible to bring the Almighty under obligations to the creature; God gains nothing from us. "If thou be righteous, what givest thou *Him?* Or what receiveth He of thine hand? Thy wickedness may hurt a man as thou art; and thy righteousness may profit the son of man" (Job 35:7, 8), but it certainly cannot affect God, who is all-blessed *in Himself.* "When ye shall have done all those things which are commanded you, say, We are unprofitable servants" (Luke 17:10) —our obedience has profited God nothing.

Nay, we go further: our Lord Jesus Christ added nothing to God in His essential being and glory, either by what He did or suffered. True, blessedly and gloriously true. He *manifested* the glory of God *to us,* but He added nought to God. He Himself expressly declares so, and there is no appeal from His words: "My goodness extendeth not to Thee" (Psa. 16:2). The whole of that Psalm is a Psalm of Christ. Christ's goodness or righteousness reached unto His saints in the earth

(Psa. 16:3), but God was high above and beyond it all, God only is "the Blessed One" (Mark 14:61, Greek).

It is perfectly true that God is both honored and dishonored by men; not in His essential being, but in His official character. It is equally true that God has been "glorified" by creation, by providence, and by redemption. This we do not and dare not dispute for a moment. But all of this has to do with His manifestative glory and the recognition of it by us. Yet had God so pleased He might have continued alone for all eternity, *without making known* His glory unto creatures. Whether He should do so or not was determined solely by His own will. He was perfectly blessed in Himself before the first creature was called into being. And what are all the creatures of His hands *unto Him* even now? Let Scripture again make answer: "Behold, the nations are as a drop of a bucket, and are counted as the small dust of the balance: behold, He taketh up the isles as a very little thing. And Lebanon is not sufficient to burn, nor the beasts thereof sufficient for a burnt offering. All nations before Him are as *nothing*; and they are counted to Him less than nothing, and vanity. To whom then will ye liken God? or what likeness will ye compare unto Him?" (Isa. 40:15-18). *That* is the God of Scripture; alas, He is still "the *unknown* God" (Acts 17:23) to the heedless multitudes. "It is He that sitteth upon the circle of the earth, and the inhabitants thereof are as grasshoppers; that stretcheth out the heavens as a curtain, and spreadeth them out as a tent to dwell in: that bringeth the princes to nothing; He maketh the judges of the earth as vanity" (Isa. 40:22, 23). How vastly different is the God of Scripture from the "god" of the average pulpit!

Nor is the testimony of the New Testament any different from that of the Old: how could it be, seeing that both have one and the same Author! There too we read, "Which in His times He shall show, who is the blessed and *only* Potentate, the King of kings, and Lord of lords: Who only hath immortality, dwelling in the light which no man can approach unto; whom no man hath seen, nor can see: to whom be honour and power everlasting, Amen" (I Tim. 6:16). Such an One is to be revered, worshipped, adored. He is solitary in His majesty, unique in His excellency, peerless in His perfections. He sustains all, but is Himself independent of all. He gives to all, but is enriched by none.

Such a God cannot be found out by searching. He can be

known only as He is *revealed* to the heart by the Holy Spirit through the Word. It is true that creation demonstrates a Creator so plainly that men are "without excuse"; yet, we still have to say with Job, "Lo, these are parts of His ways: but *how little* a portion is heard of Him? but the thunder of His power who can understand?" (26:14). The so-called argument from design by well-meaning "Apologists" has, we believe, done much more harm than good, for it has attempted to bring down the great God to the level of finite comprehension, and thereby has lost sight of His solitary excellence.

Analogy has been drawn between a savage finding a watch upon the sands, and from a close examination of it he infers a watch-maker. So far so good. But attempt to go further: suppose that savage sits down on the sand and endeavors to form to himself a conception of this watch-maker, his personal affections and manners; his disposition, acquirements, and moral character—all that goes to make up a personality; could he ever think or reason out a real man—*the* man who made the watch, so that he could say, "I am acquainted with him"? It seems trifling to ask such questions, but is the eternal and infinite God so much more within the grasp of human reason? No, indeed. The God of Scripture can only be known by those to whom He *makes Himself known.*

Nor is God known by the intellect. "God is Spirit" (John 4:24), and therefore can only be known spiritually. But fallen man is not spiritual; he is carnal. He is dead to all that is spiritual. Unless he is born again, supernaturally brought from death unto life, miraculously translated out of darkness into light, he cannot even see the things of God (John 3:3), still less apprehend them (I Cor. 2:14). The Holy Spirit has to shine in our hearts (not intellects) in order to give us "the knowledge of the glory of God in the face of Jesus Christ" (II Cor. 4:6). And even that spiritual knowledge is but fragmentary. The regenerated soul has to *grow* in grace and in the knowledge of the Lord Jesus (II Pet. 3:18).

The principal prayer and aim of Christians should be that we "walk worthy of the Lord unto all pleasing, being fruitful in every good work, and *increasing* in the knowledge of God" (Col. 1:10).

2

THE DECREES OF GOD

The decree of God is His purpose or determination with respect to future things. We have used the singular number as Scripture does (Rom. 8:28, Eph. 3:11), because there was only one act of His infinite mind about future things. But *we* speak as if there had been many, because our minds are only capable of thinking of *successive* revolutions, as thoughts and occasions arise, or in reference to the various *objects* of His decree, which being many seem to us to require a distinct purpose for each one. But an infinite understanding does not proceed by steps, from one stage to another: "Known unto God are *all* His works, from the beginning of the world" (Acts 15:18).

The Scriptures make mention of the decrees of God in many passages, and under a variety of terms. The word "decree" is found in Psa. 2:7, etc. In Eph. 3:11 we read of His "eternal purpose." In Acts 2:23 of His "determinate counsel and foreknowledge." In Eph. 1:9 of the mystery of His "will." In Rom. 8:29 that He also did "predestinate." In Eph. 1:9 of His "good pleasure." God's decrees are called His "counsel" to signify they are consummately wise. They are called God's "will" to show He was under no control, but acted according to His own pleasure. When a man's will is the rule of his conduct, it is usually capricious and unreasonable; but *wisdom* is always associated with "will" in the Divine proceedings, and accordingly, God's decrees are said to be "the counsel of His own will" (Eph. 1:11).

The decrees of God relate to all future things without exception: whatever is done in time was foreordained before time began. God's purpose was concerned with everything, whether great or small, whether good or evil, although with reference to the latter we must be careful to state that while God is the Orderer and Controller of sin, He is *not* the Author of it in the same way that He is the Author of good. Sin could not proceed from a holy God by positive and direct creation, but only by decretive permission and negative action. God's decree is as comprehensive as His government, extending to all creatures and all events. It was concerned about our life and death; about our state in time, and our state in eternity. As God works *all* things after the counsel of His own will, we learn from His works what His counsel is (was), as we judge of an architect's plan by inspecting the building which was erected under his directions.

God did not merely decree to make man, place him upon the earth, and then leave him to his own uncontrolled guidance; instead, He fixed all the circumstances in the lot of individuals, and all the particulars which will comprise the history of the human race from its commencement to its close. He did not merely decree that general laws should be established for the government of the world, but He settled the *application* of those laws to all particular cases. Our days are numbered, and so are the hairs of our heads. We may learn what is the *extent* of the Divine decrees from the dispensations of providence, in which they are executed. The care of Providence reaches to the most insignificant creatures, and the most minute events—the death of a sparrow, and the fall of a hair.

Let us now consider some of the *properties* of the Divine decrees. First, they are *eternal*. To suppose any of them to be made in time is to suppose that some new occasion has occurred; some unforeseen event or combination of circumstances has arisen, which has induced the Most High to form a new resolution. This would argue that the knowledge of the Deity is limited, and that He is growing wiser in the progress of time—which would be horrible blasphemy. No man who believes that the Divine understanding is infinite, comprehending the past, the present, and the future, will ever assent to the erroneous doctrine of temporal decrees. God is not ignorant of future events which will be executed by human volitions; He has foretold them in innumerable instances, and prophecy is but the *manifestation* of His eternal prescience. Scripture affirms that believers were chosen in Christ before the world began (Eph. 1:4), yea, that grace was "given" to them then (II Tim. 1:9).

Secondly, the decrees of God are *wise*. Wisdom is shown in the selection of the best possible ends and of the fittest means of accomplishing them. That this character belongs to the decrees of God is evident from what we know of them. They are disclosed to us *by their execution,* and every proof of wisdom in the works of God is a proof of the wisdom of the *plan,* in conformity to which they are performed. As the Psalmist declared, "O Lord, how manifold are Thy works! in wisdom hast Thou made them all" (Psalm 104:24). It is indeed but a very small part of them which falls under our observation, yet, we ought to proceed here as we do in other cases, and judge of the whole by the specimen, of what is unknown, by what is known. He who perceives the workings of admirable skill in the parts of a machine which he has an opportunity to examine, is naturally led to believe that the other parts are equally admirable. In like manner we should satisfy our minds as to God's works when doubts obtrude themselves upon us, and repel any objections that may be suggested by something that we cannot reconcile to *our* notions of what is good and wise. When we reach the bounds of the finite and gaze toward the mysterious realm of the infinite, let us exclaim, "O the depth of the riches! both of the wisdom and knowledge of God" (Rom. 11:33).

Thirdly, they are *free.* "Who hath directed the Spirit of the Lord, or being His counsellor hath taught Him? With whom took He counsel, and who instructed Him, and taught Him in the path of judgment, and taught Him knowledge, and showed to Him the way of understanding?" (Isa. 40:13, 14). God was alone when He made His decrees, and His determinations were influenced by no external cause. He was free to decree or not to decree, and to decree one thing and not another. This liberty we must ascribe to Him who is supreme, independent, and sovereign in all His doings.

Fourthly, they are *absolute and unconditional.* The execution of them is not suspended upon any condition which may, or may not be, performed. In every instance where God has decreed an end, He has also decreed every means to that end. The One who decreed the salvation of His elect also decreed to work faith in them (II Thess. 2:13). "My counsel shall stand, and I will do *all* My pleasure" (Isa. 46:10): but that could not be, if His counsel depended upon a condition which might not be performed. But God "worketh all things after the counsel of His own will" (Eph. 1:11).

Side by side with the immutability and invincibility of God's decrees, Scripture plainly teaches that man is a respon-

sible creature and answerable for his actions. And if our
thoughts are formed from God's Word the maintenance of
the one will not lead to the denial of the other. That there is
a real difficulty in defining where the one ends and the other
begins is freely granted. This is ever the case where there is a
conjunction of the Divine and the human. Real prayer is in-
dited by the Spirit, yet it is also the cry of a human heart.
The Scriptures are the inspired Word of God, yet they were
written by men who were something more than machines in
the hand of the Spirit. Christ is both God and man. He is
Omniscient, yet "increased in wisdom" (Luke 2:52). He was
Almighty, yet was "crucified through weakness" (II Cor.
13:4). He was the Prince of life, yet He died. High mysteries
are these, yet faith receives them unquestioningly.

It has often been pointed out in the past that every objec-
tion made against the eternal decrees of God applies with
equal force against His eternal foreknowledge.

Whether God has decreed all things that ever come to
pass or not, all that own the being of a God, own that
He knows all things beforehand. Now, it is self-evident
that if He knows all things beforehand, He either doth
approve of them or doth not approve of them; that is,
He either is willing they should be, or He is not willing
they should be. But to will that they *should be* is to
decree them (Jonathan Edwards).

Finally, attempt, with me, to assume and then to contemplate the opposite. To *deny* the Divine decrees would be to
predicate a world and all its concerns regulated by *un*designed
chance or blind fate. Then what peace, what assurance, what
comfort would there be for our poor hearts and minds?
What refuge would there be to fly to in the hour of need and
trial? None at all. There would be nothing better than the
black darkness and abject horror of atheism. O my reader,
how thankful should we be that everything *is* determined by
infinite wisdom and goodness! What praise and gratitude are
due unto God *for* His Divine decrees. It is because of them
that "*we know* that all things work together for good to them
that love God, to them who are the called according to His
purpose" (Rom. 8:28). Well may we exclaim, "For of Him,
and through Him, and to Him, are all things: *to whom be
glory* forever. Amen" (Rom. 11:36).

3

THE KNOWLEDGE OF GOD

God is omniscient. He knows everything: everything possible, everything actual; all events and all creatures, of the past, the present, and the future. He is perfectly acquainted with every detail in the life of every being in heaven, in earth, and in hell. "He knoweth what is in the darkness" (Dan. 2:22). Nothing escapes His notice, nothing can be hidden from Him, nothing is forgotten by Him. Well may we say with the Psalmist, "Such knowledge is too wonderful for me; it is high, I cannot attain unto it" (Psa. 139:6). His knowledge is perfect. He never errs, never changes, never overlooks anything. "Neither is there any creature that is not manifest in His sight: but all things are naked and opened unto the eyes of Him with whom we have to do" (Heb. 4:13). Yes, such is the God with whom *we* have to do"!

"Thou knowest my downsitting and mine uprising, Thou understandest my thoughts afar off. Thou compassest my path and my lying down, and art acquainted with *all* my ways. For there is not a word in my tongue but, lo, O Lord, Thou knowest it altogether" (Psa. 139:2-4). What a wondrous Being is the God of Scripture! Each of His glorious attributes should render Him honorable in our esteem. The apprehension of His omniscience ought to bow us in adoration before Him. Yet how little do we meditate upon this Divine perfection! Is it because the very thought of it fills us with uneasiness?

How solemn is this fact: nothing can be concealed from God! "For I know the things that come into your mind, every one of them" (Ezek. 11:5). Though He be invisible to us, we are not so to Him. Neither the darkness of night, the closest curtains, nor the deepest dungeon can hide any sinner from the eyes of Omniscience. The trees of the garden were not able to conceal our first parents. No human eye beheld Cain murder his brother, but his Maker witnessed his crime. Sarah might laugh derisively in the seclusion of her tent, yet was it heard by Jehovah. Achan stole a wedge of gold and carefully hid it in the earth, but God brought it to light. David was at much pains to cover up his wickedness, but ere long the all-seeing God sent one of His servants to say to him, "Thou art the man!" And to writer and reader is also said, "Be sure *your* sin will find you out" (Num. 32:23) .

Men would strip Deity of His omniscience if they could—what a proof that "the carnal mind *is* enmity against God" (Rom. 8:7) ! The wicked do as naturally hate this Divine perfection as much as they are naturally compelled to acknowledge it. They wish there might be no Witness of their sins, no Searcher of their hearts, no Judge of their deeds. They seek to banish such a God from their thoughts: "They consider not in their hearts that I remember all their wickedness" (Hosea 7:2) . How solemn is Psa. 90:8! Good reason has every Christ-rejecter for trembling before it: "Thou hast set our iniquities before Thee, our *secret* sins in the light of Thy countenance."

But to the believer, the fact of God's omniscience is a truth fraught with much comfort. In times of perplexity he says with Job, "But *He knoweth* the way that I take" (23:10) . It may be profoundly mysterious to me, quite incomprehensible to my friends, but "*He* knoweth"! In times of weariness and weakness believers assure themselves, "*He knoweth* our frame; He remembereth that we are dust" (Psa. 103:14) . In times of doubt and suspicion they *appeal* to this very attribute, saying, "*Search me,* O God, and know my heart: try me, and know my thoughts: and see if there be any wicked way in me, and lead me in the way everlasting" (Psa. 139:23, 24) . In time of sad failure, when our actions have belied our hearts, when our deeds have repudiated our devotion, and the searching question comes to us, "Lovest thou Me?", we say, as Peter did, "Lord, Thou knowest *all* things; Thou *knowest* that I love Thee" (John 21:17) .

Here is encouragement to prayer. There is no cause for fearing that the petitions of the righteous will not be heard, or that their sighs and tears shall escape the notice of God, since He knows the thoughts and intents of the heart. There is no danger of the individual saint being overlooked amidst the multitude of supplicants who daily and hourly present their various petitions, for an *infinite* Mind is as capable of paying the same attention to millions as if only one individual were seeking its attention. So too the lack of appropriate language, the inability to give expression to the deepest longing of the soul, will not jeopardize our prayers, for "It shall come to pass, that before they call, I will answer; and while they are yet speaking, I will hear" (Isa. 65:24) .

"Great is our Lord, and of great power: His understanding is infinite" (Psa. 147:5) . God not only knows whatsoever has happened in the past in every part of His vast domains, and He is not only thoroughly acquainted with everything that is now transpiring throughout the entire universe, but He is also perfectly cognizant of every event, from the least to the greatest, that ever will happen in the ages to come. God's knowledge of the future is as complete as is His knowledge of the past and the present, and that, because the future depends entirely upon Himself. Were it in anywise possible for something to occur apart from either the direct agency or permission of God, then that something would be independent of Him, and He would at once cease to be Supreme.

Now the Divine knowledge of the future is not a mere abstraction, but something which is inseparably connected with and accompanied by His purpose. God has Himself designed whatsoever shall yet be, and what He has designed *must* be effectuated. As His most sure Word affirms, "He doeth according to His will in the army of heaven, and among the inhabitants of the earth: and *none* can stay His hand" (Dan. 4:35) . And again, "There are many devices in a man's heart; nevertheless the counsel of the Lord, that *shall* stand" (Prov. 19:21) . The wisdom and power of God being alike infinite, the accomplishment of whatever He hath purposed is absolutely guaranteed. It is no more possible for the Divine counsels to fail in their execution than it would be for the thrice holy God to lie.

Nothing relating to the future is in anywise uncertain so far as the actualization of God's counsels are concerned. None of His decrees are left contingent either on creatures or secondary causes. There is no future event which is only a mere possibility, that is, something which may or may not come to pass: "*Known* unto God are *all* His works from the beginning" (Acts 15:18) . Whatever God has decreed is inexorably certain, for He is without variableness, or shadow of turning (James 1:17) . Therefore we are told at the very beginning of that book, which unveils to us so much of the future, of "Things which *must* shortly come to pass" (Rev. 1:1).

The perfect knowledge of God is exemplified and illustrated in every prophecy recorded in His Word. In the Old Testament are to be found scores of predictions concerning the history of Israel, which were fulfilled to their minutest detail, centuries after they were made. In them too are scores more foretelling the earthly career of Christ, and they too were accomplished literally and perfectly. Such prophecies could only have been given by One who knew the end from the beginning, and whose knowledge rested upon the unconditional certainty of the accomplishment of everything foretold. In like manner, both Old and New Testament contain many other announcements yet future, and they too *"must* be fulfilled" (Luke 24:44), must because foretold by Him who decreed them.

It should, however, be pointed out that neither God's knowledge nor His cognition of the future, considered simply in themselves, are causative. Nothing has ever come to pass, or ever will, merely because God knew it. The *cause* of all things is the *will* of God. The man who really believes the Scriptures knows beforehand that the seasons will continue to follow each other with unfailing regularity to the end of earth's history (Gen. 8:22), yet his knowledge is not the cause of their succession. So God's knowledge does not arise from things because they are or will be, but because He has *ordained* them to be. God knew and foretold the crucifixion of His Son many hundreds of years before He became incarnate, and this, because in the Divine purpose, He was a Lamb slain from the foundation of the world: hence we read of His being "delivered by the determinate counsel and foreknowledge of God" (Acts 2:23).

A word or two by way of application. The infinite knowledge of God should fill us with *amazement*. How far exalted above the wisest man is the Lord! None of us knows what a day may bring forth, but all futurity is open to His omniscient gaze. The infinite knowledge of God ought to fill us with holy *awe*. Nothing we do, say, or even think, escapes the cognizance of Him with whom we have to do: "The eyes of the Lord are in every place, beholding the evil and the good" (Prov. 15:3). What a curb this would be unto us, did we but meditate upon it more frequently! Instead of acting recklessly, we should say with Hagar, "Thou God seest me"

(Gen. 16:13). The apprehension of God's infinite knowledge should fill the Christian with *adoration*. The whole of my life stood open to His view from the beginning. He foresaw my every fall, my every sin, my every backsliding; yet, nevertheless, fixed His heart upon me. Oh, how the realization of this should bow me in wonder and worship before Him!

4

THE FOREKNOWLEDGE OF GOD

What controversies have been engendered by this subject in the past! But what truth of Holy Scripture is there which has not been made the occasion of theological and ecclesiastical battles? The deity of Christ, His virgin birth, His atoning death, His second advent; the believer's justification, sanctification, security; the church, its organization, officers, discipline; baptism, the Lord's supper, and a score of other precious truths might be mentioned. Yet, the controversies which have been waged over them did not close the mouths of God's faithful servants; why, then, should we avoid the vexed questions of God's Foreknowledge, because, forsooth, there are some who will charge us with fomenting strife? Let others contend if they will, our duty is to bear witness according to the light vouchsafed us.

There are two things concerning the Foreknowledge of God about which many are in ignorance: the *meaning* of the term, its Scriptural *scope*. Because this ignorance is so widespread, it is an easy matter for preachers and teachers to palm off perversions of this subject, even upon the people of God. There is only one safeguard against error, and that is to be established in the faith; and for that, there has to be prayerful and diligent study, and a receiving with meekness the engrafted Word of God. Only then are we fortified against the attacks of those who assail us. There are those today who are *mis*using this very truth in order to discredit and deny the absolute sovereignty of God in the salvation of sinners. Just as higher critics are repudiating the Divine inspiration of the Scriptures; evolutionists, the work of God in creation; so some pseudo Bible teachers are perverting His foreknowledge in order to set aside His unconditional election unto eternal life.

When the solemn and blessed subject of Divine foreordination is expounded, when God's eternal choice of certain ones to be conformed to the image of His Son is set forth, the Enemy sends along some man to argue that election is based upon the foreknowledge of God, and this "foreknowledge" is interpreted to mean that God foresaw certain ones would be more pliable than others, that they would respond more readily to the strivings of the Spirit, and that because God knew they *would* believe, He, accordingly, predestinated *them* unto salvation. But such a statement is radically wrong. It repudiates the truth of total depravity, for it argues that there is something good in some men. It takes away the independency of God, for it makes His decrees *rest upon* what He discovers in the creature. It completely turns things upside down, for in saying God foresaw certain sinners would believe in Christ, and that because of this, He predestinated them unto salvation, is the very reverse of the truth. Scripture affirms that God, in His high sovereignty, singled out certain ones to be recipients of His distinguishing favors (Acts 13:48), and therefore He determined to bestow upon them the gift of faith. False theology makes God's foreknowledge of our believing the *cause* of His election to salvation; whereas, God's election is the cause, and our believing in Christ is the *effect*.

Ere proceeding further with our discussion of this much misunderstood theme, let us pause and define our terms. What is meant by "foreknowledge"? "To know beforehand," is the ready reply of many. But we must not jump to conclusions, nor must we turn to Webster's dictionary as the final court of appeal, for it is not a matter of the etymology of the term employed. What is needed is to find out how the word is *used* in Scripture. The Holy Spirit's usage of an expression always defines its meaning and scope. It is failure to apply this simple rule which is responsible for so much confusion and error. So many people assume they already know the signification of a certain word used in Scripture, and then they are too dilatory to *test* their assumptions by means of a concordance. Let us amplify this point.

Take the word "flesh." Its meaning appears to be so obvious that many would regard it as a waste of time to look up its various connections in Scripture. It is hastily assumed that the word is synonymous with the physical body, and so no inquiry is made. But, in fact, "flesh" in Scripture frequently includes far more than what is corporeal; all that is embraced by the term can only be ascertained by a diligent comparison of *every* occurrence of it and by a study of each separate context. Take the word "world." The average reader of the Bible imagines this word is the equivalent for the human race, and consequently, many passages where the term is found are wrongly interpreted. Take the word "immortality." Surely *it* requires no study! Obviously it has reference to the indestructibility of the soul. Ah, my reader, it is foolish and wrong to assume anything where the Word of God is concerned. If the reader will take the trouble to carefully examine each passage where "mortal" and "immortal" are found, it will be seen that these words are never applied to the soul, but always to the body.

Now what has just been said on "flesh," the "world," "immortality," applies with equal force to the terms "know" and "foreknow." Instead of imagining that these words signify no more than a simple cognition, the different passages in which they occur require to be carefully weighed. The word "foreknowledge" is not found in the Old Testament. But "know" occurs there frequently. When that term is used in connection with God, it often signifies *to regard with favor,* denoting *not mere* cognition but an *affection* for the object in view. "I *know* thee by name" (Ex. 33:17). "Ye have been rebellious against the Lord from the day that I *knew* you" (Deut. 9:24). "Before I formed thee in the belly I *knew* thee" (Jer. 1:5). "They have made princes and I *knew* it *not*" (Hos. 8:4). "You only have I *known* of all the families of the earth" (Amos 3:2). In these passages "knew" signifies either *loved* or *appointed.*

In like manner, the word "know" is frequently used in the New Testament, in the same sense as in the Old Testament. "Then will I profess unto them, I *never knew* you" (Matt. 7:23). "I am the good shepherd and *know* My sheep and am *known* of Mine" (John 10:14). "If any man love God, the same is *known* of Him" (I Cor. 8:3). "The Lord *knoweth* them that are His" (II Tim. 2:19).

Now the word "foreknowledge" as it is used in the New Testament is less ambiguous than in its simple form "to know." If every passage in which it occurs is carefully studied, it will be discovered that it is a moot point whether it ever has reference to the mere perception of events which are yet to take place. The fact is that "foreknowledge" is *never* used in Scripture in connection with events or actions; instead, it always has reference to *persons.* It is persons God is said to "foreknow," not the actions of those persons. In proof of this we shall now quote each passage where this expression is found.

The first occurrence is in Acts 2:23. There we read, "Him being delivered by the determinate counsel and foreknowledge of God, ye have taken, and by wicked hands have crucified and slain." If careful attention is paid to the wording of this verse, it will be seen that the Apostle was not there speaking of God's foreknowledge of the *act* of the crucifixion, but of the *Person* crucified: "Him (Christ) being delivered *by*," etc.

The second occurrence is in Rom. 8:29, 30. "For *whom* He did foreknow, He also did predestinate to be conformed to the image of His Son, that He might be the Firstborn among many brethren. Moreover *whom* He did predestinate, them He also called," etc. Weigh well the pronoun that is used here. It is not *what* He did foreknow, but *whom* He did. It is not the surrendering of their wills nor the believing of their hearts, but the *persons* themselves that are here in view.

"God hath not cast away His people which He foreknew" (Rom. 11:2). Once more the plain reference is to persons, and to persons only.

The last mention is in I Peter 1:2: "Elect according to the foreknowledge of God the Father." *Who* are "elect according to the foreknowledge of God the Father"? The previous verse tells us: the reference is to the "strangers scattered" i. e. the Diaspora, the Dispersion, the believing Jews. Thus, here too the reference is to persons, and not to their foreseen acts.

Now in view of these passages (and there are no more) *what scriptural ground* is there for anyone saying God "foreknew" the *acts* of certain ones, viz., their "repenting and believing," and that because of those acts He elected them unto salvation? The answer is, None whatever. Scripture *never* speaks of repentance and faith as being foreseen or foreknown by God. Truly, He *did* know from all eternity that certain ones *would* repent and believe, yet this is not what Scripture refers to as the *object* of God's "foreknowledge." The word uniformly refers to God's foreknowing *persons*; then let us "hold fast the form of sound words" (II Tim. 1:13).

Another thing to which we desire to call particular attention is that the first two passages quoted above show plainly and teach implicitly that God's "foreknowledge" *is not causa-*

tive, that instead, something else lies behind, precedes it, and that something is His own *sovereign decree.* Christ was "delivered by the (1) determinate counsel and (2) foreknowledge of God" (Acts 2:23). His "counsel" or decree was the ground of His foreknowledge. So again in Rom. 8:29. That verse opens with the word "for," which tells us to look back to what immediately precedes. What, then, does the previous verse say? This: "all things work together for good to them . . . who are the called according to His purpose." Thus God's "foreknowledge" is *based upon* His "purpose" or decree (see Psa. 2:7).

God foreknows what *will be* because He has decreed what *shall be.* It is therefore a reversing of the order of Scripture, a putting of the cart before the horse, to affirm that God elects because He foreknows people. The truth is, He "foreknows" because He has *elected.* This removes the ground or cause of election from outside the creature, and places it in God's own sovereign will. God purposed in Himself to elect a certain people, not because of anything good in them or from them, either actual or foreseen, but solely out of His own mere pleasure. As to *why* He chose the ones He did, we do not know, and can only say, "Even so, Father, for so it seemed good in *Thy* sight." The plain truth of Rom. 8:29 is that God, before the foundation of the world, singled out certain sinners and appointed them unto salvation (II Thess. 2:13). This is clear from the concluding words of the verse: "Predestinated to be conformed to the image of His Son," etc. God did not predestinate those whom He foreknew *were* "conformed," but, on the contrary, those whom He "foreknew" (i. e., loved and elected) He predestinated *"to be* conformed." Their conformity to Christ is not the cause, but the effect of God's foreknowledge and predestination.

God did not elect any sinner because He foresaw that he would believe, for the simple but sufficient reason that *no* sinner ever does believe until God gives him faith; just as no man sees until God gives him sight. Sight is God's gift, seeing is the consequence of my using His gift. So faith is God's gift (Eph. 2:8, 9), believing is the consequence of my using His gift. If it were true that God had elected certain ones to be saved *because* in due time they would believe, then that would make believing a *meritorious* act, and in that event the saved sinner *would* have ground for "boasting," which Scripture emphatically denies: Eph. 2:9.

Surely God's Word is plain enough in teaching that believing is *not* a meritorious act. It affirms that Christians are a people "who have believed *through grace*" (Acts 18:27). If, then, they have believed "through grace," there is absolutely nothing meritorious about "believing," and if nothing meritorious, it could not be the ground or cause which moved God to choose them. No; God's choice proceeds not from anything in *us,* or anything from us, but solely from His own sovereign pleasure. Once more, in Rom. 11:5, we read of "a remnant according to the election of grace." There it is, plain enough; election itself is *of grace,* and grace is *unmerited* favor, something for which we had *no claim* upon God whatsoever.

It thus appears that it is highly important for us to have clear and scriptural views of the "foreknowledge" of God. Erroneous conceptions about it lead inevitably to thoughts most dishonoring to Him. The popular idea of Divine foreknowledge is altogether inadequate. God not only knew the end from the beginning, but He planned, fixed, predestinated everything from the beginning. And, as cause stands to effect, so God's purpose is the ground of His prescience. If then the reader be a real Christian, he is so because God chose him in Christ before the foundation of the world (Eph. 1:4), and chose not because He foresaw you *would* believe, but chose simply because it pleased Him to choose; chose you notwithstanding your natural unbelief. This being so, *all* the glory and praise belongs alone to Him. You have *no* ground for taking *any* credit to yourself. You have "believed *through grace*" (Acts 18:27), and that, because your very election was "of grace" (Rom. 11:5).

THE SUPREMACY OF GOD

In one of his letters to Erasmus, Luther said, "Your thoughts of God are too human." Probably that renowned scholar resented such a rebuke, the more so, since it proceeded from a miner's son; nevertheless, it was thoroughly deserved. We too, though having no standing among the religious leaders of this degenerate age, prefer the same charge against the majority of the preachers of our day, and against those who, instead of searching the Scriptures for themselves, lazily accept the teaching of others. The most dishonoring and degrading conceptions of the rule and reign of the Almighty are now held almost everywhere. To countless thousands, even among those professing to be Christians, the God of the Scriptures is quite unknown.

Of old, God complained to an apostate Israel, "Thou thoughtest that I was altogether as thyself" (Psa. 50:21). Such must now be His indictment against an apostate Christendom. Men imagine that the Most High is moved by sentiment, rather than actuated by principle. They suppose that His omnipotency is such an idle fiction that Satan is thwarting His designs on every side. They think that if He has formed any plan or purpose at all, then it must be like theirs, constantly subject to change. They openly declare that whatever power He possesses must be restricted, lest He invade the citadel of man's "free will" and reduce him to a "machine." They lower the all-efficacious Atonement, which has actually redeemed everyone for whom it was made, to a mere "remedy," which sin-sick souls may use if they feel disposed to; and they enervate the invincible work of the Holy Spirit to an "offer" of the Gospel which sinners may accept or reject as they please.

The "god" of this twentieth century no more resembles the Supreme Sovereign of Holy Writ than does the dim flickering of a candle the glory of the midday sun. The "god" who is now talked about in the average pulpit, spoken of in the ordinary Sunday School, mentioned in much of the religious literature of the day, and preached in most of the so-called Bible Conferences is the figment of human imagination, an invention of maudlin sentimentality. The heathen outside of the pale of Christendom form "gods" out of wood and stone, while the millions of heathen inside Christendom manufacture a "god" out of their own carnal mind. In reality, they are but atheists, for there is no other possible alternative between an absolutely supreme God, and no God at all. A "god" whose will is resisted, whose designs are frustrated, whose purpose is checkmated, possesses no title to Deity, and so far from being a fit object of worship, merits nought but contempt.

The supremacy of the true and living God might well be argued from the infinite distance which separates the mightiest creatures from the almighty Creator. He is the Potter, they are but the clay in His hands, to be molded into vessels of honor, or to be dashed into pieces (Psa. 2:9) as He pleases. Were all the denizens of heaven and all the inhabitants of the earth to combine in revolt against Him, it would occasion Him no uneasiness, and would have less effect upon His eternal and unassailable Throne than has the spray of Mediterranean's waves upon the towering rocks of Gibraltar. So puerile and powerless is the creature to affect the Most High, Scripture itself tells us that when the Gentile heads unite with apostate Israel to defy Jehovah and His Christ, "He that sitteth in the heavens shall *laugh*" (Psa. 2:4) .

The absolute and universal supremacy of God is plainly and positively affirmed in many scriptures. "Thine, O Lord, is the greatness, and the power, and the glory, and the victory, and the majesty: for all in the heaven and all in the earth is Thine; Thine is the Kingdom, O Lord, and Thou art exalted as Head above all. . . . And Thou reignest over all" (I Chron. 29:11, 12) —note, "reignest" now, not "will do so in the Millennium." "O Lord God of our fathers, art not Thou God in heaven? and rulest not Thou over all the kingdoms of the heathen? and in Thine hand is there not power and might, so that none (not even the Devil himself) is able to withstand Thee?" (II Chron. 20:6) . Before Him presidents and popes, kings and emperors, are less than grasshoppers.

"But He is in one mind, and who can turn Him? and what His soul desireth, *even that* He doeth" (Job 23:13) . Ah, my reader, the God of Scripture is no make-believe monarch, no mere imaginary sovereign, but King of kings, and Lord of lords. "I know that Thou canst do everything, and that *no* thought of Thine can be hindered" (Job 42:2, margin) , or, as another translator renders it, "no purpose of Thine can be frustrated." All that He has designed He does. All that He has decreed He performs. "But our God is in the heavens: He hath done *whatsoever* He hath pleased" (Psa. 115:3) ; and why has He? Because "there is no wisdom, nor understanding, nor counsel against the Lord" (Prov. 21:30) .

God's supremacy over the works of His hands is vividly depicted in Scripture. Inanimate matter, irrational creatures, all perform their Maker's bidding. At His pleasure the Red Sea divided and its waters stood up as walls (Ex. 14) ; and the earth opened her mouth, and guilty rebels went down alive into the pit (Num. 16) . When He so ordered, the sun stood still (Josh. 10) ; and on another occasion went *backward* ten degrees on the dial of Ahaz (Isa. 38:8) . To exemplify His supremacy, He made ravens carry food to Elijah (I Kings 17) , iron to swim on top of the waters (II Kings 6:5) , lions to be tame when Daniel was cast into their den, fire to burn not when the three Hebrews were flung into its flames. Thus "Whatsoever the Lord pleased, that did He in heaven, and in earth, in the seas, and all deep places" (Psa. 135:6) .

God's supremacy is also demonstrated in His perfect rule over the *wills* of men. Let the reader ponder carefully Ex. 34:24. Three times in the year all the males of Israel were required to leave their homes and go up to Jerusalem. They lived in the midst of hostile people, who hated them for having appropriated their lands. What, then, was to hinder the Canaanites from seizing their opportunity, and, during the absence of the men, slaying the women and children and taking possession of their farms? If the hand of the Almighty was not upon the wills even of wicked men, how could He make this promise beforehand, that none *should* so much as "desire" their lands? Ah, "The king's heart is in the hand of the Lord, as the rivers of water: He turneth it whithersoever He will" (Prov. 21:1) .

But, it may be objected, do we not read again and again in Scripture how that men defied God, resisted His will, broke His commandments, disregarded His warnings, and turned a deaf ear to all His exhortations? Certainly we do. And does this nullify all that we have said above? If it does, then the

Bible plainly contradicts itself. But that cannot be. What the objector refers to is simply the wickedness of man against the *external* word of God, whereas what we have mentioned above is what God has *purposed in Himself.* The rule of conduct He has given us to walk by, is perfectly fulfilled by none of us; His own eternal "counsels" are accomplished to their minutest details.

The absolute and universal supremacy of God is affirmed with equal plainness and positiveness in the New Testament. There we are told that God "worketh *all* things after the counsel of His own will" (Eph. 1:11) —the Greek for "worketh" means "to work effectually." For this reason we read, "For of Him, and through Him, and to Him, are all things: to whom be glory forever. Amen" (Rom. 11:36). Men may boast that they are free agents, with a will of their own, and are at liberty to do as they please, but Scripture says to those who boast "we will go into such a city, and continue there a year, and buy and sell. . . . Ye ought to say, *If the Lord* will" (James 4:13, 15) !

Here then is a sure resting-place for the heart. Our lives are neither the product of blind fate nor the result of capricious chance, but every detail of them was ordained from all eternity, and is now ordered by the living and reigning God. Not a hair of our heads can be touched without His permission. "A man's heart deviseth his way: *but the Lord* directeth his steps" (Prov. 16:9). What assurance, what strength, what comfort this should give the real Christian! "My times are in *Thy* hand" (Psa. 31:15). Then let me "*Rest in the Lord,* and wait patiently for Him" (Psa. 37:7).

6

THE SOVEREIGNTY OF GOD

The sovereignty of God may be defined as the *exercise* of His supremacy—see preceding chapter. Being infinitely elevated above the highest creature, He is the Most High, Lord of heaven and earth. Subject to none, influenced by none, absolutely independent; God does as He pleases, only as He pleases, always as He pleases. None can thwart Him, none can hinder Him. So His own Word expressly declares: "My counsel shall stand, and *I will do* all My pleasure" (Isa. 46:10) ; "He doeth according to *His* will in the army of heaven, and among the inhabitants of the earth: and none can stay His hand" (Dan. 4:35). Divine sovereignty means that God is God in fact, as well as in name, that He is on the Throne of the universe, directing all things, working all things "after the counsel of His own will" (Eph. 1:11).

Rightly did the late Charles Haddon Spurgeon say in his sermon on Matt. 20:15,

There is no attribute more comforting to His children than that of God's Sovereignty. Under the most adverse circumstances, in the most severe trials, they believe that Sovereignty has ordained their afflictions, that Sovereignty overrrules them, and that Sovereignty will sanctify them all. There is nothing for which the children ought more earnestly to contend than the doctrine of their Master over all creation—the Kingship of God over all the works of His own hands—the Throne of God and His right to sit upon that Throne. On the other hand, there is no doctrine more hated by worldings, no truth of which they have made such a football, as the great, stupendous, but yet most certain doctrine of the Sovereignty of the infinite Jehovah. Men will allow God to be everywhere except on His throne. They will allow Him to be in His workshop to fashion worlds and make stars. They will allow Him to be in His almonry to dispense His alms and bestow His bounties. They will allow Him to sustain the earth and bear up the pillars thereof, or light the lamps of heaven, or rule the waves of the ever-moving ocean; but when God ascends His throne, His creatures then gnash their teeth. And we proclaim an *enthroned* God, and His right to do as He wills with His own, to dispose of His creatures as *He* thinks well, without consulting them in the matter; then it is that we are hissed and execrated, and then it is that men turn a deaf ear to us, for God on His throne is not the God they love. But it is God upon the throne that we love to preach. It is God upon His throne whom we trust.

"Whatsoever the Lord pleased, that did He in heaven, and in earth, in the seas, and all deep places" (Psa. 135:6). Yes, dear reader, such is the imperial Potentate revealed in Holy Writ. Unrivalled in majesty, unlimited in power, unaffected by anything outside Himself. But we are living in a day when even the most "orthodox" seem afraid to admit the proper Godhood of God. They say that to press the sovereignty of God excludes human responsibility; whereas human responsibility is based upon Divine sovereignty, and is the product of it.

"But our God is in the heavens: He hath done whatsoever *He* hath pleased" (Psa. 115:3). He *sovereignly* chose to place each of His creatures on that particular footing which seemed good in His sight. He created angels: some He placed on a conditional footing, others He gave an immutable standing before Him (I Tim. 5:21), making Christ their head (Col. 2:10). Let it not be overlooked that the angels which sinned (II Peter 2:5), were as much His creatures as the angels that sinned not. Yet God foresaw they *would* fall, nevertheless He placed them on a mutable, creature, conditional footing, and suffered them to fall, though He was not the Author of their sin.

So too, God *sovereignly* placed Adam in the garden of Eden upon a *conditional* footing. Had He so pleased, He could have placed him upon an unconditional footing; He could have placed him on a footing as firm as that occupied by the unfallen angels, He could have placed him upon a footing as sure and as immutable as that which His saints have in Christ. But, instead, He chose to set him in Eden on the basis of creature responsibility, so that he stood or fell according as he measured up or failed to measure up to his responsibility—obedience to his Maker. Adam stood accountable to God by the law which his Creator had given him. Here was responsibility, unimpaired responsibility, tested out under the most favorable conditions.

Now God did not place Adam upon a footing of conditional, creature responsibility, because it was right He *should* so place him. No, it was right because God did it. God did not even give creatures being because it was right for Him to do so, i. e., because He was under any obligations *to* create; but it was right because He did so. God is sovereign. His will is supreme. So far from God being under any law of "right," He is a law unto Himself, so that whatsoever *He* does *is* right. And woe be to the rebel that calls His sovereignty into question: "Woe unto him that striveth with his Maker. Let the potsherd strive with the potsherds of the earth. Shall the clay say to Him that fashioned it, What makest Thou?" (Isa. 45:9).

Again; the Lord God *sovereignly* placed Israel upon a *conditional* footing. The 19th, 20th and 24th chapters of Exodus afford a clear and full proof of this. They were placed under a covenant of works. God gave to them certain laws, and made national blessing for them depend upon their observance of His statutes. But Israel were stiffnecked and uncircumcised in heart. They rebelled against Jehovah, forsook His law, turned unto false gods, apostatized. In consequence, Divine judgment fell upon them, they were delivered into the hands of their enemies, dispersed abroad throughout the earth, and remain under the heavy frown of God's displeasure to this day.

It was God in the exercise of His high sovereignty that placed Satan and his angels, Adam, and Israel in their respective *responsible* positions. But so far from His sovereignty taking away responsibility from the creature, it was by the exercise thereof that He placed them on this conditional footing, under such responsibilities as He thought proper; by virtue of which sovereignty, He is seen to be God over all. Thus, there is perfect harmony between the sovereignty of God and the responsibility of the creature. Many have most foolishly said that it is quite impossible to show where Divine sovereignty ends and creature accountability begins. *Here* is where creature responsibility begins: in the sovereign ordination of the

Creator. As to His sovereignty, there is not and never will be any "end" to it!

Let us give further proofs that the responsibility of the creature *is* based upon God's sovereignty. How many things are recorded in Scripture which were right because God *commanded* them, and which would *not* have been right had He not so commanded! What right had Adam to "eat" of the trees of the Garden? The permission of his Maker (Gen. 2:16), without which he would have been a thief! What right had Israel to "borrow" of the Egyptians' jewels and raiment (Ex. 12:35)? None, unless Jehovah had authorized it (Ex. 3:22). What right had Israel to slay so many lambs for sacrifice? None, except that God commanded it. What right had Israel to kill off all the Canaanites? None, save as Jehovah had bidden them. What right has the husband to require submission from his wife? None, unless God had appointed it. And so we might go on. Human responsibility is *based upon* Divine sovereignty.

One more example of the exercise of God's absolute sovereignty. God placed His elect upon a *different* footing from Adam or Israel. He placed His elect upon an *unconditional* footing. In the Everlasting Covenant Jesus Christ was appointed their Head, took their responsibilities upon Himself, and wrought out a righteousness for them which is perfect, indefeasible, eternal. Christ was placed upon a conditional footing, for He was "made under the law, to redeem them that were under the law," only with this infinite difference: the others failed; He did not and could not. And *who* placed Christ upon that conditional footing? The Triune God. It was sovereign will that appointed Him, sovereign love that sent Him, sovereign authority that assigned Him His work.

Certain conditions were set before the Mediator. He was to be made in the likeness of sin's flesh; He was to magnify the law and make it honorable; He was to bear all the sins of all God's people in His own body on the tree; He was to make full atonement for them; He was to endure the outpoured wrath of God; He was to die and be buried. On the fulfillment of those conditions He was promised a reward: Isa. 53:10-12. He was to be the Firstborn among many brethren; He was to have a people who should share His glory. Blessed be His name forever, He fulfilled those conditions, and because He did so, the Father stands pledged, on solemn oath, to preserve through time and bless throughout eternity every one of those for whom His incarnate Son mediated. Because He took their place, they now share His. His righteousness is theirs, His standing before God is theirs, His life is theirs. There is not a single condition for them to meet, not a single responsibility for them to discharge in order to attain their eternal bliss. "By one offering He *hath perfected* forever them that are set apart" (Heb. 10:14).

Here then is the sovereignty of God openly displayed before all, displayed in the *different* ways in which He has dealt with His creatures. Part of the angels, Adam, Israel, were placed upon a conditional footing, continuance in blessing being made dependent upon *their* obedience and fidelity to God. But in sharp contrast from them, the "little flock" (Luke 12:32), have been given an unconditional, an immutable standing in God's covenant, God's counsels, God's Son; their blessing being made dependent upon what *Christ* did for them. "The foundation of God standeth sure, having this seal: The Lord knoweth them that are His" (II Tim. 2:19). The foundation on which God's elect stand is a perfect one: nothing can be added to it, nor anything taken from it (Eccl. 3:14). Here, then, is the highest and grandest display of the absolute sovereignty of God. Verily, He *has* "mercy on whom He will have mercy, and whom He will He hardeneth" (Rom. 9:18).

THE IMMUTABILITY OF GOD

Immutability is one of the Divine perfections which is not sufficiently pondered. It is one of the excellencies of the Creator which distinguishes Him from all His creatures. God is perpetually the same: subject to no change in His being, attributes, or determinations. Therefore God is compared to a *rock* (Deut. 32:4, etc.) which remains immovable, when the entire ocean surrounding it is continually in a fluctuating state; even so, though all creatures are subject to change, God is immutable. Because God has no beginning and no ending, He can know no change. He is everlastingly "the Father of lights, with whom is no variableness, neither shadow of turning" (James 1:17).

First, God is immutable in His *essence*. His nature and being are infinite, and so, subject to no mutations. There never was a time when He was not; there never will come a time when He shall cease to be. God has neither evolved, grown, nor improved. All that He is today, He has ever been, and ever will be. "I am the Lord, I change not" (Mal. 3:6) is His own unqualified affirmation. He cannot change for the better, for He is already perfect; and being perfect, He cannot change for the worse. Altogether unaffected by anything outside Himself, improvement or deterioration is impossible. He is perpetually the same. He only can say, "I am that I am" (Ex. 3:14). He is altogether uninfluenced by the flight of time. There is no wrinkle upon the brow of eternity. Therefore His power can never diminish nor His glory ever fade.

Secondly, God is immutable in His *attributes*. Whatever the attributes of God were before the universe was called into existence, they are precisely the same now, and will remain so forever. Necessarily so; for they are the very perfections, the essential qualities of His being. *Semper idem* (always the same) is written across every one of them. His power is unabated, His wisdom undiminished, His holiness unsullied. The attributes of God can no more change than Deity can cease to be. His veracity is immutable, for His Word is "forever settled in heaven" (Psa. 119:89). His love is eternal: "I have loved thee with an everlasting love" (Jer. 31:3) and "Having loved His own which were in the world, He loved them unto the end" (John 13:1). His mercy ceases not, for it is "everlasting" (Psa. 100:5).

Thirdly, God is immutable in His *counsel*. His will never varies. Perhaps some are ready to object that we ought to read the following: "And it *repented* the Lord that He had made man" (Gen. 6:6). Our first reply is, Then do the Scriptures contradict themselves? No, that cannot be. Num. 23:19 is plain enough: "God is not a man, that He should lie; neither the son of man, that He should repent." So also in I Sam. 15:29, "The strength of Israel will not lie nor repent: for He is not a man, that He should repent." The explanation is very simple. When speaking of Himself, God frequently accommodates His language to our limited capacities. He describes Himself as clothed with bodily members, as eyes, ears, ·hands, etc. He speaks of Himself as "waking" (Psa. 78:65), as "rising early" (Jer. 7:13); yet He neither slumbers nor sleeps. When He institutes a *change in His dealings* with men, He describes His course of conduct as "repenting."

Yes, God is immutable in His counsel. "The gifts and calling of God are *without* repentance" (Rom. 11:29). It must be so, for "He is in one mind, and who can turn Him? and what His soul desireth, even that He doeth" (Job 23:13). Change and decay in all around we see, may He who changeth not abide with thee. God's purpose never alters. One of two things causes a man to change his mind and reverse his plans: want of foresight to anticipate everything, or lack of power to execute them. But as God is both omniscient and omnipotent there is never any need for Him to revise His decrees. No, "The counsel of the Lord standeth forever, the thoughts of His heart to all generations" (Psa. 33:11). Therefore do we read of "the immutability of His counsel" (Heb. 6:17).

Herein we may perceive the infinite distance which separates the highest creature from the Creator. Creaturehood and mutability are correlative terms. If the creature was not mutable by nature, it would not be a creature; it would be

God. By nature we tend toward nothingness, since we c̲___
from nothing. Nothing stays our annihilation but the will
and sustaining power of God. None can sustain himself a
single moment. We are entirely dependent on the Creator for
every breath we draw. We gladly own with the Psalmist,
Thou "holdest our soul in life" (Psa. 66:9). The realization
of this ought to make us lie down under a sense of our own
nothingness in the presence of Him "in Whom we live, and
move, and have our being" (Acts 17:28).

As fallen creatures we are not only mutable, but everything
in us is *opposed* to God. As such we are "wandering stars"
(Jude 13), out of our proper orbit. The wicked are "like the
troubled sea, when it *cannot rest*" (Isa. 57:20). Fallen man is
inconstant. The words of Jacob concerning Reuben apply with
full force to all of Adam's descendants: "unstable as water"
(Gen. 49:4). Thus it is not only a mark of piety, but also the
part of wisdom to heed that injunction, "cease ye *from man*"
(Isa. 2:22). No human being is to be depended on. "Put not
your trust in princes, in the son of man, in whom is *no* help"
(Psa. 146:3). If I disobey God, then I deserve to be deceived
and disappointed by my fellows. People who like you today
may hate you tomorrow. The multitude who cried, "Hosanna
to the Son of David," speedily changed to "Away with Him,
Crucify Him."

Herein is solid *comfort*. Human nature cannot be relied
upon; but God can! However unstable I may be, however
fickle my friends may prove, God changes not. If He varied as
we do, if He willed one thing today and another tomorrow, if
He were controlled by caprice, who could confide in Him?
But, all praise to His glorious name, He is ever the same. His
purpose is fixed, His will is stable, His word is sure. Here
then is a *rock* on which we may fix our feet, while the mighty
torrent is sweeping away everything around us. The per-
manence of God's character guarantees the fulfillment of His
promises: "For the mountains shall depart, and the hills be
removed; but My kindness shall not depart from thee, neither
shall the covenant of My peace be removed, saith the Lord
that hath mercy on thee" (Isa. 54:10).

Herein is *encouragement to prayer*. "What comfort would
it be to pray to a god that, like the chameleon, changed color
every moment? Who would put up a petition to an earthly
prince that was so mutable as to grant a petition one day, and
deny it another?" (Stephen Charnock, 1670). Should someone

ask, But what is the use of praying to One whose will is already fixed? We answer, Because He so requires it. What blessings has God promised without our seeking them? "If we ask anything according to His will, He heareth us" (I John 5:14), and He *has* willed everything that is for His child's good. To ask for anything contrary to His will is not prayer, but rank rebellion.

Herein is *terror for the wicked*. Those who defy Him, who break His laws, who have no concern for His glory, but who live their lives as though He existed not, must not suppose that, when at the last they shall cry to Him for mercy, He will alter His will, revoke His word, and rescind His awful threatenings. No, He has declared, "Therefore will I also deal in fury: Mine eye shall not spare, neither will I have pity: and though they cry in Mine ears with a loud voice, yet will I not hear them" (Ezek. 8:18). God will not deny Himself to gratify their lusts. God is holy, unchangingly so. Therefore God hates sin, eternally hates it. Hence the *eternality* of the punishment of all who die in their sins.

The Divine immutability, like the cloud which interposed between the Israelites and the Egyptian army, has a dark as well as a light side. It insures the execution of His threatenings, as well as the performance of His promises; and destroys the hope which the guilty fondly cherish, that He will be all lenity to His frail and erring creatures, and that they will be much more lightly dealt with than the declarations of His own Word would lead us to expect. We oppose to these deceitful and presumptuous speculations the solemn truth, that God is unchanging in veracity and purpose, in faithfulness and justice (John Dick, 1850).

8

THE HOLINESS OF GOD

"Who shall not fear Thee, O Lord, and glorify Thy name? for Thou only art holy" (Rev. 15:4). He only is independently, infinitely, immutably holy. In Scripture He is frequently styled "The Holy One": He is so because the sum of all moral excellency is found in Him. He is absolute Purity, unsullied even by the shadow of sin. "God is light, and in Him is no darkness at all" (I John 1:5). Holiness is the very excellency of the Divine nature: the great God is "glorious in holiness" (Ex. 15:11). Therefore do we read, "Thou art of purer eyes than to behold evil, and canst not look on iniquity" (Hab. 1:13). As God's power is the opposite of the native weakness of the creature, as His wisdom is in complete contrast from the least defect of understanding or folly, so His holiness is the very antithesis of all moral blemish or defilement. Of old God appointed singers in Israel "that they should praise the beauty of holiness" (II Chron. 20:21). "Power is God's hand or arm, omniscience His eye, mercy His bowels, eternity His duration, but holiness is His beauty" (Stephen Charnock). It is this, supremely, which renders Him lovely to those who are delivered from sin's dominion.

A chief emphasis is placed upon this perfection of God:

God is oftener styled Holy than Almighty, and set forth by this part of His dignity more than by any other. This is more fixed on as an epithet to His name than any other. You never find it expressed "His mighty name" or "His wise name," but His *great* name, and most of all, His *holy* name. This is the greatest title of honour; in this latter doth the majesty and venerableness of His name appear (Stephen Charnock).

This perfection, as none other, is solemnly celebrated before the Throne of Heaven, the seraphim crying, "Holy, holy, holy, is the Lord of hosts" (Isa. 6:3). God Himself singles out this perfection, "Once have I sworn by My holiness" (Psa. 89:35). God swears by His "holiness" because that is a *fuller* expression of Himself than anything else. Therefore are we exhorted, "Sing unto the Lord, O ye saints of His, and give thanks at the remembrance of His holiness" (Psa. 30:4). "This may be said to be a transcendental attribute, that, as it were, runs through the rest, and casts lustre upon them. It is an attribute of attributes" (John Howe, 1670). Thus we read of "the *beauty* of the Lord" (Psa. 27:4), which is none other than "the beauty of holiness" (Psa. 110:3).

As it seems to challenge an excellency above all His other perfections, so it is the glory of all the rest: as it is the glory of the Godhead, so it is the glory of every perfection in the Godhead; as His power is the strength of them, so His holiness is the beauty of them; as all would be weak without almightiness to back them, so all would be uncomely without holiness to adorn them. Should this be sullied, all the rest would lose their honour; as at the same instant the sun should lose its light, it would lose its heat, its strength, its generative and quickening virtue. As sincerity is the lustre of every grace in a Christian, so is purity the splendour of every attribute in the Godhead. His justice is a holy justice, His wisdom a holy wisdom, His arm of power a "holy arm" (Psa. 98:1), His truth or promise a "holy promise" (Psa. 105:42). His name, which signifies all His attributes in conjunction, "is holy," Psa. 103:1 (Stephen Charnock).

God's holiness is manifested in His *works*. "The Lord is righteous in all His ways, and holy in all His works" (Psa. 145:17). Nothing but that which is excellent can proceed from Him. Holiness is the rule of all His actions. At the beginning He pronounced all that He made "very good" (Gen. 1:31), which He could not have done had there been anything imperfect or unholy in them. Man was made "upright" (Eccl. 7:29), in the image and likeness of his Creator. The angels that fell were created holy, for we are told that they "kept not their first habitation" (Jude 6). Of Satan it is written, "Thou wast perfect in thy ways from the day that thou wast created, till iniquity was found in thee" (Ezek. 28:15).

God's holiness is manifested in His *law*. That law forbids sin in *all* of its modifications: in its most refined as well as its grossest forms, the intent of the mind as well as the pollution of the body, the secret desire as well as the overt act. Therefore do we read, "The law is holy, and the commandment holy, and just, and good" (Rom. 7:12). Yes, "the commandment of the Lord is pure, enlightening the eyes. The fear of the Lord is clean, enduring forever: the judgments of the Lord are true and righteous altogether" (Psa. 19:8, 9).

God's holiness is manifested *at the Cross.* Wondrously and yet most solemnly does the Atonement display God's infinite holiness and abhorrence of sin. How hateful must sin be to God for Him to punish it to its utmost deserts when it was imputed to His Son!

> Not all the vials of judgment that have or shall be poured out upon the wicked world, nor the flaming furnace of a sinner's conscience, nor the irreversible sentence pronounced against the rebellious demons, nor the groans of the damned creatures, give such a demonstration of God's hatred of sin, as the wrath of God let loose upon His Son. Never did Divine holiness appear more beautiful and lovely than at the time our Saviour's countenance was most marred in the midst of His dying groans. This He Himself acknowledges in Psa. 22. When God had turned His smiling face from Him, and thrust His sharp knife into His heart, which forced that terrible cry from Him, "My God, My God, why hast Thou forsaken me?" He adores this perfection—"Thou art holy," v. 3 (Stephen Charnock).

Because God is holy He *hates all sin.* He loves everything which is in conformity to His law, and loathes everything which is contrary to it. His Word plainly declares, "The froward is an abomination to the Lord" (Prov. 3:32). And again, "The thoughts of the wicked are an abomination to the Lord" (Prov. 15:26). It follows, therefore, that He must necessarily punish sin. Sin can no more exist without demanding His punishment than without requiring His hatred of it. God has often forgiven sinners, but He never forgives sin; and the sinner is only forgiven on the ground of Another having borne his punishment; for "without shedding of blood is no remission" (Heb. 9:22). Therefore we are told, "The Lord will take vengeance on His adversaries, and He reserveth wrath for His enemies" (Nahum 1:2). For one sin God banished our first parents from Eden. For one sin all the posterity of Canaan, a son of Ham, fell under a curse which remains over them to this day (Gen. 9:21). For one sin Moses was excluded from Canaan, Elisha's servant smitten with leprosy, Ananias and Sapphira cut off out of the land of the living.

Herein we find proof for the Divine inspiration of the Scriptures. The unregenerate do not really believe in the holiness of God. Their conception of His character is altogether one-sided. They fondly hope that His mercy will override everything else. "Thou thoughtest that I was altogether as thyself" (Psa. 50:21) is God's charge against them. They think only of a "god" patterned after their own evil hearts. Hence their continuance in a course of mad folly. Such is the holiness ascribed to the Divine nature and character in the Scriptures that it clearly demonstrates their superhuman origin. The character attributed to the "gods" of the ancients and of modern heathendom is the very reverse of that immaculate purity which pertains to the true God. An ineffably holy God, who has the utmost abhorrence of all sin, was never invented by any of Adam's fallen descendants! The fact is that nothing makes more manifest the terrible depravity of man's heart and his enmity against the living God than to have set before him One who is infinitely and immutably holy. His own idea of *sin* is practically limited to what the world calls "crime." Anything short of that man palliates as "defects," "mistakes," "infirmities," etc. And even where sin is owned at all, excuses and extenuations are made for it.

The "god" which the vast majority of professing Christians "love" is looked upon very much like an indulgent old man, who himself has no relish for folly, but leniently winks at the "indiscretions" of youth. But the Word says, "Thou hatest *all* workers of iniquity" (Psa. 5:5). And again, "God is angry with the wicked every day" (Psa. 7:11). But men refuse to believe in *this* God, and gnash their teeth when His hatred of sin is faithfully pressed upon their attention. No, sinful man was no more likely to devise a holy God than to create the Lake of fire in which he will be tormented for ever and ever.

Because God is holy, acceptance with Him on the ground of creature-doings is utterly impossible. A fallen creature could sooner create a world than produce that which would meet the approval of infinite Purity. Can darkness dwell with Light? Can the Immaculate One take pleasure in "filthy rags" (Isa. 64:6)? The best that sinful man brings forth is defiled. A corrupt tree cannot bear good fruit. God would deny Himself, vilify His perfections, were He to account as righteous and holy that which is not so in itself; and nothing is so which has the least stain upon it contrary to the nature of God. But blessed be His name, that which His holiness demanded His grace has provided in Christ Jesus our Lord. Every poor sinner who has fled to Him for refuge stands "accepted in the Beloved" (Eph. 1:6). Hallelujah!

Because God is holy the utmost reverence becomes our approaches unto Him. "God is greatly to be feared in the assembly of the saints, and to be had in reverence of all about Him" (Psa. 89:7). Then "Exalt ye the Lord our God, and worship at His footstool; He is holy" (Psa. 99.5). Yes, "at His *footstool*," in the lowest posture of humility, prostrate before Him. When Moses would approach unto the burning bush, God said, "put off thy shoes from off thy feet" (Ex. 3:5). He is to be served "with fear" (Psa. 2:11). Of Israel His demand was, "I will be sanctified in them that come nigh Me, and before all the people I will be glorified" (Lev. 10:3). The more our hearts are awed by His ineffable holiness, the more acceptable will be our approaches unto Him.

Because God is holy we should desire to be conformed to Him. His command is, "Be ye holy, for I am holy" (I Peter 1:16). We are not bidden to be omnipotent or omniscient as God is, but we are to be holy, and that "in *all* manner of deportment" (I Peter 1:15).

> This is the prime way of honouring God. We do not so glorify God by elevated admirations, or eloquent expressions, or pompous services of Him, as when we aspire to a conversing with Him with unstained spirits, and live *to* Him in living *like* Him (Stephen Charnock).

Then as God alone is the Source and Fount of holiness, let us earnestly seek holiness from Him; let our daily prayer be that He may "sanctify us *wholly*; and our whole spirit and soul and body be preserved blameless unto the coming of our Lord Jesus Christ" (I Thess. 5:23).

9

THE POWER OF GOD

We cannot have a right conception of God unless we think of Him as all-powerful, as well as all-wise. He who cannot do what he will and perform all his pleasure cannot be God. As God hath a will to resolve what He deems good, so has He power to execute His will.

The power of God is that ability and strength whereby He can bring to pass whatsoever He pleases, whatsoever His infinite wisdom may direct, and whatsoever the infinite purity of His will may resolve. . . . As holiness is the beauty of all God's attributes, so power is that which gives life and action to all the perfections of the Divine nature. How vain would be the eternal counsels, if power did not step in to execute them. Without power His mercy would be but feeble pity, His promises an empty sound, His threatenings a mere scarecrow. God's power is like Himself: infinite, eternal, incomprehensible; it can neither be checked, restrained, nor frustrated by the creature (Stephen Charnock).

"God hath spoken once; twice have I heard this, that power belongeth unto God" (Psa. 62:11). "God hath spoken once": nothing more is necessary! Heaven and earth shall pass away, but His word abideth forever. "God hath spoken once": how befitting His Divine majesty! We poor mortals may speak often and yet fail to be heard. He speaks but once and the thunder of His power is heard on a thousand hills. "The Lord also thundered in the heavens, and the Highest gave His voice; hailstones and coals of fire. Yea, He sent out His arrows, and scattered them; and He shot out lightnings, and discomfited them. Then the channels of waters were seen and the foundations of the world were discovered at Thy rebuke, O Lord, at the blast of the breath of Thy nostrils" (Psa. 18:13-15).

"God hath spoken once": behold His unchanging authority. "For who in the heavens can be compared unto the Lord? who among the sons of the mighty can be likened unto the Lord?" (Psa. 89:6). "And all the inhabitants of the earth are reputed *as nothing*: and He doeth according to His will in the army of heaven, and among the inhabitants of the earth: and none can stay His hand, or say unto Him, What doest Thou?" (Dan. 4:35). This was openly displayed when God became incarnate and tabernacled among men. To the leper He said, "I will, be thou clean, and *immediately* his leprosy *was* cleansed" (Matt. 8:3). To one who had lain in the grave four days He cried, "Lazarus, come forth," and the dead came forth. The stormy wind and the angry wave were hushed at a single word from Him. A legion of demons could not resist His authoritative command.

"Power *belongeth* unto God," and to Him alone. Not a creature in the entire universe has an atom of power save what God delegates. But God's power is not acquired, nor does it depend upon any recognition by any other authority. It belongs to Him inherently.

God's power is like Himself, self-existent, self-sustained. The mightiest of men cannot add so much as a shadow of increased power to the Omnipotent One. He sits on no buttressed throne and leans on no assisting arm. His court is not maintained by His courtiers, not does it borrow its splendor from His creatures. He is Himself the great central source and Originator of all power (C. H. Spurgeon).

Not only does all creation bear witness to the great power of God, but also to his entire independency of all created things. Listen to His own challenge: "Where wast *thou* when *I* laid the foundations of the earth? declare, if thou hast understanding. Who hath laid the measures thereof, if thou knowest? or who hath stretched the line upon it? Whereupon are the foundations thereof fastened or who laid the cornerstone thereof?" (Job 38:4-6). How completely is the pride of man laid in the dust!

Power is also used as a name of God, "the Son of man sitting at the right hand of power" (Mark 14:62), that is, at the right hand of God. God and power are so inseparable that they are reciprocated. As His essence is immense, not to be confined in place; as it is eternal, not to be

measured in time; so it is almighty, not to be limited in
regard of action (Stephen Charnock).

"Lo, these are parts of His ways: but how little a portion is
heard of Him? but the thunder of His power who can understand? (Job 26:14). Who is able to count all the monuments
of His power? Even that which is displayed of His might in
the visible creation is utterly beyond our powers of comprehension, still less are we able to conceive of omnipotence itself. There is infinitely more power lodged in the nature of
God than is expressed in all His works.

"Parts of His ways" we behold in creation, providence, redemption, but only a "little part" of *His* might is seen in
them. Remarkably is this brought out in Hab. 3:4: "and *there
was the hiding of His power.*" It is scarcely possible to imagine anything more grandiloquent than the imagery of this
whole chapter, yet nothing in it surpasses the nobility of this
statement. The prophet (in vision) beheld the mighty God
scattering the hills and overturning the mountains, which one
would think afforded an amazing demonstration of His
power. Nay, says our verse, *that* is rather the "hiding" than
the displaying of *His* power. What is meant? This: so inconceivable, so immense, so uncontrollable is the power of
Deity, that the fearful convulsions which He works in nature
conceal more than they reveal of His infinite might!

It is very beautiful to link together the following passages:
"He walketh upon the waves of the sea" (Job 9:8), which
expresses God's uncontrollable power. "He walketh in the cir-
cuit of Heaven" (Job 22:14), which tells of the immensity of
His presence. "He walketh upon the wings of the wind" (Psa.
104:3), which signifies the amazing swiftness of His operations. This last expression is very remarkable. It is not that
"He flieth," or "runneth," but that He "walketh" and that, on
the very "wings of the wind"—on the most impetuous of the
elements, tossed into utmost rage, and sweeping along with almost inconceivable rapidity, yet they are *under* His feet,
beneath His perfect control!

Let us now consider God's power *in creation*. "The heavens
are Thine, the earth also is Thine, as for the world and the
fulness thereof, Thou has founded them. The north and the
south Thou hast created them" (Psa. 89:11, 12). Before man
can work he must have both tools and materials, but God began with nothing, and by His word alone out of nothing
made all things. The intellect cannot grasp it. God "spake

and it was done, He commanded and it stood fast" (Psa. 33:9). Primeval matter heard His voice. "God said, Let there be ... and it *was* so" (Gen. 1). Well may we exclaim, "Thou hast a mighty arm: strong is Thy hand, high is Thy right hand" (Psa. 89:13).

Who, that looks upward to the midnight sky; and, with an eye of reason, beholds its rolling wonders; who can forbear enquiring, Of *what* were their mighty orbs *formed?* Amazing to relate, they were produced without materials. They sprung from emptiness itself. The stately fabric of universal nature emerged out of *nothing.* What instruments were used by the Supreme Architect to fashion the parts with such exquisite niceness, and give so beautiful a polish to the whole? How was it all connected into one finely-proportioned and nobly finished structure? A *bare fiat* accomplished all. *Let them be,* said God. He added no more; and at once the marvelous edifice arose, adorned with every beauty, displaying innumerable perfections, and declaring amidst enraptured seraphs its great Creator's praise. "By the *word* of the Lord were the heavens made, and all the host of them by the *breath* of His mouth," Psa. 33:6 (James Hervey, 1789).

Consider God's power *in preservation.* No creature has power to preserve itself. "Can the rush grow up without mire? can the flag grow up without water?" (Job 8:11). Both man and beast would perish if there were not herbs for food, and herbs would wither and die if the earth were not refreshed with fruitful showers. Therefore is God called the Preserver of "man and beast" (Psa. 36:6). He "upholdeth all things by the word of His power" (Heb. 1:3). What a marvel of Divine power is the prenatal life of every human being! That an infant can live at all, and for so many months, in such cramped and filthy quarters, and that without breathing, is unaccountable without the power of God. Truly He "holdeth our soul in life" (Psa. 66:9).

The preservation of the earth from the violence of the sea is another plain instance of God's might. How is that raging element kept pent within those limits wherein He first lodged it, continuing its channel, without overflowing the earth and dashing in pieces the lower part of the creation? The natural situation of the water is to be above the earth, because it is lighter, and to be immediately under the air, because it is heavier. Who restrains the natural quality of it? Certainly man does not, and cannot. It is the fiat of its Creator which alone bridles it: "Hitherto shalt thou come, but no further: and here shall thy proud waves be stayed" (Job 38:11). What a standing monument of the power of God is the preservation of the world!

Consider God's power *in government*. Take His restraining of the malice of Satan. "The devil, as a roaring lion, walketh about, seeking whom he may devour" (I Peter 5:8). He is filled with hatred against God, and with fiendish enmity against men, particularly the saints. He that envied Adam in paradise envies us the pleasure of enjoying any of God's blessings. Could he have his will, he would treat all the same way he treated Job: he would send fire from heaven on the fruits of the earth, destroy the cattle, cause a wind to overthrow our houses, and cover our bodies with boils. But, little as men may realize it, God bridles him to a large extent, prevents him from carrying out his evil designs, and confines him within *His* ordinations.

So too God restrains the natural corruption of men. He suffers sufficient outbreakings of sin to show what fearful havoc has been wrought by man's apostasy from his Maker, but who can conceive the frightful lengths to which men would go were God to remove His curbing hand? "Their mouth is full of cursing and bitterness, their feet are swift to shed blood" (Rom. 3:14, 15). This is the nature of *every* descendant of Adam. Then what unbridled licentiousness and headstrong folly would triumph in the world, if the power of God did not interpose to lock down the floodgates of it! See Psa. 93:3, 4.

Consider God's power *in judgment*. When He smites, none can resist Him: see Ezek. 22:14. How terribly this was exemplified at the Flood! God opened the windows of heaven and broke up the great fountains of the deep, and (excepting those in the ark) the entire human race, helpless before the storm of His wrath, was swept away. A shower of fire and brimstone from heaven, and the cities of the plain were exterminated. Pharaoh and all his hosts were impotent when God blew upon them at the Red Sea. What a terrific word is that in Rom. 9:22: "What if God, willing to show His wrath, and to make His *power* known, endured with much longsuffering the vessels of wrath fitted to destruction." God is going to display His mighty power upon the reprobate not merely by incarcerating them in Gehenna, but by supernaturally preserving their bodies as well as souls amid the eternal burnings of the Lake of Fire.

Well may all *tremble* before such a God! To treat with impudence One who can crush us more easily than we can a moth, is a suicidal policy. To openly defy Him who is clothed with omnipotence, who can rend us in pieces or cast us into Hell any moment He pleases, is the very height of insanity. To put it on its lowest ground, it is but the part of wisdom to heed His command, "Kiss the Son, lest He be angry, and ye perish from the way, when His wrath is kindled but a little" (Psa. 2:12).

Well may the enlightened soul *adore* such a God! The wondrous and infinite perfections of such a Being call for fervent worship. If men of might and renown claim the admiration of the world, how much more should the power of the Almighty fill us with wonderment and homage. "Who is like unto Thee, O Lord, among the gods, who is like Thee, glorious in holiness, fearful in praises, doing wonders?" (Ex. 15:11).

Well may the saint *trust* such a God! He is worthy of implicit confidence. Nothing is too hard for Him. If God were stinted in might and had a limit to His strength we might well despair. But seeing that He is clothed with omnipotence, no prayer is too hard for *Him* to answer, no need too great for Him to supply, no passion too strong for Him to subdue; no temptation too powerful for Him to deliver from, no misery too deep for Him to relieve. "The Lord is the strength of my life; of whom shall I be afraid?" (Psa. 27:1). "Now unto Him that is able to do exceeding abundantly above all that we ask or think, according to the power that worketh in us, unto Him be glory in the church by Christ Jesus throughout all ages, world without end. Amen" (Eph. 3:20, 21).

10

THE FAITHFULNESS OF GOD

Unfaithfulness is one of the most outstanding sins of these evil days. In the business world, a man's word is, with exceedingly rare exceptions, no longer his bond. In the social world, marital infidelity abounds on every hand, the sacred bonds of wedlock being broken with as little regard as the discarding of an old garment. In the ecclesiastical realm, thousands who have solemnly covenanted to preach the truth make no scruple to attack and deny it. Nor can reader or writer claim complete immunity from this fearful sin: in how many ways have we been unfaithful to Christ, and to the light and privileges which God has entrusted to us! How refreshing, then, how unspeakably blessed, to lift our eyes above this scene of ruin, and behold One who *is* faithful, faithful in all things, faithful at all times.

"Know therefore that the Lord Thy God, He is God, the *faithful* God" (Deut. 7:9). This quality is essential to His being, without it He would not be God. For God to be unfaithful would be to act contrary to His nature, which were impossible: "If we believe not, yet He abideth faithful; He cannot deny Himself" (II Tim. 2:13). Faithfulness is one of the glorious perfections of His being. He is as it were clothed with it: "O Lord God of hosts, who is a strong Lord like unto Thee? or to Thy faithfulness *round about* Thee?" (Psa. 89:8). So too when God became incarnate it was said, "Righteousness shall be the girdle of His loins, and faithfulness the girdle of His reins" (Isa. 11:5).

What a word is that in Psa. 36:5, "Thy mercy, O Lord, is in the heavens; and Thy faithfulness unto the clouds." Far above all finite comprehension is the unchanging faithfulness of God. Everything about God is great, vast, incomparable. He never forgets, never fails, never falters, never forfeits His word. To every declaration of promise or prophecy the Lord has exactly adhered, every engagement of covenant or threatening He will make good, for "God is not a man, that He should lie; neither the son of man, that He should repent: hath He said, and shall He not do it? or hath He spo-

ken, and shall He not make it good?" (Num. 23:19). Therefore does the believer exclaim, "His compassions fail not, they
are new every morning: *great* is Thy faithfulness" (Lam.
3:22, 23).

Scripture abounds in illustrations of God's faithfulness.
More than four thousand years ago He said, "While the earth
remaineth, seedtime and harvest, and cold and heat, and summer and winter, and day and night shall not cease" (Gen.
8:22). Every year that comes furnishes a fresh witness to
God's fulfillment of this promise. In Gen. 15 we find that
Jehovah declared unto Abraham, "Thy seed shall be a
stranger in a land that is not theirs, and shall serve them ...
But in the fourth generation they shall come hither again"
(vv. 13-16). Centuries ran their weary course. Abraham's
descendants groaned amid the brick-kilns of Egypt. Had God
forgotten His promise? No, indeed. Read Ex. 12:41, "And it
came to pass at the end of the four hundred and thirty years,
even the selfsame day it came to pass, that all the hosts of the
Lord went out from the land of Egypt." Through Isaiah the
Lord declared, "Behold, a virgin shall conceive, and bear a
son, and shall call His name Immanuel" (7:14). Again centuries passed, but "When the fulness of the time was come,
God sent forth His Son, made of a woman" (Gal. 4:4).

God is true. His Word of Promise is sure. In all His relations with His people God is faithful. He may be safely relied
upon. No one ever yet really trusted Him in vain. We find
this precious truth expressed almost everywhere in the Scriptures, for His people need to know that faithfulness is an essential part of the Divine character. This is the basis of our
confidence in Him. But it is one thing to accept the faithfulness of God as a Divine truth, it is quite another to *act upon
it.* God has given us many "exceeding great and precious
promises," but are we really counting on His fulfillment of
them? Are we actually *expecting* Him to do for us all that He
has said? Are we resting with implicit assurance on these
words, "He is *faithful* that promised" (Heb. 10:23)?

There are seasons in the lives of all when it is not easy, no
not even for Christians, to believe that God *is* faithful. Our
faith is sorely tried, our eyes bedimmed with tears, and we
can no longer trace the outworkings of His love. Our ears are
distracted with the noises of the world, harassed by the atheis-
tic whisperings of Satan, and we can no longer hear the sweet
accents of His still small voice. Cherished plans have been

thwarted, friends on whom we relied have failed us, a professed brother or sister in Christ has betrayed us. We are staggered. We sought to be faithful to God, and now a dark cloud hides Him from us. We find it difficult, yea, impossible, for carnal reason to harmonize His frowning providence with His gracious promises. Ah, faltering soul, severely tried fellow pilgrim, seek grace to heed Isa. 50:10, "Who is among you that feareth the Lord, that obeyeth the voice of His servant, that walketh in darkness and hath no light? let him trust in the name of the Lord, and *stay upon his God.*"

When you are tempted to doubt the faithfulness of God, cry out, "Get thee hence, Satan." Though you cannot now harmonize God's mysterious dealings with the avowals of His love, wait on Him for more light. In His own good time He will make it plain to you. "What I do thou knowest not *now*, but thou shalt know hereafter" (John 13:7). The sequel will yet demonstrate that God has neither forsaken nor deceived His child. "And therefore will the Lord *wait* that He may be gracious unto you, and therefore will He be exalted, that He may have mercy upon you: for the Lord is a God of judgment: blessed are all they *that wait for Him*" (Isa. 30:18).

> "Judge not the Lord by feeble sense,
> But trust Him for His grace,
> Behind a frowning providence
> He hides a smiling face.
> Ye fearful saints, fresh courage take,
> The clouds ye so much dread,
> Are rich with mercy, and shall break
> In blessing o'er your head."

"Thy testimonies which Thou hast commanded are righteous and very faithful" (Psa. 119:138). God has not only told us the best, but He has not withheld the worst. He has faithfully described the ruin which the Fall has effected. He has faithfully diagnosed the terrible state which sin has produced. He has faithfully made known his inveterate hatred of evil, and that He must punish the same. He has faithfully warned us that He is "a consuming fire" (Heb. 12:29). Not only does His Word abound in illustrations of His fidelity in fulfilling His promises, but it also records numerous examples of His faithfulness in making good His threatenings. Every stage of Israel's history exemplifies that solemn fact. So it was with individuals: Pharaoh, Korah, Achan and a host of others are so many proofs. And thus it will be with *you,* my reader: unless you have fled or do flee to Christ for refuge, the everlasting burning of the Lake of Fire will be your sure and certain portion. God *is* faithful.

God is faithful in *preserving* His people. "God is faithful, by whom ye are called unto the fellowship of His Son" (I Cor. 1:9). In the previous verse promise was made that God would confirm unto the end His own people. The Apostle's confidence in the absolute security of believers was founded not on the strength of their resolutions or ability to persevere, but on the veracity of Him that cannot lie. Since God has promised to His Son a certain people for His inheritance, to deliver them from sin and condemnation, and to make them participants of eternal life in glory, it is certain that He will not allow any of them to perish.

God is faithful in *disciplining* His people. He is faithful in what He withholds, no less than in what He gives. He is faithful in sending sorrow as well as in giving joy. The faithfulness of God is a truth to be confessed by us not only when we are at ease, but also when we are smarting under the sharpest rebuke. Nor must this confession be merely of our mouths, but of our hearts, too. When God smites us with the rod of chastisement, it is *faithfulness* which wields it. To acknowledge this means that we humble ourselves before Him, own that we fully deserve His correction, and instead of murmuring, thank Him for it. God never afflicts without a reason. "For *this cause* many are weak and sickly among you" (I Cor. 11:30), says Paul, illustrating this principle. When His rod falls upon us let us say with Daniel, "O Lord, righteousness belongeth unto Thee, but unto us confusion of faces" (9:7).

"I know, O Lord, that Thy judgments are right, and that Thou *in faithfulness* hast afflicted me" (Psa. 119:75). Trouble and affliction are not only consistent with God's love pledged in the everlasting covenant, but they are parts of the administration of the same. God is not only faithful notwithstanding afflictions, but faithful in sending them. "Then will I visit their transgression with the rod, and their iniquity with stripes: My lovingkindness will I not utterly take from him nor suffer My faithfulness to fail" (Psa. 89:32, 33). Chastening is not only reconcilable with God's lovingkindness, but it is the effect and expression of it. It would much quieten the minds of God's people if they would remember that His covenant love binds Him to lay on them seasonable correction. Afflictions are necessary for us: "In their affliction they will seek Me early" (Hos. 5:15).

God is faithful in *glorifying* His people. "Faithful is He which calleth you, who also will do" (I Thess. 5:24). The immediate reference here is to the saints being "preserved blameless unto the coming of our Lord Jesus Christ." God deals with us not on the ground of our merits (for we have none), but for His own great name's sake. God is constant to Himself and to His own purpose of grace: "whom He called ... them He also glorified" (Rom. 8:30). God gives a full demonstration of the constancy of His everlasting goodness toward His elect by effectually calling them out of darkness into His marvelous light, and this should fully assure them of the certain continuance of it. "The foundation of God *standeth sure*" (II Tim. 2:19). Paul was resting on the faithfulness of God when he said, "I know whom I have believed, and am persuaded that He is able to keep that which I have committed unto Him against that day" (II Tim. 1:12).

The apprehension of this blessed truth will *preserve us from worry*. To be full of care, to view our situation with dark forebodings, to anticipate the morrow with sad anxiety, is to reflect poorly upon the faithfulness of God. He who has cared for His child through all the years will not forsake him in old age. He who has heard your prayers in the past will not refuse to supply your need in the present emergency. Rest on Job 5:19, "He *shall* deliver thee in six troubles: yea, in seven there shall no evil touch thee."

The apprehension of this blessed truth will *check our murmurings*. The Lord knows what is best for each one of us, and one effect of resting on this truth will be the silencing of our petulant complainings. God is greatly honored when, under trial and chastening, we have good thoughts of Him, vindicate His wisdom and justice, and recognize His love in His very rebukes.

The apprehension of this blessed truth will beget increasing *confidence in God*. "Wherefore let them that suffer according to the will of God commit the keeping of their souls to Him in well doing, as unto a faithful Creator" (I Peter 4:19). When we trustfully resign ourselves, and all our affairs into God's hands, fully persuaded of His love and faithfulness, the sooner shall we be satisfied with His providences and realize that "He doeth *all* things well."

11

THE GOODNESS OF GOD

"The goodness of God endureth continually" (Psa. 52:1).
The "goodness" of God refers to the perfection of His nature:
"God is light, and in Him is *no* darkness at all" (I John 1:5).
There is such an absolute perfection in God's nature and
being that nothing is wanting to it or defective in it, and
nothing can be added to it to make it better.

> He is originally good, good of Himself, which nothing else
> is; for all creatures are good only by participation and
> communication from God. He is essentially good; not
> only good, but goodness itself: the creature's good is a su-
> peradded quality, in God it is His essence. He is infinitely
> good; the creature's good is but a drop, but in God there
> is an infinite ocean or gathering together of good. He is
> eternally and immutably good, for He cannot be less
> good than He is; as there can be no addition made to
> Him, so no subtraction from Him (Thomas Manton).

God is *summum bonum*, the highest good.

God is not only the Greatest of all beings, but the Best. All
the goodness there is in any creature has been imparted from
the Creator, but *God's* goodness is underived, for it is the
essence of His eternal nature. As God is infinite in power
from all eternity, before there was any display thereof, or any
act of omnipotency put forth, so He was eternally good before there was any communication of His bounty, or any
creature to whom it might be imparted. Thus, the first manifestation of this Divine perfection was in giving being to all
things. "Thou art good, and *doest* good" (Psa. 119:68). God
has in Himself an infinite and inexhaustible treasure of all
blessedness, enough to fill all things.

All that emanates from God—His decrees, His creation, His
laws, His providences—cannot be otherwise than good: as it is
written, "And God saw everything that He had made, and,

behold, it was *very good*" (Gen. 1:31). Thus, the "goodness" of God is *seen*, first, in creation. The more closely the creature is studied, the more the beneficence of its Creator becomes apparent. Take the highest of God's earthly creatures, man. Abundant reason has he to say with the Psalmist, "I will praise Thee, for I am fearfully and wonderfully made: marvelous are Thy works, and that my soul knoweth right well" (139:14). Everything about the structure of our bodies attests the goodness of their Maker. How suited the hands to perform their allotted work! How good of the Lord to appoint sleep to refresh the wearied body! How benevolent His provision to give to the eyes lids and brows for their protection! And so we might continue indefinitely.

Nor is the goodness of the Creator confined to man; it is exercised toward all His creatures. "The eyes of all wait upon Thee; and Thou givest them their meat in due season. Thou openest Thine hand, and satisfiest the desire of every living thing" (Psa. 145:15, 16). Whole volumes might be written, yea have been, to amplify this fact. Whether it be the birds of the air, the beasts of the forest, or the fish in the sea, abundant provision has been made to supply their every need. God "giveth food to all flesh, for His mercy endureth forever" (Psa. 136:25). Truly, "The earth is full of the goodness of the Lord" (Psa. 33:5).

The goodness of God is seen in the variety of natural pleasures which He has provided for His creatures. God might have been pleased to satisfy our hunger without the food being pleasing to our palates—how His benevolence appears in the varied flavors which He has given to meats, vegetables, and fruits! God has not only given us senses, but also that which gratifies them; and this too reveals His goodness. The earth might have been as fertile as it is without its surface being so delightfully variegated. Our physical lives could have been sustained without beautiful flowers to regale our eyes with their colors, and our nostrils with their sweet perfumes. We might have walked the fields without our ears being saluted by the music of the birds. Whence, then, this loveliness, this charm, so freely diffused over the face of nature? Verily, "The *tender* mercies of the Lord are over *all* His works" (Psa. 145:9).

The goodness of God is seen in that when man transgressed the law of His Creator a dispensation of unmixed wrath did not at once commence. Well might God have deprived His fallen creatures of every blessing, every comfort, every pleasure. Instead, He ushered in a regime of a mixed nature, of mercy and judgment. This is very wonderful if it be duly considered, and the more thoroughly that regime be examined the more will it appear that "mercy rejoiceth against judgment" (James 2:13). Notwithstanding all the evils which attend our fallen state, the balance of good greatly preponderates. With comparatively rare exceptions, men and women experience a far greater number of days of health than they do of sickness and pain. There is much more creature-happiness than creature-misery in the world. Even our sorrows admit of considerable alleviation, and God has given to the human mind a pliability which adapts itself to circumstances and makes the most of them.

Nor can the benevolence of God be justly called into question because there *is* suffering and sorrow in the world. If man *sins against* the goodness of God, if he despises "the riches of His goodness and forbearance and longsuffering," and after the hardness and impenitency of his heart treasurest up unto himself wrath against the day of wrath (Rom. 2:4, 5), who is to blame but himself? Would God *be* "good" if He punished not those who ill-use His blessings, abuse His benevolence, and trample His mercies beneath their feet? It will be no reflection upon God's goodness, but rather the brightest exemplification of it, when He shall rid the earth of those who have broken His laws, defied His authority, mocked His messengers, scorned His Son, and persecuted those for whom He died.

The goodness of God appeared most illustriously when He sent forth His Son "made of woman, made under the law, to redeem them that were under the law, that we might receive the adoption of sons" (Gal. 4:4, 5). Then it was that a multitude of the heavenly host praised their Maker and said, "Glory to God in the highest and on earth peace, *goodwill* toward men" (Luke 2:14). Yes, in the Gospel the *"grace* (which word in Greek conveys the idea of *benevolence* or *goodness*) of God that bringeth salvation hath appeared to all men" (Titus 2:11). Nor can God's benignity be called into question because He has not made every sinful creature to be a subject of His redemptive grace. He did not bestow it upon the fallen angels. Had God left all to perish it would have been no reflection on His *goodness*. To any who would challenge this statement we will remind him of our Lord's sovereign prerogative: "Is it not lawful for Me to do what I will with Mine own? Is thine eye evil, because I am good?" (Matt. 20:15).

"O that men would praise the Lord for His goodness, and for His wonderful works to the children of men" (Psa. 107:8). Gratitude is the return justly required from the objects of His beneficence; yet it is often withheld from our great Benefactor simply because His goodness is so constant and so abundant. It is lightly esteemed because it is exercised toward us in the common course of events. It is not felt because we daily experience it. "Despisest *thou* the riches of His goodness?" (Rom. 2:4). His goodness is "despised" when it is not improved as a means to lead men to repentance, but, on the contrary, serves to harden them from the supposition that God entirely overlooks their sin.

The goodness of God is the life of the believer's trust. It is this excellency in God which most appeals to our hearts. Because His goodness endureth forever, we ought never to be discouraged: "The Lord is good, a stronghold in the day of trouble, and He knoweth them that trust in Him" (Nahum 1:7).

When others behave badly to us, it should only stir us up the more heartily to give thanks unto the Lord, because *He* is good; and when we ourselves are conscious that we are far from being good, we should only the more reverently bless Him that *He* is good. We must never tolerate an instant's unbelief as to the goodness of the Lord; whatever else may be questioned, this is absolutely certain, that Jehovah is good; His dispensations may vary, but His nature is always the same (C. H. Spurgeon).

12

THE PATIENCE OF GOD

Far less has been written upon this than the other excellencies of the Divine character. Not a few of those who have expatiated at length upon the Divine attributes have passed over the patience of God without any comment. It is not easy to suggest a reason for this, for surely the longsuffering of God is as much one of the Divine perfections as is His wisdom, power, or holiness, and as much to be admired and revered by us. True, the actual term will not be found in a concordance as frequently as the others, but the glory of this grace itself shines forth on almost every page of Scripture. Certain it is that we lose much if we do not frequently meditate upon the patience of God and earnestly pray that our hearts and ways may be more completely conformed thereto.

Most probably the principal reason why so many writers have failed to give us anything, separately, upon the patience of God was because of the difficulty of distinguishing this attribute from the Divine goodness and mercy, particularly the latter. God's longsuffering is mentioned in conjunction with His grace and mercy again and again, as may be seen by consulting Ex. 34:6, Num. 14:18, Psa. 86:15, etc. That the *patience* of God is really a display of His *mercy,* that it is indeed one way in which it is frequently manifested, cannot be denied. But that patience and mercy are one and the same excellency, and are not to be separated, we cannot concede. It may not be easy to discriminate between them, nevertheless, Scripture fully warrants us in affirming some things about the one which we cannot about the other.

Stephen Charnock, the Puritan, defines God's patience, in part, thus:

It is part of the Divine goodness and mercy, yet differs from both. God being the greatest goodness, hath the greatest mildness; mildness is always the companion of true goodness, and the greater the goodness, the greater the mildness. Who so holy as Christ, and who so meek? God's slowness to anger is a branch . . . from His mercy: "The Lord is full of compassion, slow to anger" (Psa. 145:8). It differs from mercy in the formal consideration of the object: mercy respects the creature as miserable, patience respects the creature as criminal; mercy pities him in his misery, and patience bears with the sin which engendered the misery, and is giving birth to more.

Personally, we would define the Divine patience as that power of control which God exercises over Himself, causing Him to bear with the wicked and forebear so long in punishing them. In Nahum 1:3 we read, "The Lord is slow to anger and great in power," upon which Mr. Charnock said,

Men that are great in the world are quick in passion, and are not so ready to forgive an injury, or bear with an offender, as one of a meaner rank. It is a want of power over that man's self that makes him do unbecoming things upon a provocation. A prince that can bridle his passions is a king over himself as well as over his subjects. God is slow to anger *because* great in power. He has no less power over Himself than over His creatures.

It is at the above point, we think, that God's patience is most clearly distinguished from His mercy. Though the creature is benefitted thereby, the patience of God chiefly respects Himself, a restraint placed upon His acts by His will; whereas His mercy terminates wholly upon the creature. The patience of God is that excellency which causes Him to sustain great injuries without immediately avenging Himself. He has a power of patience as well as a power of justice. Thus the Hebrew word for the Divine longsuffering is rendered "slow to anger" in Nehemiah 9:17, Psa. 103:8, etc. Not that there are any passions in the Divine nature, but that God's wisdom and will is pleased to act with that stateliness and sobriety which is becoming to His exalted majesty.

In support of our definition above let us point out that it was to this excellency in the Divine character that Moses appealed, when Israel sinned so grievously at Kadesh-Barnea, and there provoked Jehovah so sorely. Unto His servant the Lord said, "I will smite them with the pestilence and disinherit them." Then it was that the mediator Moses, as a type of the Christ to come, pleaded, "I beseech Thee, let *the power* of my Lord be great according as Thou hast spoken, saying, The Lord is *longsuffering,"* etc. (Num. 14:17). Thus, His "longsuffering" is His "power" of self-restraint.

Again, in Rom. 9:22 we read, "What if God, willing to show His wrath, and to make His *power* known, endured with much *longsuffering* the vessels of wrath fitted to destruction . . . ?" Were God to immediately break these reprobate vessels into pieces, His power of self-control would not so eminently appear; by bearing with their wickedness and forebearing punishment so long, the power of His patience is gloriously demonstrated. True, the wicked interpret His longsuffering quite differently—"Because sentence against an evil work is not executed speedily, therefore the heart of the sons of men is fully set in them to do evil" (Eccl. 8:11)—but the anointed eye adores what they abuse.

"The God of patience" (Rom. 15:5) is one of the Divine titles. Deity is thus denominated, first, because God is both the Author and Object of the grace of patience in the saint. Secondly, because this is what He is in Himself: patience is one of His perfections. Thirdly, as a pattern for us: "Put on therefore, as the *elect of God,* holy and beloved, bowels of mercy, kindness, humbleness of mind, meekness, *longsuffering*" (Col. 3:12). And again, "Be ye therefore followers (emulators) of God, as dear children" (Eph. 5:2). When tempted to be disgusted at the dullness of another, or to be revenged on one who has wronged you, call to remembrance God's infinite patience and longsuffering with yourself.

The patience of God is *manifested* in His dealings with sinners. How strikingly was it displayed toward the antediluvians. When mankind was universally degenerate, and all flesh had corrupted its way, God did not destroy them till He had forewarned them. He "waited" (I Peter 3:20), probably no less than one hundred and twenty years (Gen. 6:3), during which time Noah was a "preacher of righteousness" (II Peter 2:5). So, later, when the Gentiles not only worshipped and served the creature more than the Creator, but also committed the vilest abominations contrary even to the dictates of nature (Rom. 1:19-26) and thereby filled up the measure of their iniquity, yet, instead of drawing His sword for the extermination of such rebels, God "suffered all nations to walk in their own ways," and gave them "rain from heaven and fruitful seasons" (Acts 14:16, 17).

Marvelously was God's patience exercised and manifested toward *Israel.* First, He "suffered their manners" for forty years in the wilderness (Acts 13:18). Later, when they had entered Canaan, but followed the evil customs of the nations around them, and turned to idolatry, though God chastened them sorely, He did not utterly destroy them, but in their distress, raised up deliverers for them. When their iniquity was raised to such a height that none but a God of infinite patience could have borne them, He spared them many years before He allowed them to be carried down into Babylon. Finally, when their rebellion against Him reached its climax by crucifying His Son, He waited forty years ere He sent the Romans against them, and that, only after they had judged themselves "unworthy of eternal life" (Acts 13:46).

How wondrous is God's patience with the world today. On every side people are sinning with a high hand. The Divine law is trampled under foot and God Himself openly despised. It is truly amazing that He does not instantly strike dead those who so brazenly defy Him. Why does He not suddenly cut off the haughty infidel and blatant blasphemer, as He did Ananias and Sapphira? Why does He not cause the earth to open its mouth and devour the persecutors of his people, so that, like Dathan and Abiram, they shall go down alive into the Pit? And what of apostate Christendom, where every possible form of sin is now tolerated and practiced under cover of the holy name of Christ? Why does not the righteous wrath of Heaven make an end of such abominations? Only one answer is possible: because God bears with "*much* longsuffering the vessels of wrath fitted to destruction."

And what of the writer and the reader? Let us review our own lives. It is not long since *we* followed a multitude to do evil, had no concern for God's glory, and lived only to gratify self. How patiently He bore with our vile conduct! And now that grace has snatched us as brands from the burning, giving us a place in God's family, and has begotten us unto an eternal inheritance in glory, how miserably we requite Him. How shallow our gratitude, how tardy our obedience, how frequent our backslidings! One reason why God suffers the flesh to remain in the believer is that He may exhibit His "longsuffering *to usward*" (II Peter 3:9). Since this Divine attribute is manifested only in this world, God takes advantage to display it toward "His own."

May our meditation upon this Divine excellency soften our hearts, make our consciences tender, and may we learn in the school of holy experience the "patience of saints," namely, submission to the Divine will and continuance in well doing. Let us earnestly seek grace to emulate this Divine excellency. "Be ye therefore perfect, even as your Father which is in heaven is perfect" (Matt. 5:48). In the immediate context of this verse Christ exhorts us to love our enemies, bless them that curse us, do good to them that hate us. God bears long with the wicked notwithstanding the multitude of their sins, and shall we desire to be revenged because of a single injury?

13

THE GRACE OF GOD

Grace is a perfection of the Divine character which is exercised only toward the elect. Neither in the Old Testament nor in the New is the grace of God ever mentioned in connection with mankind generally, still less with the lower orders of His creatures. In this it is distinguished from "mercy," for the mercy of God is "over all His works" (Psa. 145:9). Grace is the sole source from which flows the goodwill, love, and salvation of God unto His chosen people. This attribute of the Divine character was defined by Abraham Booth in his helpful book *The Reign of Grace* thus: "It is the eternal and absolute free favour of God, manifested in the vouchsafement of spiritual and eternal blessings to the guilty and the unworthy."

Divine grace is the sovereign and saving favor of God exercised in the bestowment of blessings upon those who have no merit *in* them and for which no compensation is demanded *from* them. Nay, more; it is the favor of God shown to those who not only have no positive deserts of their own, but who are thoroughly ill-deserving and hell-deserving. It is completely unmerited and unsought, and is altogether unattracted by anything in or from or by the objects upon which it is bestowed. Grace can neither be bought, earned, nor won by the creature. If it could be, it would cease to be *grace*. When a thing is said to be of "grace" we mean that the recipient has no claim upon it, that it was in nowise due him. It comes to him as pure charity, and, at first, unasked and undesired.

The fullest exposition of the amazing grace of God is to be found in the Epistles of the Apostle Paul. In his writings "grace" stands in direct opposition to works and worthiness, *all* works and worthiness, of whatever kind or degree. This is abundantly clear from Rom. 11:6, "And if by grace, then it is no more of works: otherwise grace is no more grace. If it be of works, then is it no more grace, otherwise work is no more work." Grace and works will no more unite than an acid and an alkali. "By grace are ye saved through faith; and that not of yourselves; it is the gift of God: not of works, lest any man should boast" (Eph. 2:8, 9). The absolute favor of God can no more consist with human merit than oil and water will fuse into one (see also Rom. 4:4, 5).

There are three principal characteristics of Divine grace. First, it is *eternal*. Grace was planned before it was exercised, purposed before it was imparted: "Who hath saved us, and called us with a holy calling, not according to our works, but according to His own purpose and grace, which was given us in Christ Jesus *before* the world began" (II Tim. 1:9). Secondly, it is *free,* for none did ever purchase it: "Being justified *freely* by His grace" (Rom. 3:24). Thirdly, it is *sovereign,* because God exercises it toward and bestows it upon whom He pleases: "Even so might grace *reign*" (Rom. 5:21). If grace "reigns" then it is on the throne, and the occupant of the throne is sovereign. Hence "the *throne* of grace" (Heb. 4:16).

Just because grace *is unmerited* favor, it must be exercised in a *sovereign* manner. Therefore does the Lord declare, "I will be gracious to whom I will be gracious" (Ex. 33:19). Were God to show grace to all of Adam's descendants, men would at once conclude that He was righteously compelled to take them to heaven as a meet compensation for allowing the human race to fall into sin. But the great God is under no obligation to any of His creatures, least of all to those who are rebels against Him.

Eternal life is a *gift*, therefore it can neither be earned by good works, nor claimed as a right. Seeing that salvation *is* a "gift," who has any right to tell God on whom He ought to bestow it? It is not that the Giver ever *refuses* this gift to any who seek it wholeheartedly, and according to the rules which He has prescribed. No! He refuses none who come to Him empty-handed and in the way of His appointing. But if out of a world of impenitent and unbelieving rebels, God is determined to exercise His sovereign right by choosing a limited number to be saved, who is wronged? Is God *obliged* to force His gift on those who value it not? Is God compelled to save those who are determined to go *their own* way?

But nothing more riles the natural man and brings to the surface his innate and inveterate enmity against God than to press upon him the eternality, the freeness, and the absolute sovereignty of Divine grace. That God should have formed

His purpose from everlasting, without in anywise consulting the creature, is too abasing for the unbroken heart. That grace cannot be earned or won by any efforts of man is too self-emptying for self-righteousness. And that grace singles out whom it pleases to be its favored objects arouses hot protests from haughty rebels. The clay rises up against the Potter and asks, "Why hast Thou made me thus?" A lawless insurrectionist dares to call into question the justice of Divine sovereignty.

The distinguishing grace of God is seen in saving those people whom He has sovereignly singled out to be His high favorites. By "distinguishing" we mean that grace discriminates, makes differences, chooses some and passes by others. It was distinguishing grace which selected Abraham from the midst of his idolatrous neighbors and made him "the friend of God." It was distinguishing grace which saved "publicans and sinners," but said of the religious Pharisees, "Let them alone" (Matt. 15:14). Nowhere does the glory of God's free and sovereign grace shine more conspicuously than in the unworthiness and unlikeliness of its objects. Beautifully was this illustrated by James Hervey, (1751):

Where sin has abounded, says the proclamation from the court of heaven, grace doth much more abound. *Manasseh* was a monster of barbarity, for he caused his own children to pass through the fire, and filled Jerusalem with innocent blood. Manasseh was an adept in iniquity, for he not only multiplied, and to an extravagant degree, his own sacrilegious impieties, but he poisoned the principles and perverted the manners of his subjects, making them do worse than the most detestable of the heathen idolators (see II Chron. 33). Yet, through this superabundant grace he is humbled, he is reformed, and becomes a child of forgiving love, an heir of immortal glory.

Behold that bitter and bloody persecutor, *Saul;* when, breathing out threatenings and bent upon slaughter, he worried the lambs and put to death the disciples of Jesus. The havoc he had committed, the inoffensive families he had already ruined, were not sufficient to assuage his vengeful spirit. They were only a taste, which, instead of glutting the bloodhound, made him more closely pursue the track, and more eagerly pant for destruction. He is still athirst for violence and murder. So eager and insatiable is his thirst, that he even *breathes out* threatening and slaughter (Acts 9:1). His words are spears and arrows, and his tongue a sharp sword. 'Tis as natural for him to menace the Christians as to breathe the air. Nay, they bled every hour in the purposes of his rancorous heart. It is only owing to want of power that every syllable he utters, every breath he draws, does not deal out deaths, and cause some of the innocent disciples to fall. Who, upon the principles of human judgment, would not have pronounced *him* a vessel of wrath, destined to unavoidable damnation? Nay, would not have been ready to conclude that, if there were heavier chains and a deeper dungeon in the world of woe, they must surely be reserved for such an implacable enemy of true godliness? Yet, admire and adore the inexhaustible treasures of grace—*this* Saul is admitted into the goodly fellowship of the prophets, is numbered with the noble army of martyrs and makes a distinguished figure among the glorious company of the apostles.

The *Corinthian*s were flagitious even to a proverb. Some of them wallowed in such abominable vices, and habituated themselves to such outrageous acts of injustice, as were a reproach to human nature. Yet even these sons of violence and slaves of sensuality were washed, sanctified, justified (I Cor 6:9-11). "Washed," in the precious blood of a dying Redeemer; "sanctified," by the powerful operations of the blessed Spirit; "justified," through the infinitely tender mercies of a gracious God. Those who were once the burden of the earth are now the joy of heaven, the delight of angels.

Now the grace of God is manifested in and by and through the Lord Jesus Christ. "The law was given by Moses, grace and truth came by Jesus Christ" (John 1:17). This does not mean that God never exercised grace toward any before His Son became incarnate—Gen. 6:8, Ex. 33:19, etc., clearly show otherwise. But grace and truth were fully revealed and perfectly exemplified when the Redeemer came to this earth, and died for His people upon the cross. It is through Christ the Mediator alone that the grace of God flows to His elect. "Much more the grace of God, and the gift by grace, which is *by* one man, Jesus Christ . . . . much more they which receive abundance of grace, and of the gift of righteousness, shall reign in life *by* one, Jesus Christ . . . . so might grace reign through righteousness, unto eternal life, *by* Jesus Christ our Lord" (Rom. 5:15, 17, 21).

The grace of God is *proclaimed* in the Gospel (Acts 20:24), which is to the self-righteous Jew a "stumbling block," and to the conceited and philosophizing Greek "foolishness." And why so? Because there is nothing whatever in it that is adapted to the gratifying of the pride of man. It announces that unless we are saved by grace, we cannot be saved at all. It declares that apart from Christ, the unspeakable Gift of God's grace, the state of every man is desperate, irremediable, hopeless. The Gospel addresses men as guilty, condemned, perishing criminals. It declares that the chastest moralist is in the same terrible plight as is the most voluptuous profligate; and the zealous professor, with all his religious performances, is no better off than the most profane infidel.

The Gospel contemplates every descendant of Adam as a fallen, polluted, hell-deserving and helpless sinner. The grace which the Gospel publishes is his only hope. All stand before God convicted as transgressors of His holy law, as guilty and condemned criminals, who are not merely awaiting sentence, but the execution of sentence already passed upon them (John 3:18; Rom 3:19). To complain against the partiality of grace is suicidal. If the sinner insists upon bare justice, then the Lake of Fire must be his eternal portion. His only hope lies in bowing to the sentence which Divine justice has passed upon him, owning the absolute righteousness of it, casting himself on the mercy of God, and stretching forth empty hands to avail himself of the grace of God now made known to him in the Gospel.

The third Person in the Godhead is the *Communicator* of grace, therefore is He denominated "the Spirit of grace" (Zech. 12:10). God the Father is the Fountain of all grace, for He purposed in Himself the everlasting covenant of redemption. God the Son is the only Channel of grace. The Gospel is the Publisher of grace. The Spirit is the Bestower. He is the One who applies the Gospel in saving power to the soul: quickening the elect while spiritually dead, conquering their rebellious wills, melting their hard hearts, opening their blind eyes, cleansing them from the leprosy of sin. Thus we may say with the late G. S. Bishop,

> Grace is a provision for men who are so fallen that they cannot lift the axe of justice, so corrupt that they cannot change their own natures, so averse to God that they can-

not turn to Him, so blind that they cannot see Him, so deaf that they cannot hear Him, and so dead that He Himself must open their graves and lift them into resurrection.

14

THE MERCY OF GOD

"O give thanks unto the Lord: for He is good, for His mercy endureth forever" (Psa. 136:1). For this perfection of the Divine character God is greatly to be praised. Three times over in as many verses does the Psalmist here call upon the saints to give thanks unto the Lord for this adorable attribute. And surely this is the least that can be asked for from those who have been recipients of such bounty. When we contemplate the characteristics of this Divine excellency, we cannot do otherwise than bless God for it. His mercy is "great" (I Kings 3:6), "plenteous" (Psa. 86:5), "tender" (Luke 1:78), "abundant" (I Peter 1:3); it is "from everlasting to everlasting upon them that fear Him" (Psa. 103:17). Well may we say with the Psalmist, "I will sing aloud of Thy mercy" (59:16).

"I will make all My goodness pass before thee, and I will proclaim the name of the Lord before thee; and will be gracious to whom I will be gracious, and will show mercy on whom I will show mercy" (Ex. 33:19). Wherein differs the "mercy" of God from His "grace"? The mercy of God has its spring in the Divine goodness. The first issue of God's goodness is His benignity or bounty, by which He gives liberally to His creatures as creatures; thus has He given being and life to all things. The second issue of God's goodness is His mercy, which denotes the ready inclination of God to relieve the misery of fallen creatures. Thus, "mercy" presupposes *sin*.

Though it may not be easy at the first consideration to perceive a real difference between the grace and the mercy of God, it helps us thereto if we carefully ponder His dealings with the unfallen angels. He has never exercised mercy toward them, for they have never stood in any need thereof, not having sinned or come beneath the effects of the curse. Yet, they certainly are the objects of God's free and sovereign grace. First, because of His *election* of them from out of the whole angelic race (I Tim. 5:21). Secondly, and in consequence of their election, because of His *preservation* of them from apostacy, when Satan rebelled and dragged down with him one-third of the celestial hosts (Rev. 12:4). Thirdly, in making Christ their *Head* (Col. 2:10; I Peter 3:22), whereby they are eternally secured in the holy condition in which they were created. Fourthly, because of the exalted *position* which has been assigned them: to live in God's immediate presence (Dan. 7:10), to serve Him constantly in His heavenly temple, to receive honorable commissions from Him (Heb. 1:14). This is abundant *grace* toward them; but "mercy" it is not.

In endeavoring to study the mercy of God as it is set forth in Scripture, a threefold distinction needs to be made, if the Word of Truth is to be "rightly divided" thereon. First, there is a *general* mercy of God, which is extended not only to all men, believers and unbelievers alike, but also to the entire creation: "His tender mercies are over *all* His works" (Psa. 145:9); "He giveth to all life, and breath, and all things" (Acts 17:25). God has pity upon the brute creation in their needs, and supplies them with suitable provision. Secondly, there is a *special* mercy of God, which is exercised toward the children of men, helping and succoring them, notwithstanding their sins. To them also He communicates all the necessities of life: "for He maketh His sun to rise on the evil and on the good, and sendeth rain on the just and on the unjust" (Matt. 5:45). Thirdly, there is a *sovereign* mercy which is reserved for the heirs of salvation, which is communicated to them in a covenant way, through the Mediator.

Following out a little further the difference between the second and third distinctions pointed out above, it is important to note that the mercies which God bestows on the wicked are solely of a *temporal* nature; that is to say, they are confined strictly to this present life. There will be no mercy extended to them beyond the grave: "It is a people of no understanding: therefore He that made them will not have mercy on them, and He that formed them will show them no favour" (Isa. 27:11). But at this point a difficulty may suggest itself to some of our readers, namely, Does not Scripture affirm that "His mercy endureth forever" (Psa. 136:1)? Two things need to be pointed out in that connection. God can never cease to be merciful, for this is a quality of the Divine essence (Psa. 116:5); but the *exercise* of His mercy is regulated by His sovereign will. This must be so, for there is nothing outside Himself which obliges Him to act; if there were, that "something" would be *supreme,* and God would cease to be *God.*

It is pure sovereign grace which alone determines the exercise of Divine mercy. God expressly affirms this fact in Rom. 9:15, "For He saith to Moses, I will have mercy on whom *I will* have mercy." It is not the wretchedness of the creature which causes Him to show mercy, for God is not influenced by things outside of Himself as we are. If God *were* influenced by the abject misery of leprous sinners, He would cleanse and save *all* of them. But He does not. Why? Simply because it is not His pleasure and purpose so to do. Still less is it the merits of the creatures which causes Him to bestow mercies upon them, for it is a contradiction in terms to speak of *meriting* "mercy." "*Not* by works of righteousness which we have done, but according to His mercy. He saved us" (Titus 3:5) —the one standing in direct antithesis to the other. Nor is it the merit of Christ which moves God to bestow mercies on His elect: that would be substituting the effect for the cause. It is "through" or because of the tender mercy of our God that Christ was sent here to His people (Luke 1:78). The merits of Christ make it possible for God to *righteously* bestow spiritual mercies on His elect, justice having been fully satisfied by the Surety! No, mercy arises *solely* from God's imperial pleasure.

Again, though it be true, blessedly and gloriously true, that God's mercy "endureth forever," yet we must observe carefully the objects *to whom* His "mercy" is shown. Even the casting of the reprobate into the Lake of Fire is an act of *mercy.* The punishment of the wicked is to be contemplated from a threefold viewpoint. From God's side, it is an act of *justice,* vindicating His honor. The mercy of God is never shown to the prejudice of His holiness and righteousness. From their side, it is an act of *equity,* when they are made to suffer the due reward of their iniquities. But from the standpoint of the redeemed, the punishment of the wicked is an act of unspeakable *mercy.* How dreadful would it be if the present order of things, when the children of God are obliged to live in the midst of the children of the Devil, should continue forever! Heaven would at once cease to be heaven if the ears of the saints still heard the blasphemous and filthy language of the reprobate. What a mercy that in the New

Jerusalem "there shall in nowise enter into it any thing that defileth, neither worketh abomination" (Rev. 21:27) !

Lest the reader might think in the last paragraph we have been drawing upon our imagination, let us appeal to Holy Scripture in support of what has been said. In Psa. 143:12 we find David praying, "And of Thy *mercy* cut off mine enemies, and destroy all them that afflict my soul: for I am Thy servant." Again; in Psa. 136:15 we read that God "overthrew Pharaoh and his hosts in the Red Sea: *for* His *mercy* endureth forever." It was an act of vengeance upon Pharaoh and his hosts, but it was an act of "mercy" unto the Israelites. Again, in Rev. 19:1-3 we read, "I heard a great voice of much people in heaven, saying, Alleluia; Salvation, and glory, and honour, and power, unto the Lord our God: *for* true and righteous are His judgments: for He hath *judged* the great whore, which did corrupt the earth with her fornication, and hath *avenged* the blood of His servants at her hand. And again they said, *Alleluia*. And her smoke rose up forever and ever."

From what has just been before us, let us note how vain is the presumptuous hope of the wicked, who, notwithstanding their continued defiance of God, nevertheless count upon His being merciful to them. How many there are who say, I do not believe that God will ever cast me into Hell; He is too merciful. Such a hope is a viper, which if cherished in their bosoms will sting them to death. God is a God of justice as well as mercy, and He has expressly declared that He will "by no means clear the guilty" (Ex. 34:7). Yea, He has said, "The wicked *shall* be turned into hell, all the nations that forget God" (Psa. 9:17). As well might men reason thus: I do not believe that if filth be allowed to accumulate and sewage become stagnant and people deprive themselves of fresh air, that a merciful God will let them fall a prey to a deadly fever. The fact is that those who neglect the laws of health *are* carried away by disease, notwithstanding God's mercy. Equally true is it that those who neglect the laws of spiritual health shall forever suffer the Second Death.

Unspeakably solemn is it to see so many *abusing* this Divine perfection. They continue to despise God's authority, trample upon His laws, continue in sin, and yet presume upon His mercy. But God will not be unjust to Himself. God shows mercy to the truly penitent, but not to the impenitent (Luke 13:3). To continue in sin and yet reckon upon Divine mercy remitting punishment is diabolical. It is saying, "Let us do evil that good may come," and of all such it is written that their "damnation is just" (Rom. 3:8). Presumption shall most certainly be disappointed; read carefully Deut. 29:18-20. Christ is the spiritual Mercyseat, and all who despise and reject His Lordship shall "perish from the way, when His wrath is kindled but a little" (Psa. 2:12).

But let our final thought be of God's spiritual mercies unto His own people. "Thy mercy is great unto the heavens" (Psa. 57:10). The riches thereof transcend our loftiest thought. "For as the heaven is high above the earth, so great is His mercy toward them that fear Him" (Psa. 103:11). None can measure it. The elect are designated "vessels of mercy" (Rom. 9:23). It is mercy that quickened them when they were dead in sins (Eph. 2:4, 5). It is mercy that saves them (Titus 3:5). It is His abundant mercy which begat them unto an eternal inheritance (I Peter 1:3). Time would fail us to tell of His preserving, sustaining, pardoning, supplying mercy. Unto His own, God is "the Father of mercies" (II Cor. 1:3).

> "When all Thy mercies, O my God,
> My rising soul surveys,
> Transported with the view I'm lost,
> In wonder, love, and praise."

15

THE LOVE OF GOD

There are three things told us in Scripture concerning the *nature* of God. First, "God is spirit" (John 4:24). In the Greek there is no indefinite article, and to say "God is *a* spirit" is most objectionable, for it places Him in a class with others. God is "spirit" in the highest sense. Because He is "spirit" He is incorporeal, having no visible substance. Had God a tangible body, He would not be omnipresent, He would be limited to one place; because He is "spirit" He fills heaven and earth. Secondly, "God is light" (I John 1:5), which is the opposite of darkness. In Scripture "darkness" stands for sin, evil, death, and "light" for holiness, goodness, life. "God is light" means that He is the *sum* of all excellency. Thirdly, "God is love" (I John 4:8). It is not simply that God "loves," but that He *is* Love itself. Love is not merely one of His attributes, but His very nature.

There are many today who talk about the love of God, who are total strangers to the God of love. The Divine love is commonly regarded as a species of amiable weakness, a sort of good-natured indulgence; it is reduced to a mere sickly sentiment, patterned after human emotion. Now the truth is that on this, as on everything else, our thoughts need to be formed and regulated by what is revealed thereon in Holy Scripture. That there is urgent need for this is apparent not only from the ignorance which so generally prevails, but also the low state of spirituality which is now so sadly evident everywhere among professing Christians. How little real love there is for God. One chief reason for this is because our hearts are so little occupied with His wondrous love for His people. The better we are acquainted with His love—its character, fulness, blessedness—the more will our hearts be drawn out in love to Him.

1. The love of God is *uninfluenced*. By this we mean, there

was nothing whatever in the objects of His love to call it into exercise, nothing in the creature to attract or prompt it. The love which one creature has for another is because of something in the object; but the love of God is free, spontaneous, uncaused. The only reason why God loves any is found in His own sovereign will: "The Lord did not set His love upon you, nor choose you because ye were more in number than any people; for ye were the fewest of all people: but *because* the Lord loved thee" (Deut. 7:7, 8). God has loved His people from everlasting, and therefore nothing about the creature can be the cause of what is found in God from eternity. He loves *from* Himself: "according to His own purpose" (II Tim. 1:9).

"We love Him, because He first loved us" (I John 4:19). God did not love us because we loved Him, but He loved us before we had a particle of love for Him. Had God loved us in return for ours, then it would not be spontaneous on His part; but because He loved us when we were loveless, it is clear that His love was uninfluenced. It is highly important, if God is to be honored and the heart of His child established, that we should be quite clear upon this precious truth. God's love for me and for each of "His own" was entirely unmoved by anything in us. What was there in me to attract the heart of God? Absolutely nothing. But, to the contrary, there was everything to repel Him, everything calculated to make Him loathe me—sinful, depraved, a mass of corruption, with *"no good thing"* in me.

> "What was there in me that could merit esteem,
>   Or give the Creator delight?
> 'Twas even so, Father, I ever must sing,
>   Because it seemed good in Thy sight."

2. It is *eternal*. This of necessity. God Himself is eternal, and God *is* love; therefore, as God Himself had no beginning, His love had none. Granted that such a concept far transcends the grasp of our feeble minds, nevertheless, where we cannot comprehend we can bow in adoring worship. How clear is the testimony of Jer. 31:3, "I have loved thee with an everlasting love, therefore with lovingkindness have I drawn thee." How blessed to know that the great and holy God loved His people before heaven and earth were called into existence, that He had set His heart upon them from all eter-

nity. Clear proof is this that His love is spontaneous, for He loved them endless ages before they had any being.

The same precious truth is set forth in Eph. 1:4,5: "According as He hath chosen us in Him *before* the foundation of the world, that we should be holy and without blame before Him. *In love* having predestinated us." What praise should this evoke from each of His children! How tranquilizing for the heart: since God's love toward me had no beginning, it can have no ending! Since it is true that "from everlasting to everlasting" He is God, and since God is "love," then it is equally true that "from everlasting *to* everlasting" He loves His people.

3. It is *sovereign*. This also is self-evident. God Himself is sovereign, under obligations to none, a law unto Himself, acting always according to His own imperial pleasure. Since God is sovereign, and since He is love, it necessarily follows that His love is sovereign. Because God *is* God, He does as He pleases; because God is love, He loves whom He pleases. Such is His own express affirmation: "Jacob have I loved, but Esau have I hated" (Rom. 9:13). There was no more reason in Jacob why he should be the object of Divine love than there was in Esau. They both had the same parents, and were born at the same time, being twins; yet God loved the one and hated the other! Why? Because it pleased Him to do so.

The sovereignty of God's love necessarily follows from the fact that it is uninfluenced by anything in the creature. Thus, to affirm that the cause of His love lies in God Himself is only another way of saying, He loves whom He pleases. For a moment, assume the opposite. Suppose God's love were regulated by anything else than His will: in such a case He would love by rule, and loving by rule He would be under a law of love, and then so far from being free, God would Himself be *ruled by law*. "In love having predestinated us unto the adoption of children by Jesus Christ to Himself, according to"— what? Some excellency which He foresaw in them? No! What then? "According to the good pleasure of His will" (Eph. 1:4, 5).

4. It is *infinite*. Everything about God is infinite. His *essence* fills heaven and earth. His *wisdom* is illimitable, for He knows everything of the past, present, and future. His *power* is unbounded, for there is nothing too hard for Him. So His love is without limit. There is a depth to it which none can fathom; there is a height to it which none can scale;

there is a length and breadth to it which defies measurement, by any creature-standard. Beautifully is this intimated in Eph. 2:4: "But God, who is rich in mercy, for His *great* love where-with He loved us": the word "great" there is parallel with the "God *so* loved" of John 3:16. It tells us that the love of God is so transcendent it cannot be estimated.

No tongue can fully express the infinitude of God's love, or any mind comprehend it: it "passeth knowledge" (Eph. 3:19). The most extensive ideas that a finite mind can frame about Divine love, are infinitely below its *true* nature. The heaven is not so far above the earth as the goodness of God is beyond the most raised conceptions which we are able to form of it. It is an *ocean* which swells higher than all the mountains of opposition in such as are the objects of it. It is a *fountain* from which flows all necessary good to all those who are interested in it (John Brine, 1743).

5. It is *immutable*. As with God Himself there is "no varia-bleness, neither shadow of turning" (James 1:17), so His love knows neither change nor diminution. The worm Jacob sup-plies a forceful example of this: "Jacob have I loved," de-clared Jehovah, and despite all his unbelief and waywardness, He never ceased to love him. John 13:1 furnishes another beautiful illustration. That very night one of the apostles would say, "Show us the Father"; another would deny Him with cursings; all of them would be scandalized by and for-sake Him. Nevertheless, "having loved His own which were in the world, He loved them *unto the end*." The Divine love is subject to no vicissitudes. Divine love is "strong as death . . . many waters cannot quench it" (Song of Sol. 8:6, 7). Nothing can separate from it (Rom. 8:35-39).

> "His love no end nor measure knows,
>   No change can turn its course,
>   Eternally the same it flows
>   From one eternal source."

6. It is *holy*. God's love is not regulated by caprice, passion, or sentiment, but by principle. Just as His grace reigns not at the expense of it, but "through righteousness" (Rom. 5:21), so His love never conflicts with His holiness. "God is light" (I John 1:5) is mentioned *before* "God is love" (I John 4:8).

God's love is no mere amiable weakness or effeminate
softness. Scripture declares that "whom the Lord loveth He
chasteneth, and scourgeth every son whom He receiveth"
(Heb. 12:6). God will not wink at sin, even in His own
people. His love is *pure,* unmixed with any maudlin sentimentality.

7. It is *gracious.* The love and favor of God are inseparable.
This is clearly brought out in Rom. 8:32-39. What that love
is, from which there can be no "separation," is easily perceived from the design and scope of the immediate context: it
is that goodwill and grace of God which determined Him to
give His Son for sinners. That *love* was the impulsive power
of Christ's incarnation: "God so loved the world that He gave
His only begotten Son" (John 3:16). Christ died not in order
to make God love us, but because He did love His people.
Calvary is the supreme demonstration of Divine love. Whenever you are tempted to doubt the love of God, Christian
reader, go back to Calvary.

Here then is abundant cause for trust and patience under
Divine affliction. Christ was beloved of the Father, yet *He* was
not exempted from poverty, disgrace, and persecution. *He*
hungered· and thirsted. Thus, it was *not* incompatible with
God's *love* for Christ when He permitted men to spit upon
and smite Him. Then let no Christian call into question
God's love when he is brought under painful afflictions and
trials. God did not enrich Christ on earth with temporal pros-
perity, for "He had not where to lay His head." But He *did*
give Him the Spirit "without measure" (John 3:34). Learn
then that *spiritual* blessings are the principal gifts of Divine
love. How blessed to know that when the world hates us, God
loves us!

16

THE WRATH OF GOD

It is sad indeed to find so many professing Christians who appear to regard the wrath of God as something for which they need to make an apology, or who at least wish there were no such thing. While some would not go so far as to openly admit that they consider it a blemish on the Divine character, yet they are far from regarding it with delight; they like not to think about it, and they rarely hear it mentioned without a secret resentment rising up in their hearts against it. Even with those who are more sober in their judgment, not a few seem to imagine that there is a severity about the Divine wrath that makes it too terrifying to form a theme for profitable contemplation. Others harbor the delusion that God's wrath is not consistent with His goodness, and so seek to banish it from their thoughts.

Yes, many there are who turn away from a vision of God's wrath as though they were called to look upon some blotch in the Divine character or some blot upon the Divine government. But what saith the Scriptures? As we turn to them we find that God has made no attempt to conceal the facts concerning His wrath. *He* is not ashamed to make it known that vengeance and fury belong unto Him. His own challenge is, "See now that I, even I, am He, and there is no god with Me: I kill, and I make alive; I wound, and I heal; neither is there any that can deliver out of My hand. For I lift up My hand to heaven, and say, I live forever. If I whet My glittering sword, and Mine hand take hold on judgment; I will render vengeance to Mine enemies, and will reward them that hate Me" (Deut. 32:39-41). A study of the concordance will show that there are *more* references in Scripture to the anger, fury, and wrath of God, than there are to His love and tenderness. Because God is holy, He hates all sin; and because

He hates all sin, His anger burns against the sinner (Psa. 7:11).

Now the wrath of God is as much a Divine perfection as is His faithfulness, power, or mercy. It *must be* so, for there is no blemish whatever, not the slightest defect in the character of God; yet there *would be* if "wrath" were absent from Him! Indifference to sin is a moral blemish, and he who hates it not is a moral leper. How could He who is the Sum of all excellency look with equal satisfaction upon virtue and vice, wisdom and folly? How could He who is infinitely holy disregard sin and refuse to manifest His "severity" (Rom. 9:22) toward it? How could He, who delights only in that which is pure and lovely, not loathe and hate that which is impure and vile? The very nature of God makes Hell as real a necessity, as imperatively and eternally requisite, as Heaven is. Not only is there no imperfection in God, but there is no perfection in Him that is less perfect than another.

The wrath of God is His eternal detestation of all unrighteousness. It is the displeasure and indignation of Divine equity against evil. It is the holiness of God stirred into activity against sin. It is the moving cause of that just sentence which He passes upon evildoers. God is angry against sin because it is a rebelling against His authority, a wrong done to His inviolable sovereignty. Insurrectionists against God's government shall be made to know that God *is* the Lord. They shall be made to feel how great that Majesty is which they despise, and how dreadful is that threatened wrath which they so little regarded. Not that God's anger is a malignant and malicious retaliation, inflicting injury for the sake of it, or in return for injury received. No, though God will vindicate His dominion as the Governor of the universe, He will not be vindictive.

That Divine wrath *is* one of the *perfections* of God is not only evident from the considerations presented above, but is also clearly established by the express declarations of His own Word. "For the wrath of God is revealed *from heaven*" (Rom. 1:18). Robert Haldane comments on this verse as follows:

It was revealed when the sentence of death was first pronounced, the earth cursed, and man driven out of the earthly paradise, and afterwards by such examples of punishment as those of the Deluge, and the destruction of the Cities of the Plain by fire from heaven, but especially by the reign of death throughout the world. It was proclaimed in the curse of the law on every transgression, and was intimated in the institution of sacrifice, and in all the services of the Mosaic dispensation. In the eighth chapter of this epistle, the Apostle calls the attention of believers to the fact that the whole creation has become subject to vanity, and groaneth and travaileth together in pain. The same creation which declares that there is a God, and publishes His glory, also proves that He is the Enemy of sin and the Avenger of the crimes of men. . . . But above all, the wrath of God was revealed from heaven when the Son of God came down to manifest the Divine character, and when that wrath was displayed in His sufferings and death, in a manner more awful than by all the tokens God had before given of His displeasure against sin. Besides this, the future and eternal punishment of the wicked is now declared in terms more solemn and explicit than formerly. Under the new dispensation, there are two revelations given from heaven, one of wrath, the other of grace.

Again, that the wrath of God is a Divine perfection is plainly demonstrated by what we read in Psa. 95:11: "Unto whom I sware in My wrath." There are two occasions of God's "swearing": in making promises (Gen. 22:16); and in pronouncing judgments (Deut. 1:34 ff). In the former, He swears in mercy to His children; in the latter, He swears to deprive a wicked generation of its inheritance because of murmuring and unbelief. An oath is for solemn confirmation (Heb. 6:16). In Gen. 22:16 God says, *"By Myself* have I sworn." In Psa. 89:35 He declares, "Once have I sworn *by My holiness."* While in Psa. 95:11 He affirms, "I swear *in My wrath."* Thus the great Jehovah Himself appeals to His "wrath" as a perfection equal to His "holiness": He swears by the one as much as by the other! Again, as in Christ "dwelleth all the fulness of the Godhead bodily" (Col. 2:9), and as all the Divine perfections are illustriously displayed by Him (John 1:18), therefore do we read of "the *wrath* of the Lamb" (Rev. 6:16).

The wrath of God is a perfection of the Divine character upon which we need to frequently meditate. First, that our hearts may be duly impressed by God's detestation of sin. We are ever prone to regard sin lightly, to gloss over its hideousness, to make excuses for it. But the more we study and ponder God's abhorrence of sin and His frightful vengeance upon it, the more likely are we to realize its heinousness. Secondly, to beget a true fear in our souls for God: "Let us have grace whereby we may serve God acceptably with reverence and godly fear: for our God is a consuming fire" (Heb. 12:28, 29). We cannot serve Him "acceptably" unless there is due "reverence" for His awful Majesty and "godly fear" of His righteous anger; and these are best promoted by frequently calling to mind that "our God is a consuming fire." Thirdly, to draw out our souls in fervent praise for our having been delivered *from* "the wrath to come" (I Thess. 1:10).

Our readiness or our reluctancy to *meditate* upon the wrath of God becomes a sure test of our hearts' true attitude toward Him. If we do not truly rejoice in God, for what He is in Himself, and that because of *all* the perfections which are eternally resident in Him, then how dwelleth *the love of God* in us? Each of us needs to be most prayerfully on his guard against devising an image of God in our thoughts which is patterned after our own evil inclinations. Of old the Lord complained, "Thou thoughtest that I was altogether as *thyself*" (Psa. 50:21). If we rejoice not "at the remembrance of His *holiness*" (Psa. 97:12), if we rejoice not to know that in a soon-coming Day God will make a most glorious display of His *wrath* by taking vengeance upon all who now oppose Him, it is proof positive that our hearts are *not* in subjection to Him, that we are yet in our sins, and that we are on the way to the everlasting burnings.

"*Rejoice,* O ye nations (Gentiles) His people, *for* He will avenge the blood of His servants, and will render vengeance to His adversaries" (Deut. 32:43). And again we read, "I heard a great voice of much people in heaven, saying, Alleluia; Salvation, and glory, and honour, and power, unto the Lord our God: *For* true and righteous are His judgments: for He hath judged the great whore, which did corrupt the earth with her fornication, and hath avenged the blood of His servants at her hand. And again they said, Alleluia" (Rev. 19:1-3). Great will be the rejoicing of the saints in that day when the Lord shall vindicate His majesty, exercise His awful dominion, magnify His justice, and overthrow the proud rebels who have dared to defy Him.

"If thou Lord, shouldest mark (impute) iniquities, O Lord, who shall stand?" (Psa. 130:3). Well may each of us ask this question, for it is written, "the ungodly shall not stand in the judgment" (Psa. 1:5). How sorely was *Christ's* soul exercised with thoughts of God's marking the iniquities of His people when they were upon Him! He was "amazed and very heavy" (Mark 14:33). His awful agony, His bloody sweat, His strong cries and supplications (Heb. 5:7), His reiterated prayers ("If it be possible, let this cup pass from Me"), His last dreadful cry ("My God, My God, why hast Thou forsaken Me?") all manifest what fearful apprehensions He had of *what* it was for God to "mark iniquities." Well may poor sinners cry out, "Lord *who* shall stand," when the Son of God Himself so trembled beneath the weight of His wrath! If thou, my reader, hast not "fled for refuge" to Christ, the only Savior, "how wilt thou do in the swelling of the Jordan?" (Jer. 12:5).

When I consider how the goodness of God is abused by the greatest part of mankind, I cannot but be of his mind that said, The greatest miracle in the world is God's patience and bounty to an ungrateful world. If a prince hath an enemy got into one of his towns, he doth not send them in provision, but lays close siege to the place, and doth what he can to starve them. But the great God, that could wink all His enemies into destruction, bears with them, and is at daily cost to maintain them. Well may He command us to bless them that curse us, who Himself does good to the evil and unthankful. But think not, sinners, that you shall escape thus; God's mill goes slow, but grinds small; the more admirable His patience and bounty now is, the more dreadful and unsupportable will that fury be which ariseth out of His abused goodness. Nothing smoother than the sea, yet when stirred into a tempest, nothing rageth more. Nothing so sweet as the patience and goodness of God, and nothing so terrible as His wrath when it takes fire (William Gurnall, 1660).

Then "flee," my reader, flee to Christ; "flee *from* the wrath to come" (Matt. 3:7) ere it be too late. Do not, we earnestly beseech you, suppose that this message is intended for somebody else. It is *to you!* Do not be contented by *thinking* you *have* already fled to Christ. Make *certain!* Beg the Lord to search your heart and show you yourself.

*   *   *   *

A Word to Preachers. Brethren, do we in our oral ministry, preach on this solemn subject as much as we ought? The Old Testament prophets frequently told their hearers that their wicked lives provoked the Holy One of Israel, and that they were treasuring up to themselves wrath against the day of wrath. And conditions in the world are no better now than they were then! Nothing is so calculated to arouse the careless and cause carnal professors to search their hearts, as to enlarge upon the fact that "God is angry with the wicked every day" (Psa. 7:11). The forerunner of Christ warned his hearers to "flee from the wrath to come" (Matt. 3:7). The Savior bade His auditors, "Fear Him, which after He hath killed, hath power to cast into Hell; yea, I say unto you, Fear Him" (Luke 12:5). The Apostle Paul said, "Knowing therefore the *terror* of the Lord, we persuade men" (II Cor. 5:11). Faithfulness demands that we speak as plainly about Hell as about Heaven.

17

THE CONTEMPLATION OF GOD

In the previous chapters we have had in review some of the wondrous and lovely perfections of the Divine character. From this most feeble and faulty contemplation of His attributes, it should be evident to us all that God is, *first,* an *incomprehensible* Being, and, lost in wonder at His infinite greatness, we are constrained to adopt the words of Zophar, "Canst thou by searching find out God? canst thou find out the Almighty unto perfection? It is high as heaven; what canst thou do? deeper than hell; what canst thou know? The measure thereof is longer than the earth, and broader than the sea" (Job 11:7-9). When we turn our thoughts to God's eternity, His immateriality, His omnipresence, His almightiness, our minds are overwhelmed.

But the incomprehensibility of the Divine nature is not a reason why we should desist from reverent inquiry and prayerful strivings to apprehend what He has so graciously revealed to Himself in His Word. Because we are unable to acquire perfect knowledge, it would be folly to say we will therefore make no efforts to attain to *any* degree of it. It has been well said that, "Nothing will so enlarge the intellect, nothing so magnify the whole soul of man, as a devout, earnest, continued, investigation of the great subject of the Deity. The most excellent study for expanding the soul is the science of Christ and Him crucified and the knowledge of the Godhead in the glorious Trinity" (C. H. Spurgeon). Let us quote a little further from this prince of preachers:

The proper study of the Christian is the Godhead. The highest science, the loftiest speculation, the mightiest philosophy, which can engage the attention of a child of God is the name, the nature, the person, the doings, and the existence of the great God which he calls his Father. There is something exceedingly improving to the mind in a contemplation of the Divinity. It is a subject so vast, that all our thoughts are lost in its immensity; so deep, that our pride is drowned in its infinity. Other subjects we can comprehend and grapple with; in them we feel a kind of self-contentment, and go on our way with the thought, "Behold I am wise." But when we come to this master science, finding that our plumbline cannot sound its depth, and that our eagle eye cannot see its height, we turn away with the thought, "I am but of yesterday and know nothing" (Sermon on Mal. 3:6).

Yes, the incomprehensibility of the Divine nature should teach us humility, caution, and reverence. After all our searchings and meditations we have to say with Job, "Lo, these are parts of His ways: but how little a portion is heard of Him!" (26:14). When Moses besought Jehovah for a sight of His glory, He answered him, "I will proclaim the name of the Lord before thee" (Ex. 33:19), and, as another has said, "the name is the collection of His attributes." Rightly did the Puritan John Howe declare:

> The notion therefore we can hence form of His glory, is only such as we may have of a large volume by a brief synopsis, or of a spacious country by a little landscape. He hath here given us a true report of Himself, but not a full; such as will secure our apprehensions—being guided thereby—from error, but not from ignorance. We can apply our minds to contemplate the several perfections whereby the blessed God discovers to us His being, and can in our thoughts attribute them all to Him, though we have still but low and defective conceptions of each one. Yet so far as our apprehensions can correspond to the discovery that He affords us of His several excellencies, we have a present view of His glory.

As the difference is indeed great between the knowledge of God which His saints have in this life and that which they shall have in Heaven, yet, as the former should not be undervalued because it is imperfect, so the latter is not to be magnified above its reality. True, the Scripture declares that we shall see "face to face" and "know" even as we are known (I Cor. 13:12). But to infer from this that we shall then know God as fully as He knows us is to be misled by the mere sound of words, and to disregard the restriction of that knowledge that our finiteness necessarily requires. There is a vast difference between the saints being glorified and their being made Divine. In their glorified state, Christians will still be finite creatures, and therefore, never able to fully comprehend the infinite God.

The saints in heaven will see God with the eye of the mind, for He will be always invisible to the bodily eye. They will see Him more clearly than they could see Him by reason and faith, and more extensively than all His works and dispensations had hitherto revealed Him. But their minds will not be so enlarged as to be capable of contemplating at once, or in detail, the whole excellence of His nature. To comprehend infinite perfection, they must become infinite themselves. Even in Heaven, their knowledge will be partial, but at the same time their happiness will be complete, because their knowledge will be perfect in this sense, that it will be adequate to the capacity of the subject, although it will not exhaust the fulness of the object. We believe that it will be progressive, and that as their views expand, their blessedness will increase. But it will never reach a limit beyond which there is nothing to be discovered, and when ages after ages have passed away, He will still be the incomprehensible God (John Dick, 1840).

Secondly, from a review of the perfections of God, it appears that He is an *all-sufficient* Being. He is all-sufficient in Himself and to Himself. As the First of beings, He could receive nothing from another, nor be limited by the power of another. Being infinite, He is possessed of all possible perfection. When the Triune God existed all alone, He was all to Himself. His understanding, His love, His energies, found an adequate object in Himself. Had He stood in need of anything external He would not have been *independent,* and therefore He would not have been God. He created all things, and that "for Himself" (Col. 1:16), yet it was not in order to supply a lack, but that He might communicate life and happiness to angels and men, and admit them to the vision of His glory. True, He demands the allegiance and services of His intelligent creatures, yet *He* derives no benefit from their offices; all the advantage redounds to themselves (Job 22:2, 3). He makes use of means and instruments to accomplish His ends, yet not from a deficiency of power, but oftentimes to more strikingly display His power through the feebleness of the instruments.

The all-sufficiency of God makes Him to be the Supreme

Object which is ever to be sought unto. True happiness consists only in the enjoyment of God. His favor is life, and His lovingkindness is better than life. "The Lord is my portion, saith my soul; therefore will I hope in Him" (Lam. 3:24). His love, His grace, and His glory are the chief objects of the saints' desire and the springs of their highest satisfaction. "There be many that say, Who will show us any good? Lord, lift Thou up the light of *Thy* countenance upon us. Thou hast put gladness in my heart, more than in the time that their corn and their wine increased" (Psa. 4:6, 7). Yea, the Christian, when in his right mind, is able to say, "Although the fig tree shall not blossom, neither shall fruit be in the vines; the labour of the olive shall fail, and the fields shall yield no meat; the flock shall be cut off from the fold, and there shall be no herd in the stalls: *yet* I will rejoice *in the Lord,* I will joy in the God of my salvation" (Hab. 3:17, 18).

Thirdly, from a review of the perfections of God, it appears that He is the *Supreme Sovereign* of the universe. It has been rightly said:

No dominion is so absolute as that which is founded on creation. He who might not have made any thing, had a right to make all things according to His own pleasure. In the exercise of His uncontrolled power, He has made some parts of the creation mere inanimate matter, of grosser or more refined texture, and distinguished by different qualities, but all inert and unconscious. He has given organization to other parts, and made them susceptible of growth and expansion, but still without life in the proper sense of the term. To others He has given not only organization, but conscious existence, organs of sense and self-motive power. To these He has added in man the gift of reason, and an immortal spirit, by which he is allied to a higher order of beings who are placed in the superior regions. Over the world which He has created, He sways the scepter of omnipotence. "I praised and honoured Him that liveth forever, whose dominion is an everlasting dominion, and His kingdom is from generation to generation: and all the inhabitants of the earth are reputed as nothing: and He doeth according to His will in the army of heaven, and among the inhabitants of the earth: and none can stay His hand, or say unto Him, What doest Thou?"—Dan. 4:34, 35 (John Dick).

A creature, considered as such, has no rights. He can demand nothing from his Maker; and in whatever manner he may be treated, has no title to complain. Yet, when thinking of the absolute dominion of God over all, we ought never to lose sight of His moral perfections. God is just and good, and ever does that which is right. Nevertheless, He exercises His sovereignty according to His own imperial and righteous pleasure. He assigns each creature his place as seemeth good in His own sight. He orders the varied circumstances of each according to His own counsels. He molds each vessel according to His own uninfluenced determination. He has mercy on whom He will, and whom He will He hardens. Wherever we are, His eye is upon us. Whoever we are, our life and everything is held at His disposal. To the Christian, He is a tender Father; to the rebellious sinner He will yet be a consuming fire. "Now unto the King eternal, immortal, invisible, the only wise God, be honour and glory for ever and ever. Amen" (I Tim. 1:17).

INDEX OF SCRIPTURES QUOTED

INDEX OF AUTHORS QUOTED

SPECIAL PROBLEMS IN
MANAGING EATING DISORDERS

Clinical Practice

Number 20

Judith H. Gold, M.D., F.R.C.P.(C)
Series Editor

SPECIAL PROBLEMS IN
MANAGING EATING DISORDERS

Edited by

Joel Yager, M.D.
Department of Psychiatry and Biobehavioral Sciences
School of Medicine
University of California, Los Angeles
West Los Angeles Veterans Administration
    Medical Center (Brentwood Division)
Los Angeles, California

Harry E. Gwirtsman, M.D.
Unit on Eating Disorders
Clinical Neuroendocrinology Branch
Department of Intramural Research Programs
National Institute of Mental Health
Bethesda, Maryland

Carole K. Edelstein, M.D.
Department of Psychiatry and Biobehavioral Sciences
School of Medicine
University of California, Los Angeles
Los Angeles, California

Washington, DC
London, England

Copyright © 1992 American Psychiatric Press, Inc.
ALL RIGHTS RESERVED
Manufactured in the United States of America on acid-free paper
First Edition 94 93 92 91 4 3 2 1

American Psychiatric Press, Inc.
1400 K Street, N.W., Washington, DC 20005

Library of Congress Cataloging-in-Publication Data

Special problems in managing eating disorders / edited by Joel Yager,
    Harry E. Gwirtsman, Carole K. Edelstein. — 1st ed.
        p.   cm. — (Clinical practice ; no. 20)
    Includes bibliographical references and index.
    ISBN 0-88048-457-8
    1. Eating disorders—Complications and sequelae. 2. Eating
disorders—Treatment. I. Yager, Joel, 1941– II. Gwirtsman, Harry E.,
1950–   .   III. Edelstein, Carole K., 1943–   .   IV. Series.
    [DNLM: 1. Eating Disorders—therapy. W1 CL767J no. 20/WM 175
S741]
RC552.E18S64   1991
616.85′26—dc20
DLC
for Library of Congress   91-4580
                                                                  CIP

British Library Cataloguing in Publication Data

A CIP record is available from the British Library.

Contents

Contributors

Arnold E. Andersen, M.D.
Associate Professor, Department of Psychiatry and Behavioral
Sciences, Johns Hopkins University School of Medicine;
Director, Eating and Weight Disorders Clinic, Johns Hopkins Hospital,
Baltimore, Maryland

Carole K. Edelstein, M.D.
Assistant Clinical Professor, Department of Psychiatry and
Biobehavioral Sciences, School of Medicine, University of
California, Los Angeles, Los Angeles, California

Harry E. Gwirtsman, M.D.
Chief, Unit on Eating Disorders, Clinical Neuroendocrinology Branch,
Department of Intramural Research Programs, National Institute of
Mental Health, Bethesda, Maryland

Karen Hanson, B.A.
Community Program Assistant, Department of Psychiatry,
University of Minnesota School of Medicine, Minneapolis,
Minnesota

Bryan H. King, M.D.
Assistant Professor, Department of Psychiatry and Biobehavioral
Sciences, School of Medicine, University of California, Los
Angeles, Los Angeles, California

James E. Mitchell, M.D.
Professor and Director of Adult Psychiatry, University of
Minnesota School of Medicine, Minneapolis, Minnesota

Richard L. Pyle, M.D.
Associate Professor, Department of Psychiatry, University of
Minnesota School of Medicine, Minneapolis, Minnesota

Shiela Specker, M.D.
Assistant Professor, Department of Psychiatry, University of Minnesota School of Medicine, Minneapolis, Minnesota

Stephen A. Wonderlich, Ph.D.
Assistant Professor, Division of Psychiatry and Behavioral Science, University of North Dakota; Co-Director, Fargo Clinic Eating Disorders Program, Fargo, North Dakota

Joel Yager, M.D.
Professor and Director of Residency Education, Department of Psychiatry and Biobehavioral Sciences, School of Medicine, University of California, Los Angeles; Associate Chief of Staff for Residency Education, West Los Angeles Veterans Administration Medical Center (Brentwood Division), Los Angeles, California

Roy T. Young, M.D.
Professor and Executive Vice-Chairman, Department of Medicine, School of Medicine, University of California, Los Angeles, Los Angeles, California

Introduction
to the Clinical Practice Series

*O*ver the years of its existence the series of monographs entitled *Clinical Insights* gradually became focused on providing current, factual, and theoretical material of interest to the clinician working outside of a hospital setting. To reflect this orientation, the name of the Series has been changed to *Clinical Practice.*

The Clinical Practice Series will provide readers with books that give the mental health clinician a practical clinical approach to a variety of psychiatric problems. These books will provide up-to-date literature reviews and emphasize the most recent treatment methods. Thus, the publications in the Series will interest clinicians working both in psychiatry and in the other mental health professions.

Each year a number of books will be published dealing with all aspects of clinical practice. In addition, from time to time when appropriate, the publications may be revised and updated. Thus, the Series will provide quick access to relevant and important areas of psychiatric practice. Some books in the Series will be authored by a person considered to be an expert in that particular area; others will be edited by such an expert who will also draw together other knowledgeable authors to produce a comprehensive overview of that topic.

Some of the books in the Clinical Practice Series will have their foundation in presentations at an annual meeting of the American Psychiatric Association. All will contain the most recently available information on the subjects discussed. Theoretical and scientific data will be applied to clinical situations, and case illustrations will be utilized in order to make the material even more relevant for the practitioner. Thus, the Clinical Practice Series should provide educational reading in a compact format especially written for the mental health clinician–psychiatrist.

Judith H. Gold, M.D., F.R.C.P.(C)
Series Editor
Clinical Practice Series

Clinical Practice Series Titles

Treating Chronically Mentally Ill Women (#1)
Edited by Leona L. Bachrach, Ph.D., and Carol C. Nadelson, M.D.

Divorce as a Developmental Process (#2)
Edited by Judith H. Gold, M.D., F.R.C.P.(C)

Family Violence: Emerging Issues of a National Crisis (#3)
Edited by Leah J. Dickstein, M.D., and Carol C. Nadelson, M.D.

Anxiety and Depressive Disorders in the Medical Patient (#4)
By Leonard R. Derogatis, Ph.D., and Thomas N. Wise, M.D.

Anxiety: New Findings for the Clinician (#5)
Edited by Peter Roy-Byrne, M.D.

The Neuroleptic Malignant Syndrome and Related Conditions (#6)
By Arthur Lazarus, M.D., Stephan C. Mann, M.D., and
Stanley N. Caroff, M.D.

Juvenile Homicide (#7)
Edited by Elissa P. Benedek, M.D., and Dewey G. Cornell, Ph.D.

**Measuring Mental Illness: Psychometric Assessment
for Clinicians (#8)**
Edited by Scott Wetzler, Ph.D.

Family Involvement in Treatment of the Frail Elderly (#9)
Edited by Marion Zucker Goldstein, M.D.

Psychiatric Care of Migrants: A Clinical Guide (#10)
By Joseph Westermeyer, M.D., M.P.H., Ph.D.

Office Treatment of Schizophrenia (#11)
Edited by Mary V. Seeman, M.D., F.R.C.P.(C), and
Stanley E. Greben, M.D., F.R.C.P.(C)

The Psychosocial Impact of Job Loss (#12)
By Nick Kates, M.B.B.S., F.R.C.P.(C), Barrie S. Greiff, M.D., and
Duane Q. Hagen, M.D.

New Perspectives on Narcissism (#13)
Edited by Eric M. Plakun, M.D.

Introduction

*A*lthough much has been written about the "typical" eating-disordered patient—the best little girl in the world with anorexia nervosa or the bulimic college student, for example—a great percentage, if not the large majority, of patients with eating disorders present challenging and complicated combinations of problems that can be daunting to the most experienced clinicians. The presence of one or more comorbid psychiatric conditions along with an eating disorder diagnosis may be the rule rather than the exception. Clinicians are faced with questions of diagnosis and differential diagnosis, the need to prioritize clinical problems in the development of treatment plans, and tricky questions of integrating various psychological, social, and biological treatment strategies in the care of these patients.

In this book a group of experienced clinicians and clinical researchers address some of the most prevalent and troubling problems facing clinicians who deal with complex eating-disordered patients in their day-to-day practice. Rather than "textbook" cases, the patients whose problems are addressed here represent the variety of complicated cases frequently seen in clinical settings. These patients are often excluded from research studies because they are not "pure culture" eating-disordered subjects. As a result, the current literature on such patients offers few practical treatment recommendations based on systematically obtained clinical research data. In the absence of such a data base, the authors in this book have attempted to fill the gap by developing practice guidelines and practice options based on a synthesis of what knowledge does exist and their extensive clinical experience.

In Chapter 1, James E. Mitchell, Richard L. Pyle, Shiela Specker, and Karen Hanson, from the extremely productive eating disorders group at the University of Minnesota, discuss the relationship of eating disorders and chemical dependency problems. More than 30% of patients with eating disorders may have a concurrent substance abuse problem, particularly patients with bulimia nervosa. The authors consider issues of diagnosis, treatment philosophies, and the staging of interventions for the eating disorder and chemical dependency problems.

The complicated relationships of affective disorders and eating disorders are discussed by Carole K. Edelstein and Joel Yager in Chapter 2. The authors focus on the genesis of symptoms often characteristic of mood disorders (which may occur as a result of malnutrition), resulting in a difficult and often confusing diagnostic picture as eating disorders and mood disorders overlap. The authors present suggestions for teasing apart mood and eating disorder components and for developing treatment strategies for several of the different patterns that exist.

Stephen A. Wonderlich and James E. Mitchell discuss the comorbidity of eating disorders and personality disorders in Chapter 3. Because patients with eating disorders more often than not meet diagnostic criteria for concurrent personality disorders and because the preexisting personality disorder appears to be a fertile field in which eating disorders may develop, the treatment of these patients is often dictated as much by the nature and extent of the personality disorder as by the eating disorder. Furthermore, many aspects of personality are strained and warped by the presence of an eating disorder, and many of the psychopathologic personality traits commonly seen in acutely symptomatic eating-disordered patients may subside "spontaneously" as the eating disorder symptoms abate. This chapter offers clues on how to approach such entanglements.

Arnold E. Andersen, director of the Eating Disorders Program at The Johns Hopkins University, may well have accumulated more extensive clinical experience with male eating-disordered patients than any other American psychiatrist. In Chapter 4, he elegantly discusses his close examination of these patients, their special concerns, and treatment considerations that differ from those for female patients.

In Chapter 5, Arnold E. Andersen presents a thorough review of the medical complications encountered in eating-disordered patients and sets forth guidelines for their assessment and management. His assessment guidelines are thoughtful and balanced, representing a judicious and complete selection of necessary laboratory procedures while avoiding an indiscriminate and costly "shotgun" approach to the workup. He also emphasizes the need for a high degree of suspicion and concern about the potential presence of serious medical complications in these patients.

Next, Harry E. Gwirtsman considers the assessment and management of the patient who purges by means of laxative abuse in Chapter 6. A substantial percentage of patients with bulimia nervosa—perhaps as many as 40% of the patients in some series—have become chronic abusers of laxatives, and this symptom is often extremely difficult for patients to surrender, even with inpatient treatment. The author offers a protocol for treating these problems that has met with a fair degree of success in several settings.

The pregnant eating-disordered patient presents special concerns for the well-being of the fetus and child as well as for the mother. In Chapter 7, Carole K. Edelstein and Bryan H. King review what little literature exists in this area and describe several pregnant patients they followed in both individual and group psychotherapy. Based on their experiences, they offer suggestions for clinicians faced with similar cases.

The bulimic patient with diabetes mellitus presents potentially life-threatening problems to psychiatrists, other mental health clinicians, dietitians, and primary care physicians. Because these patients have novel forms of purging at their disposal, such as simply not taking their insulin or not following their diets, and because dietary and insulin noncompliance often results in hypoglycemic or hyperglycemic episodes that may result in seizures, confusion, and other neurologically and medically serious sequelae, special care must be given both to the management of their illnesses and to the close working alliance among all the health professionals involved with their care. These considerations are discussed by Joel Yager and Roy T. Young in Chapter 8.

Finally, even in the best of hands, some patients with eating disorders will have an inexorably chronic course; sometimes remaining remarkably stable for years, sometimes resulting in death through suicide or malnutrition. In Chapter 9 Joel Yager discusses the various management strategies available to clinicians and considers some of the ethical and legal issues involved in attempts to deliver care to these patients and their families while dealing with their concerns, fears, and frustrations.

We see the chapters in this book as momentary views of rapidly changing fields. We hope that authors writing on these topics in the future will be able to rely on a considerably expanded research base and a more extensive accumulation of clinical experience so subsequent guidelines can provide increasing degrees of wisdom.

Joel Yager, M.D.
Harry E. Gwirtsman, M.D.
Carole K. Edelstein, M.D.

Chapter 1

Eating Disorders and Chemical Dependency

James E. Mitchell, M.D.
Richard L. Pyle, M.D.
Shiela Specker, M.D.
Karen Hanson, B.A.

Although the co-occurrence of eating disorders and problems associated with drug and alcohol abuse has frequently been noted in the psychiatric literature (Brisman and Siegel 1984; Hatsukami et al. 1986; Zweben 1987), many important questions about it remain. Why, for example, does this comorbidity appear to be more common than would be predicted given the prevalence of these disorders among women in the general population? What is the best approach to the serious clinical problems associated with treating this comorbidity (patients with both types of disorders appear to be particularly difficult to treat)?

In this chapter we review much of the published literature about the relationship between eating disorders and chemical dependency, focusing on reports of series of patients and controlled studies. We also discuss the similarities and differences between these types of disorders.

From the Eating Disorders Program, Department of Psychiatry, University of Minnesota Medical School. Supported in part by Public Health Service grants R01-40377 and R01-43296.

Drug and Alcohol Abuse Among Women With Bulimia Nervosa

Case example

Ms. J was a 25-year-old white woman who presented for treatment with a 6-year history of binge eating on a daily basis, usually followed by self-induced vomiting. During this time she had become increasingly depressed with initial insomnia, decreased energy, and suicidal ideas. A related problem was alcohol abuse. She had begun using alcohol in high school on weekends. However, for the previous 3 years she had been drinking to the point of intoxication 4 or 5 nights a week. There was a positive family history of depression in her mother and alcohol abuse in her father. She had made a serious suicide attempt about 1 year before evaluation while she had been intoxicated.

The case example above illustrates this comorbidity and the associated family and psychiatric problems often seen in such individuals.

In one of the early reports of a series of patients with bulimia nervosa (Pyle et al. 1981), 24% of the patients were noted to have been treated for chemical dependency before presenting for treatment for their eating disorder. The median age of this group was 24, suggesting that many of these women had not traversed the age of risk for chemical dependency. In 1983 Hudson et al. reported that 31% of 49 bulimic women aged 17–49 met lifetime criteria for substance use disorders using the structured Diagnostic Interview Schedule (DIS; Robins et al. 1981). This same group later reported that 49% of 70 bulimic patients aged 18–45 had a lifetime prevalence of substance use disorders using the DIS (Hudson et al. 1987b).

Our group previously published data on substance use disorders in two separate series of patients using clinical assessment. In the first study (Hatsukami et al. 1984), we found that 18.5% of a series of 108 bulimic women met criteria for alcohol or drug abuse. In the second (Mitchell et al. 1985), we found that 34% of a series of 275 patients with bulimia had a history of alcohol or drug abuse problems and 18% had a history of treatment for such problems at the time of evaluation for their eating disorder.

Several other observations also contribute to our understanding of the comorbidity risk for these two disorders. In 1987 we published a comparison of women with early onset (by age 20) versus late onset (age 25 or above) bulimia and found that the late onset patients were far more likely to have had substance use problems (36%) than were the early onset patients (5%) (Mitchell et al. 1987). A correlation between an increasing prevalence of substance use disorders and age among bulimic patients was also suggested in a report by Beary et al. (1986) who found that by age 35, 50% of their bulimic patients had developed problems with alcohol abuse.

Four reports in the literature contain data that allow for a comparison of the rates of alcohol and drug abuse problems among bulimic women and controls. Pyle et al. (1983) reported that the rate of alcohol and drug abuse problems was considerably higher among individuals who met criteria for bulimia nervosa (13.3%) compared with those who did not (3.6%) in a questionnaire survey of 1,355 college freshman. Killen et al. (1987) reported similar results in a survey of 1,728 tenth graders. In their findings, individuals who admitted to purging were also more likely to be drinking heavily than those who denied purging. Two additional studies involved direct interviews of patients. Bulik (1987) reported that the rate of alcohol and drug abuse problems among 35 patients with bulimia (mean age 30) was 48%, whereas the rate among 35 controls (mean age 31) was 8.6%. Hudson et al. (1987a) reported that the rate of substance use disorders was 48% among 70 bulimic women (mean age 26) but only 3% among 28 controls (mean age 31).

Taken together, both uncontrolled and controlled studies suggest an exaggerated prevalence for alcohol and drug abuse problems among individuals with bulimia nervosa compared with many women in the general population.

Drug and Alcohol Abuse Among Women With Anorexia Nervosa

The comorbidity problem between alcohol and drug abuse and anorexia nervosa is less clear, and the data here are far less consistent. Eckert et al. (1979) reported that 7 (6.7%) of a series of 105 patients with anorexia nervosa had a lifetime diagnosis of alcohol abuse using DSM-III criteria (American Psychiatric Association 1980). Viesselman and Roig (1985) reported that none of their 13 subjects who satisfied Feighner's criteria (Feighner et al. 1972) for anorexia nervosa had problems with alcohol or drug abuse, and Henzel (1984) found that 5 of 15 anorexic patients had this problem. In a study using the DIS-structured interview, Hudson et al. (1983) found that 19% of 16 anorexic patients met criteria for substance use problems.

It is noteworthy that when anorexic patients are grouped into the restricting and bulimic subtypes, it becomes apparent that the problem with alcohol and drug abuse is more common among those in the bulimic subgroup. For example, Cantwell et al. (1977) reported that of seven patients with anorexia nervosa who developed alcohol and drug abuse problems, six were bulimic. Therefore, although the question of exaggerated prevalence of alcohol and drug abuse problems among anorexia nervosa patients in general remains controversial, when this comorbidity problem is encountered it appears to center primarily on the bulimic subgroup of anorexia nervosa patients.

Eating Disorders Among Persons With Drug and Alcohol Abuse Problems

Paralleling the literature on chemical dependency problems among eating-disordered patients is a separate literature on the prevalence of eating disorders among chemically dependent patients. Several reports support such an association. In 1986 Beary et al. reported that 7 (35%) of 20 women with chemical dependency problems also had an active eating disorder. Lacey and Moureli (1986) reported in an expanded series that 11 (40%) of 27 patients met criteria for an eating disorder.

Jonas et al. (1987) reported data obtained through the systematic assessment of 259 consecutive callers to a national cocaine hot line. Thirty-two percent of the callers met criteria for an eating disorder; 22% met DSM-III criteria for bulimia; 9% met DSM-III criteria for bulimia plus the additional criterion of self-induced vomiting; 7% met criteria for anorexia nervosa, bulimic subtype; and 2% met criteria for anorexia nervosa, restricting subtype. Of particular interest, 44% of those who met criteria for bulimia were male.

Two studies have systematically examined the prevalence of bulimia nervosa and anorexia nervosa in large populations of individuals with alcohol or drug abuse problems. Hudson et al. (in press) reported that 15% of women and 3% of men in a series of 386 individuals undergoing chemical dependency treatment satisfied DSM-III-R criteria

(American Psychiatric Association 1987) for anorexia nervosa or bulimia nervosa. E. D. Eckert and R. L. Pyle (October 1990, unpublished observations) compared the rates of eating disorders among 1,355 college students and 440 women undergoing chemical dependency treatment. Although 7.8% of the female college students satisfied DSM-III criteria for bulimia, 17.8% of the chemically dependent patients met these criteria. Using the more stringent criteria of the DSM-III bulimia criteria coupled with binge eating and self-induced vomiting or laxative abuse on at least a weekly basis, 1% of the female college students satisfied the criteria, whereas 6.7% of the women undergoing chemical dependency did, again strongly suggesting an increased rate of eating disorders among substance abusers.

Familial Association Between Chemical Dependency and Eating Disorders

Several investigators have examined the prevalence of chemical abuse problems among the relatives of patients with eating disorders in an attempt to delineate the familial relationships between the two disorders. Rivinus et al. (1984) reported the morbid risk for alcohol and drug abuse in the relatives of 40 patients with anorexia nervosa to be 21.6%; the risk for relatives of 23 controls was only 8%. In retrospectively examining the family histories of 94 patients with anorexia nervosa, Halmi and Loney (1973) found that 2 of the mothers and 12 of the fathers had problems with alcohol abuse. The relationship between bulimic and restricting subgroups and the risk of alcohol and drug abuse among anorexic individuals seems to hold true also for their families—that is, the relatives of the bulimic subgroup appear to be at particular risk. Strober et al. (1982) reported that the rate of alcoholism among the relatives of patients with anorexia nervosa, restricting subtype, was 4%; the rate among relatives of those with the bulimic subtype was 16%.

Two controlled studies have examined the prevalence of chemical dependency among relatives of normal-weight bulimic patients. Bulik (1987) reported that alcohol and drug abuse was increased in the first- and second-degree relatives of 35 normal-weight bulimic subjects compared with 35 age-matched controls. Hudson et al. (1987b) reported an increased role of substance abuse problems among relatives of 69 bulimic women compared with the rate among the relatives of 28 controls.

Therefore, the available studies suggest an exaggerated risk for chemical dependency problems among patients with eating disorders and their relatives, compared with controls and their relatives. The data on elevated risk are particularly compelling for individuals with normal-weight bulimia and individuals with anorexia nervosa, bulimic subtype, and their families. Whether this exaggerated prevalence for alcohol and drug dependency is unique to eating-disordered patients and their families, as compared with individuals with other types of psychopathology and their families, has yet to be tested.

To further evaluate the relationship between familial alcohol and drug abuse and eating disorders, we hypothesized that there might be interesting differences among bulimic patients who came from families where there was a heavy loading for chemical dependency problems, compared with patients who came from families without this history (Mitchell et al. 1988a). Of interest, those patients with a positive family history of alcohol or other drug abuse reported a higher current body weight and higher maximum body weight, were more likely to report a family history of depression and criminality, and were more likely to report having been previously treated for chemical dependency problems. Their eating patterns, however, were quite similar to those of the patients in the negative family history group.

Behavioral Similarities

As several authors have discussed (Filstead et al. 1988; Hatsukami et al. 1984; Jones et al. 1985; Scott 1983) there are many behavioral similarities between alcohol and drug abuse problems and the eating disorders. These similarities include the misuse of an ingested substance, preoccupation with use of the substance, repeated attempts at self-control (and repeated failure), a habit pattern of repeated use, the use of the substance for mood-altering effects, and the development of adverse physical, psychological, and social sequelae. This model particularly holds true for bulimia nervosa either in association with anorexia nervosa or in normal-weight individuals. The concept is at times expanded to include anorexia nervosa as an "addiction" to starvation or weight loss.

The similarities between eating disorders and chemical dependency and the ascendancy of addictionology as a theoretical model behind treatment strategies for several types of disorders have lead many treatment programs to adapt traditional chemical dependency 12-step treatment models for the treatment of eating disorders. Some of the theoretical problems in grouping these disorders under one category recently have been eloquently argued by Vendereycken (1990). What many of these programs fail to acknowledge is that there is a very important difference between eating disorders and chemical dependency. Patients with eating disorders need to learn control—they cannot avoid the substance of abuse as can someone with active chemical dependency. This is not a minor philosophical discrepancy, but a difference with important treatment implications.

Atypical Substances of Abuse

In addition to what are regarded as usual substances of abuse, many patients with eating disorders abuse several other classes of drugs that are normally not encountered in chemical dependency treatment programs. These are agents that are used to promote weight loss or rid oneself of food. They include laxatives, diuretics, diet pills, and the emetic agent ipecac (Mitchell et al. 1988c). The problem of laxative abuse is discussed elsewhere in this volume. Here we focus our attention on the other three classes of drugs.

Diet Pills

In our previous description of a series of 275 patients with bulimia nervosa (Mitchell et al. 1985), we noted that 52.2% reported having used diet pills for weight control purposes, and 25.1% had used them at least once a day during the course of their eating disorder. In a separate series of 100 patients, 26 reported having used diet pills in the month before evaluation (Mitchell et al. 1988c). Eight (31%) of these patients used the diet pills several times a day, 10 (38%) several times a week or weekly, and 8 (31%) less than weekly. The most commonly ingested diet pills were the over-the-counter agents, such as Dexatrim, Dietac, and Acutrim. Several of the patients used multiple diet pills a day.

Most of the over-the-counter diet pills sold in the United States contain phenylpropanolamine hydrochloride and are dosed so the individual consumes 75 mg/day. Some also contain other active substances such as vitamins, minerals, and iron. These drugs have been shown to facilitate weight loss on a short-term basis in individuals with obesity (Altschuler et al. 1982). However, there have been reports of untoward effects including elevated blood pressure (Horowitz et al. 1980; Lee et al. 1979; Shapiro 1977), renal failure (Swenson et al. 1982), seizures (Howrie and Wolfson 1983), and a variety of adverse central nervous system effects. The effects of these agents in normal-weight women with bulimia nervosa have not been adequately studied.

Diuretics

In our series of 275 bulimic women, we found that 33.9% reported having used diuretics for weight control purposes and 10.2% reported using diuretics on at least a daily basis (Mitchell et al. 1985). This is a markedly exaggerated prevalence compared with the use of these substances by young women in the general population. For example, in a survey of 355 college students (59.8% of whom were women), 4.2% reported that they had used diuretics (Halmi et al. 1981). In a separate survey of 1,268 high school students by Johnson et al. (1983), 4% reported using diuretics.

Over-the-counter diuretic preparations are commonly used by members of the general population for control of "idiopathic edema" and symptoms associated with premenstrual fluid retention. Idiopathic edema remains a controversial topic. In 1977 Bailey noted that women with idiopathic edema are at times prescribed diuretics and that on occasion they do not tell other physicians about their use of these products. MacGregor et al. (1975, 1979) suggested that idiopathic edema may result from the misuse of diuretics. Clearly not all women who use diuretics for idiopathic edema or relief of premenstrual syndrome symptoms abuse the drugs or have clinically significant eating problems, but there does appear to be an association.

Eating-disordered patients may obtain diuretics from several sources: over-the-counter (diuretics that contain a variety of active diuretic ingredients including pamabrom, caffeine, and ammonium chloride), prescription diuretics for appropriate or questionable medical reasons, prescription diuretics prescribed for someone else, and misappropriation of diuretics in the workplace (Katz et al. 1972).

In our experience most bulimic patients who misuse diuretics use over-the-counter preparations. However, there is a small subgroup who specifically abuse prescription diuretics and who may see multiple physicians for such prescriptions (Mitchell et al. 1988d).

Ipecac

Pope et al. (1986) were the first to study the prevalence of ipecac misuse among women with bulimia. They reported that in a consecutive series of 100 bulimic women, 28 reported having used ipecac. Of these, 7 reported having used the drug 10 to 99 times, and 4 reported having used the drug more than 100 times. Ipecac is dispensed in the United States as a syrup containing the emetine base. The alkaloid emetine can be responsible for myopathies, including cardiomyopathies, and several case histories of such problems have been reported (Bennett et al. 1982; Brotman et al. 1981; Friedman 1984; Palmer and Guay 1985).

The medical assessment of these patients involves careful delineation of any possible toxicity from the drug, especially cardiomyopathy. Assessment should include an electrocardiogram, and strong consideration should be given to an echocardiogram.

Implications and Conclusions

The available literature clearly suggests a problem of comorbidity between eating disorders and drug and alcohol abuse problems. The reasons for this remain unclear, and the specificity of this comorbidity relative to other forms of psychopathology is yet to be adequately addressed in research studies.

This comorbidity as well as the similarities between the two disorders has led many treatment programs to modify existing treatment approaches for drug and alcohol abuse problems for the treatment of eating disorders. In many of these programs, eating disorders are seen as another form of "addiction." Such patients are often taught that they are inherently different from others, that there are certain foods they cannot eat, that they need to be "abstinent" from these certain foods. The implication is clearly that they will be someone with an eating disorder for the rest of their life. Do these theoretical notions fit with our knowledge of eating disorders? We think not. Although there are significant similarities, there are also important differences, the most important of which is that people with eating disorders need to learn to eat appropriately; they cannot really "avoid" food or be "abstinent" from the substance of abuse. Follow-up research has clearly documented that many patients with eating disorders, particularly those with bulimia nervosa, can make a full recovery (Mitchell et al. 1988b). Furthermore, as has been argued by Fairburn and Cooper (1984), a strong case can be made that patients should not be taught to exclude certain foods from their diet but should be encouraged to reintroduce "trigger" or binge foods during the course of treatment so they will not continue to have "feared" foods.

Patients with eating disorders—particularly those with normal-weight bulimia nervosa and anorexia nervosa, bulimic subtype—appear to have an exaggerated risk for abusing several other "atypical" classes of compounds, including laxatives, diet pills, diuretics, and ipecac. The misuse of such drugs can pose significant medical risks. If present, a history of the misuse of these substances needs to be documented at the time of evaluation so these problems can be incorporated into treatment planning.

This comorbidity has significant implications for the assessment and treatment of patients with either bulimia nervosa or alcohol and drug abuse problems. Because the focus of this work is on eating disorders, we will discuss these implications from that perspective.

First, it is of utmost importance to take a very careful history regarding the use of typical substances of abuse (i.e., amphetamines, alcohol, and marijuana) and atypical substances of abuse (i.e., laxatives, diuretics, and ipecac) when evaluating patients with eating disorders. It is also important to delineate the relationship between the two conditions. For example, does the patient tend to be disinhibited when intoxicated and then to binge eat? Or does he or she tend to substitute these behaviors, binge eating when not using alcohol or vice versa? The nature of the relationship and the temporal correlations between the two conditions may be useful in planning treatment strategies.

Next, treatment decisions must be made. Because concurrent treatments for both conditions are rarely available, one has to decide which treatment will be primary. This depends on the medical state of the patient. If one is dealing with a patient with normal-weight bulimia nervosa whose eating behavior and chemical usage are not endangering her life, the usual approach is to treat her chemical dependency first, while attempting to at least moderate the abnormal eating behavior during the process of that treatment. However, in a patient with low-weight anorexia nervosa, eating disorder treatment may be the priority, particularly inpatient treatment and medical stabilization. An alternate possibility would be when the severity of the substance abuse problem poses immediate health hazards requiring intervention for that problem. Practical suggestions concerning the management of eating-disordered patients on a substance abuse unit have been offered by Marcus and Katz (1990). These authors stress the need for nutritional evaluation and rehabilitation as well as specific strategies to interrupt bulimic symptoms in such settings.

The ideal program would combine elements of a traditional 12-step addiction treatment program and the behavioral and cognitive behavioral components that are favored in the treatment of eating disorders. Unfortunately, in the minds of many therapists these approaches are antithetical, and the therapists of each camp frequently are antagonistic to the other camp. This is probably one of the main reasons for the lack of many dual diagnosis programs. However, in situations where a staff can be assembled that can be rigorous in the applications of the various treatment principles, yet flexible enough to effectively employ both types, a combined approach may be best.

References

Altschuler S, Conte A, Sebok M, et al: Three controlled trials of weight loss with phenylpropanolamine. Int J Obes 6:549–556, 1982

American Psychiatric Association: Diagnostic and Statistical Manual of Mental Disorders, 3rd Edition. Washington, DC, American Psychiatric Association, 1980

American Psychiatric Association: Diagnostic and Statistical Manual of Mental Disorders, 3rd Edition, Revised. Washington, DC, American Psychiatric Association, 1987

Bailey RR: Water-logged women: idiopathic oedema. N Z Med J 85:129–132, 1977

Beary MD, Lacey JH, Merry J: Alcoholism and eating disorder in women of fertile age. Br J Addict 81:685–689, 1986

Bennett HS, Spiro AJ, Pollack MA, et al: Ipecac-induced myopathy simulating dermatomyositis. Neurology 32:91–94, 1982

Brisman J, Siegel M: Bulimia and alcoholism: two sides of the same coin? J Subst Abuse Treat 1:113–118, 1984

Brotman MC, Forbath N, Garfinkel PE, et al: Myopathy due to ipecac syrup poisoning in a patient with anorexia nervosa. Can Med Assoc J 125:453–473, 1981

Bulik CM: Drug and alcohol abuse by bulimic women and their families. Am J Psychiatry 144:1604–1606, 1987

Cantwell DP, Struzenberger S, Burroughs J, et al: Anorexia nervosa: an affective disorder? Arch Gen Psychiatry 34:1087–1093, 1977

Eckert ED, Goldberg SC, Halmi KA, et al: Alcoholism in anorexia nervosa, in

Psychiatric Factors in Drug Abuse. Edited by Pickens RW, Heston LL. New York, Grune & Stratton, 1979, pp 267–283

Feighner JP, Robins E, Guze SB, et al: Diagnostic criteria for use in psychiatric research. Arch Gen Psychiatry 26:57–63, 1972

Fairburn CG, Cooper PJ: The clinical features of bulimia nervosa. Br J Psychiatry 144:238–246, 1984

Filstead WJ, Parrella DP, Ebbit J: High-risk situations for engaging in substance abuse and binge-eating behaviors. J Stud Alcohol 49:136–141, 1988

Friedman EJ: Death from ipecac intoxication in a patient with anorexia nervosa. Am J Psychiatry 141:702–703, 1984

Halmi KA, Loney J: Familial alcoholism in anorexia nervosa. Br J Psychiatry 123:53–54, 1973

Halmi KA, Falk JR, Schwartz E: Binge-eating and vomiting: a survey of a college population. Psychol Med 11:697–706, 1981

Hatsukami D, Eckert E, Mitchell JE, et al: Affective disorder and substance abuse in women with bulimia. Psychol Med 14:701–704, 1984

Hatsukami D, Mitchell JE, Eckert ED, et al: Characteristics of patients with bulimia only, bulimia with affective disorder, and bulimia with substance abuse problems. Addict Behav 11:399–406, 1986

Henzel HA: Diagnosing alcoholism in patients with anorexia nervosa. Am J Drug Alcohol Abuse 10:461–466, 1984

Horowitz JD, Howes LG, Christophidis N, et al: Hypertensive responses induced by phenylpropanolamine in anorectic and decongestant preparations. Lancet 1:60–61, 1980

Howrie DL, Wolfson JH: Phenylpropanolamine-induced hypertensive seizures. J Pediatr 102:143–145, 1983

Hudson JI, Pope HG, Jonas JM, et al: Family history study of anorexia nervosa and bulimia. Br J Psychiatry 142:133–138, 1983

Hudson JI, Pope HG, Jonas JM, et al: A controlled family history study of bulimia. Psychol Med 17:883–890, 1987a

Hudson JI, Pope HG, Yurgelun-Todd D, et al: A controlled study of lifetime prevalence of affective and other psychiatric disorders in bulimic outpatients. Am J Psychiatry 144:1283–1287, 1987b

Hudson JI, Weiss RD, Pope HG, et al: Eating disorders in hospital substance abusers. J Clin Psychiatry (in press)

Johnson CL, Lewis C, Love S, et al: A descriptive survey of dieting and bulimic behavior in a female high school population. Report of the Fourth Ross Conference in Medical Research, Phoenix, AZ, September 1983, pp 14–18

Jonas JM, Gold MS, Sweeney D, et al: Eating disorders and cocaine abuse: a survey of 259 cocaine abusers. J Clin Psychiatry 48:47–50, 1987

Jones DA, Cheshire N, Moorhouse H: Anorexia nervosa, bulimia and alcoholism: association of eating disorder and alcohol. J Psychiatr Res 19:377–380, 1985

Katz FH, Eckert R, Gebott MD: Hypokalemia caused by surreptitious self-administration of diuretics. Ann Intern Med 76:85–90, 1972

Killen JD, Taylor CB, Telch MJ, et al: Evidence for an alcohol-stress link among normal weight adolescents reporting purging behavior. International Journal of Eating Disorders 6:349–356, 1987

Lacey JH, Moureli E: Bulimic alcoholics: some features of a clinical subgroup. Br J Addict 81:389–393, 1986

Lee KY, Vandogen R, Beilin LM: Severe hypertension after ingestion of an appetite suppressant (phenylpropanolamine) with indomethacin. Lancet 1:1110–1111, 1979

MacGregor GA, Tasker PRW, deWardener HE: Diuretic-induced oedema. Lancet 1:489–492, 1975

MacGregor GA, Markandu ND, Roulston JE, et al: Is "idiopathic" oedema idiopathic? Lancet 1:397–400, 1979

Marcus RN, Katz JL: Inpatient care of the substance-abusing patient with a concomitant eating disorder. Hosp Community Psychiatry 41:59–63, 1990

Mitchell JE, Hatsukami D, Eckert ED, et al : Characteristics of 275 patients with bulimia. Am J Psychiatry 142:482–485, 1985

Mitchell JE, Hatsukami D, Pyle RL, et al: Late onset bulimia. Compr Psychiatry 28:323–328, 1987

Mitchell JE, Hatsukami D, Pyle R, et al: Bulimia with and without a family history of drug abuse. Addict Behav 13:245–251, 1988a

Mitchell JE, Pyle RL, Hatsukami D, et al: A 2–5-year follow-up study of patients treated for bulimia. International Journal of Eating Disorders 8:157–165, 1988b

Mitchell JE, Pomeroy C, Huber M: A clinician's guide to the eating disorders medicine cabinet. International Journal of Eating Disorders 7:211–223, 1988c

Mitchell JE, Pomeroy C, Seppala M, et al: Diuretic use as a marker for eating problems and affective disorders among women. J Clin Psychiatry 49:267–270, 1988d

Palmer EP, Guay AT: Reversible myopathy secondary to abuse of ipecac in patients with major eating disorders. N Engl J Med 313:1457–1459, 1985

Pope HG, Hudson JI, Nixon RA, et al: The epidemiology of ipecac abuse (ltr). N Engl J Med 314:245, 1986

Pyle RL, Mitchell JE, Eckert ED: Bulimia: a report of 34 cases. J Clin Psychiatry 42:60–64, 1981

Pyle RL, Mitchell JE, Eckert ED et al: The incidence of bulimia in freshman college students. International Journal of Eating Disorders 2:75–85, 1983

Rivinus TM, Biederman J, Herzog DB, et al: Anorexia nervosa and affective disorders: a controlled family history study. Am J Psychiatry 141:1414–1418, 1984

Robins LN, Helzer JE, Croughan J, et al: National Institute of Mental Health Diagnostic Interview Schedule: its history, characteristics, and validity. Arch Gen Psychiatry 38:381–389, 1981

Scott DW: Alcohol and food abuse: some comparisons. Br J Addict 78:339–349, 1983

Shapiro SR: Hypertension due to anorectic agent. N Engl J Med 280:1363, 1977

Strober M, Salkin B, Burroughs J, et al: Validity of the bulimia-restrictor distinction in anorexia nervosa: parental personality characteristics and family psychiatric morbidity. J Nerv Ment Dis 170:345–351, 1982

Swenson RD, Golper TA, Bennett WM: Acute renal failure and rhabodomyolysis after ingestion of phenylpropanolamine-containing diet pills. JAMA 248:1216, 1982

Vendereycken W: The addiction model in eating disorders: some critical remarks and a selected bibliography. International Journal of Eating Disorders 9:95–101, 1990

Viesselman JO, Roig M: Depression and suicidality in eating disorders. J Clin Psychiatry 46:118–124, 1985

Zweben JE: Eating disorders and substance abuse. J Psychoactive Drugs 19:181–192, 1987

Chapter 2

Eating Disorders and Affective Disorders

Carole K. Edelstein, M.D.
Joel Yager, M.D.

*D*epression and eating disorders are common comorbid conditions. In this chapter we examine the effects of their joint occurrence on the traditional clinical activities of diagnosis, assessment, treatment with antidepressant medications, and psychotherapy. We present our guidelines for using medications—focusing on when we have and have not found them to be helpful—and illustrate through three case examples how medications can provide important benefits in different ways. As background we discuss how dysphoric moods emerge from and interact with other eating disorder symptoms.

Why is depression a common finding among patients with eating disorders? To begin with, sources of dysphoria and demoralization are abundant in these patients. Figure 2–1 shows contributions from at least four areas. First is the abnormal eating itself. Episodes of bingeing can lower self-esteem in the bulimic patient and lead to feelings of fragmentation, disorganization, and even depersonalization. The term "bingeing" may be too neutral to adequately convey the frantic overeating and frenzied stuffing that occur.

Cooper et al. (1988), who studied mood changes over the binge-purge cycle in depressed and nondepressed bulimic patients and binge-eating patients, found the postbinge period to be "an emphatically unpleasant mood state." Patients reported low levels of energy and excitement, high levels of panic and helplessness, and very high levels of guilt, disgust, and anger. There were no differences reported in this experience between the depressed and nondepressed subgroups, suggesting that intense dysphoria can exist independent of major affective disorder and in direct relationship to eating behaviors. Furthermore, most patients who binge are constantly exhorting themselves, "I'm not going

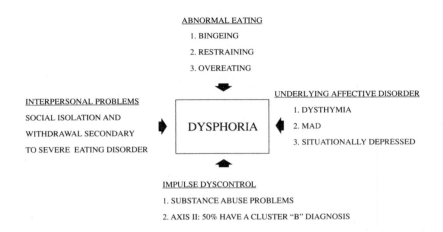

Figure 2–1.   Sources of dysphoria in the eating-disordered patient.

to do this ever again"; thus with each new binge they violate their own internal standards and disappoint themselves.

Ordinarily, individuals who binge eat are highly restrained in their eating, consuming and retaining fewer calories than they require physiologically (i.e., when they are not actually binge eating). As a result, they intermittently feel deprived and may become dysphoric. Overeating can also be disruptive and produce negative moods.

Even subjective overeating of relatively low caloric loads, *not* major bingeing, may overwhelm patients by sensations of fullness and result in states of acute anxiety and demoralization. Although laboratory studies of eating behavior show that binge-purge episodes transiently decrease anxiety and tension, this brief respite may be followed by rebound or withdrawal-mediated increases in dysphoria (Kaye et al. 1988).

Second, 25–80% of eating-disordered patients have categorically defined major mood disorder as diagnosed by structured interviews (see Strober and Katz 1988), and more than two dozen studies using standardized instruments such as the Beck Depression Inventory (Beck 1978), the Hopkins Symptom Checklist-90 (HSCL-90; Derogatis et al. 1974), and the Hamilton Rating Scale for Depression (Hamilton 1967) have found a high prevalence of depression to be present in patients with eating disorders.

A third contributing factor to affective symptoms among patients with eating disorders is the combination of impulse dyscontrol and affective instability associated with acting-out character pathology and/or associated substance abuse (Hatsukami et al. 1984; Levin and Hyler 1986; Piran et al. 1988).

Finally, patients are at risk for developing or exacerbating interpersonal problems as their eating disorders become more severe and their symptoms increasingly require them to withdraw into relative isolation because of their time consuming and socially unappealing nature. Patients with good instrumental role functioning—successful professionals—come home from work and may binge and vomit repetitively. As their social supports diminish, their dysphoria mounts.

Diagnosis

When an eating-disordered patient presents with or develops dysphoria, the clinician's first task is to determine whether the patient has a concurrent Axis I mood syndrome (according to DSM-III-R criteria; American Psychiatric Association 1987) or brief reactive dysphoria/demoralization either from the sources outlined in Figure 2–1 or from starvation effects. This disentangling is not easy. Keys et al.'s landmark study (1950) showed how many symptoms of depression may result from starvation. After 6 months of consuming about one-half their baseline total of daily calories their patients noted anergia, fragmented sleep, decreased concentration and libido, anhedonia, dysphoria, and social withdrawal.

Although symptoms of depression due to the starvation syndrome are to be expected among patients with anorexia nervosa, Pirke et al. (1985) found evidence that normal-weight patients with bulimia nervosa are also starved. Therefore, concurrent mood disturbances may be expected among some patients whose weights fall within statistically normal group ranges. Pirke et al. (1985) reported significant differences between bulimic patients and controls, based on several metabolic indices, which when affected in concert and in specific patterns indicate starvation (e.g., glucose tolerance, norepinephrine response to standing, elevated levels of ketones and free fatty acids, and decreased triiodothyronine [T3] levels). These data suggest that irritability and other mood changes in normal-weight patients may be physiologically driven in relation to starvation.

Even though starvation may generate symptoms suggesting mood disorder, the attractive physical appearances these patients can present with may partially mask their underlying depression and further confound diagnosis. Recent research, however, suggests that certain aspects of eating-disordered patients' clinical depression may distinguish it from other mood syndromes.

For example, although commonly used measures of anhedonia and dysphoria fail to distinguish patients with anorexia nervosa from unipolar depressed patients, the latter have significantly more sleep disturbances and psychomotor retardation (Piran et al. 1985). Keller et al.'s 1989 study of patients with bulimia and concurrent mood disorder showed that the two disorders had discrete periods of onset and offset. The researchers followed 30 outpatients for 18 months and identified periods of recovery and relapse from episodes of bulimia and affective disorder. Their key finding was that the course of the two disorders did not coincide.

When Cooper and Fairburn (1986) compared bulimic patients to unipolar depressed patients, they found that the eating-disordered patients scored higher on Present State Exam (PSE; Wing et al. 1974) measures of anxiety, guilt, and obsessionality, whereas depressed patients scored higher on social withdrawal, loss of usual interest, suicidality, low mood, and loss of libido. Furthermore, the authors felt that the guilt, rumination, and dysphoria seen in the bulimic patients might be epiphenomena of eating behaviors because they were transient and appeared related to exacerbations of the eating disorders.

The high prevalence of affective disturbance within the eating-disordered patient population has stimulated much discussion and controversy about possible models for interaction between the mood and the eating disorders (Altschuler and Weiner 1985; Chaitin 1988; Cooper et al. 1988; Hudson et al. 1987; Katz 1987; Kaye et al. 1988; Keller et al. 1989; Keys et al. 1950; Laessle et al. 1988; Levy et al. 1988; Mitchell et al. 1986; Piran et al. 1985; Pope et al. 1985; Strober and Katz 1987, 1988; Szmukler 1987; Wamboldt et al. 1987; Wilson and Lindholm 1987).

Without attempting to resolve all the extant controversies or review various theories in detail, our own distillation of key conclusions for the clinician that have emerged from currently available data is as follows:

- Some individuals merit two or more concurrent Axis I diagnoses, with their mood syndromes well described by current categorical definitions. The mood symptoms may predominate or not; they may remit or recur even as eating disorder symptoms wax and wane.

- Some individuals have depressive symptoms that do not meet a usual mood disorder diagnosis but that are typical for eating-disordered patients, with an emphasis on rumination, guilt, and anxiety. For many patients these symptoms are worse than their eating symptoms.
- Some individuals may have depressive symptoms secondary to inadequate energy supplies. These starvation effects remit after weight restoration and/or the normalization of eating.

What are the implications of these conclusions for clinicians faced with eating-disordered patients who appear depressed? Clearly, there are benefits to be gained from teasing apart the symptoms of dysphoria and trying to identify whether they are due to coexisting disorders or are predominately eating and weight related. Our approach to assessing these problems follows.

Assessment

The goal of assessment is to identify whether the interactions between dysphoria and impulsive eating behaviors in a given patient are linked or to determine that the mood disorder and eating behaviors are relatively independent, although concurrent. When linked, the interactions are probably best conceptualized as circular. As shown in Figure 2–2—derived from typical Minnesota Multiphasic Personality Inventory (MMPI) profile peaks as seen in patients with anorexia nervosa and bulimia nervosa (Norman and Herzog 1983)—uncomfortable negative affective states (D) are avoided via actions (Pd). Because these actions often provide immediate relief, they are highly reinforcing. However, these same actions ultimately intensify regret and remorse and thus reinitiate the cycle of overeating followed by purging.

Tools that clinicians may find useful in documenting this interaction can identify the eating-related waxing and waning of dysphoric affects. Such tools include daily journals, life history time lines, checklists for following eating behaviors, and mood rating scales.

Daily journals can be used to chart not only the location of eating but also the emotional environment in which it occurred (e.g., before a work deadline, alone at night, or after an argument). These charts should include descriptions of mood states at different points in the binge-purge

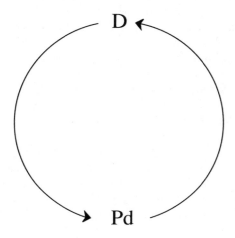

Circular path of acting out → Remorse →
Increased depression → Acting out to relieve
depression → Temporary relief (highly
reinforcing → Later regret → Remorse → Etc.

Figure 2–2. How depression and eating disorder symptoms may be linked. D= Depression; Pd = Psychopathic deviance.

cycle (before bingeing, postbinge, before purging, and postpurge). Patients who have difficulty identifying their feelings can be given charts of labelled emotions illustrated by line drawings of faces portraying the named state.

A life history time line can be used to correlate past episodes of depression with weight and eating symptoms. The clinician should carefully question and review with the patient her recollections of the persistence of low mood and of the presence of low mood at different weights and during times when the eating disorder was active or quiescent. For example, a 23-year-old binge-eating graduate student who experienced an episode of mild, spontaneously remitting anorexia nervosa in high school, but who had persistent weight and food preoccupation and dysphoria related to being unable to exercise, found and brought her long-discarded high school diary into therapy. It documented weights, preoccupations, and family events in the 18 months that preceded weight loss and poignantly illustrated the shift in concern from boys and grades to foods and weight. Even in the absence of such personal diaries, most patients can be helped to reconstruct key life events. The clinician can have the patient start with the important life events and then fill in probable weights and behaviors by recalling, for example, clothes worn and their sizes. When such information is entered on a time line the emerging pattern often prompts additional recall.

The clinician should find or devise a paper and pencil checklist system for monitoring eating disorder symptoms: binge frequency, vomit frequency, hours exercising, meals skipped, number of times per day used scale, etc. Using such a checklist the clinician can focus at each visit on the key variables for the specific profile of symptoms the patient exhibits. Our checklist appears in Appendix 1 (Eating Disorders Clinic Medication Visit Progress Note).

Among mood rating scales, the Beck Depression Inventory (Beck 1978) is easy to use in the office. It can be filled out in minutes while the patient is in the waiting room and scored by the clinician in less than 1 minute at the start of the session. Combining the eating disorders rating scale with a frequently administered depression checklist can provide ongoing information about the relationships of eating symptoms and mood, especially if the history is unclear. It can also provide systematic feedback about the progress of treatment, the need for medication, and the conjoint or independent responses of eating and mood symptoms to treatment. Such an approach allows for continuing reassessment of treatment strategies as various clusters of symptoms improve, remain unchanged, or worsen with different treatment approaches.

Finally, clinicians need to be wary about their preconscious mindsets about the interrelationships between physical appearance and mood. Unlike classic mood syndromes, depressed eating-disordered patients can look like (and be) exquisitely dressed and groomed fashion models. The use of checklists as described above will amplify and correct impressions derived from superficial appearances.

General Guidelines for Treatment With Antidepressant Medications

At the start of treatment, it should be recognized that using medications in this patient population is often problematic. Many patients are reluctant to take medications and may report many side effects.

When Not to Start Treatment With Medication

Whatever the outcome of the assessment, we hesitate suggesting antidepressant medications adjunctly in three circumstances. The first is if the patient's belief system is opposed to medication due to fears of becoming fat, of becoming addicted, and/or of losing control. Because vigorous lobbying efforts by the physician may only increase resistance, one must gently examine the patient's attitudes, provide information, dispel myths, and educate the patient in hopes that he or she will come to regard pharmacologic intervention as an option at least worth thinking about periodically.

The second circumstance is when the clinician believes the medication's side effects could outweigh its efficacy. These drugs are potentially dangerous in patients who are using recreational drugs or drinking alcohol (and driving) and those who may feel suicidal. Because nondrug modalities such as cognitive behavioral therapy have been shown to be quite useful for some eating-disordered patients, one might hesitate to treat with medication when efficacious nondrug alternatives are available.

Finally, we hesitate suggesting medication when the patient makes clear a strong desire to get better without medication so that he or she can feel internally enhanced rather than dependent on medication.

When to Start Treatment With Medication

There are several circumstances in which we would readily initiate treatment with medication. First is when the patient is clearly depressed and has a history of depressive episodes at normal weight or a positive family history for depression. Second, we would recommend a medication trial to any patient (whether depressed or not) whose reasonably conceived and executed multidimensional eating disorder treatment plan has failed to curb the eating disorder and/or ameliorate low mood (see Case 1 below).

We wish to emphasize that we are not advocating the introduction of medication to resolve a psychotherapy stalemate (Perry 1989). The sources of such an impasse may often be found in some unyielding defensive style of the patient or in therapist countertransference difficulties. Issues in therapist competence and choice of therapy can also be factors. For example, there are several effective treatments for normal-weight bulimia nervosa, but finding the right one may mean shuffling and reshuffling the elements of the different approaches.

A therapist skilled in only one approach may not be able to offer what is required to promote improvement in that patient. However, when the focused efforts of a skilled treatment team (utilizing, as appropriate, nutritional counseling, cognitive behavioral or behavioral individual treatment, and group and family treatment) cannot break the grip of an eating disorder, a medication trial should be strongly considered.

What can antidepressants offer?   The rationale for using antidepressants is based primarily on their demonstrated efficacy in treating normal-weight bulimia nervosa in more than a dozen placebo-controlled, double-blind studies (Freeman and Mundro 1988; Pope and Hudson 1989). These studies are summarized in Table 2–1.

In anorexia nervosa, medication studies have been inconclusive, although further study of noradrenergic mechanisms has been suggested (Herzog and Brotman 1987). Furthermore, new data suggest that pharmacologic manipulation of the serotonergic system may be productive (Weltzin et al. 1990). The major medication studies for anorexia nervosa are summarized in Table 2–2.

It has also been suggested that the development of an eating disorder may represent a biological defense against depression because running and starving generate endorphins, which may help alleviate depressed mood. Finally, using antidepressant medication may help reduce the patient's vulnerability to the eating disorder as mood, reality testing, and active coping all improve. As depression lifts, patients may be less inclined to catastrophize and become better able to substitute adaptive tension-reducing behaviors such as socializing, pleasurable exercise, and even working or studying for binge eating and purging.

Proposed mechanisms through which antidepressant benefits may be derived are numerous. An early hypothesis suggested that medications resolved an underlying depression that was being expressed through the eating disorder (Altschuler and Weiner 1985; Pope and Hudson 1986),

Table 2–1. Controlled studies of bulimia nervosa treated with antidepressants

Study	Medication	Sample size	Patient source[a]	Duration (wk)	Dose (mg)	Results
	Tricyclics					
Agras et al. 1987	Imipramine	22	Adv & Clin	16	300	Significant
Blouin et al. 1988	Crossover Desmethyl					
	imipramine	10	Adv & local ref	6	150	Significant
	Fenfluramine	12	Adv & local ref	6	60	Significant
Hughes et al. 1986	Desmethyl imipramine	23	Adv & local ref	6	200	Significant
Mitchell and Groat 1984	Amitriptyline	32	Clin	8+	150	NS
Pope et al. 1983	Imipramine	22	Adv	6	200	$P < .01$
Sabine et al. 1983	Mianserin	50	Clin	8	60	NS
	MAOIs					
Kennedy et al. 1988	Isocarboxazid	18	Clin	12	60	Significant
Walsh et al. 1988	Phenelzine	50	Adv & local ref	6	60–90	Significant
	Other					
Enas et al. 1989	Fluoxetine	382	Adv & Clin	8	20 or 60	Both dosages outperform placebo; 60 mg more effective
Freeman et al. 1988	Fluoxetine	40	Clin	6	60	Effective
Horne et al. 1988	Bupropion	55	Adv & Clin	—	225–450	Significant; risk of seizure
Pope et al. 1985	Nomifensine	—	—	—	—	Effective; drug withdrawn
Pope et al. 1989a	Trazodone	42	Adv	4	400	Significant

[a]Patient sources: Clin = Eating disorder or psychiatric clinic patients; Adv = Recruited from advertisements; Local ref = Referrals from local MDs or therapists.

Note: MAOI = Monoamine oxidase inhibitors.

Table 2–2. Medication trials for patients with anorexia nervosa

Study	Medication	Duration (wk)	Dose (mg)	Results
Placebo-controlled trial				
Biederman et al. 1985	Amitriptyline	5	3[a]	NS
Gross et al. 1981	Lithium carbonate	4	NA	Active drug group gained more weight
Halmi et al. 1986	Amitriptyline	8	160	NS
	Cyproheptadine	8	32	NS; marginal effects on weight gain
Lacey and Crisp 1980	Clomipramine	10	50	NS; very low dose
Vandereycken and Pierloot 1982	Pimozide	3	4–6	NS
Open trial				
Andersen 1987	Benzodiazepines	NA	NA	Caution; dependency and withdrawal symptoms
Gwirtsman et al. 1990	Fluoxetine	NA	20–40	All 6 patients had decreased depression; most increased weight; no weight loss
Hudson et al. 1985	Multiple TCAs	NA	NA	Four out of 10 patients improved
Luby et al. 1987	Naltrexone	NA	50–100	Six of 8 patients improved; 4 relapsed off medication
Weltzin et al. 1990	Fluoxetine	NA	40	Restricting patients improved more than did bulimic patients (presumably dose related) with 9 out of 22 asymptomatic

[a]mg/kg body weight.
Note: TCA = tricyclic antidepressant.

but neuroendocrine studies, sleep studies, and family studies seem to have laid to rest the always controversial notion that eating disorders and affective disorders share a common etiology (Levy et al. 1988).

Appetite suppression by these medications, enough to reduce intake below binge threshold, has also been suggested (Mitchell 1988), and this mechanism may in fact partly explain the effectiveness of monoamine oxidase inhibitors (MAOIs) in bulimia. Antidepressant medications may facilitate satiety or modify the neural control of eating behavior in other unknown ways (Rossiter et al. 1988). They also have antianxiety effects that may be particularly important, given the high concordance of anxiety disorders in patients with eating disorders (Hudson et al. 1983) and the fact that they are effective in nondepressed as well as in depressed patients with eating disorders (Hughes et al. 1986). Finally, a primary antibinge action, possibly mediated via effects on norepinephrine and serotonin systems, may explain how these drugs modify bulimic eating.

Additional considerations.　Clinicians who have identified appropriate candidates and who are familiar with the possible mechanisms of antidepressant medication efficacy in these patients must still weigh some practical difficulties. First, although almost all eating-disordered patients experience some degree of affective impairment (Chaitin 1988), depression remains difficult to diagnose in the eating-disordered patient. Despite careful assessment, depression sometimes remains masked behind the patient's pleasing, well-groomed facades and determined secrecy. In situations where a full-blown mood disorder is not clearly present, one may hesitate to add a potentially problematic treatment.

Second, clinicians need to consider the high variability in patients' responses to medication. The literature suggests that some patients derive antibinge-eating effects, some derive antidepressant effects (see Case 3 below), and some derive both (see Case 2 below). Of course, some derive no benefits. Uncertainty as to outcomes can test the therapeutic alliance, which may threaten to unravel as both doctor and patient wait for the medication to work; and a long wait may be in store. Follow-up studies (Pope and Hudson 1989) have shown that most patients who ultimately respond require several adjustments, either dosage changes or switches to alternate medications. These changes are prompted either by troublesome side effects or inadequate therapeutic response.

A third issue that may deter some clinicians is the difficulty of translating the results of research protocols to the management realities of everyday clinical life. Some treatments are not as useful in practice as they appear to be in the explanatory research studies (Fairburn 1990). Side effects, drop outs, other concurrent diagnoses and problems, and the select nature of research subjects who respond to advertisements and who are heavily screened rather than sequential clinic cases may amplify these differences (Edelstein et al. 1989; Mitchell 1988).

Case examples. To illustrate these management issues, we present three case examples that demonstrate how medications can provide important benefits, but in different ways. The cases reflect the diverse origins of dysphoria, the unpredictable interrelationships between depression and abnormal eating, and the diverse responses to medication treatment in typical patients.

Case 1, the most straightforward, demonstrates the effectiveness of adding an antidepressant medication to the treatment of a previously mildly dysphoric young woman with bulimia nervosa whose mood state had already normalized with eating disorder treatment, but whose eating disorder symptoms had only partially responded.

Case 2 demonstrates the course of symptoms in an unintended active medication→no medication→active medication treatment sequence in a moderately depressed patient whose parents persuaded her "to get off drugs." The stepwise concurrent disappearance, return, and disappearance of both eating disorder and mood disorder symptoms illustrate how powerfully but unexpectedly linked these symptoms may be.

Case 3 involves a young woman who met full criteria for three distinct eating disorders at different times over a 6-year period: bulimia nervosa (with intermittent severe laxative abuse), restrained normal eating, and anorexia nervosa, restricting subtype. She also had major mood disorder with several discrete episodes. At times the onsets and offsets of these episodes seemed related to shifts in her eating disorder, and at other times they seemed to be associated with dramatic changes in weight.

Case 1: Normal-weight bulimia nervosa in a healthy outpatient with minimal mood symptoms

Ms. A, a 21-year-old woman studying to be a court reporter, presented to the University of California, Los Angeles (UCLA), outpatient clinic complaining of daily episodes of binge eating and self-induced vomiting. She had minimal mood symptoms (primarily irritability and remorse tied mostly to her eating episodes), and she was assigned to an open-ended outpatient treatment group. The group therapists used cognitive behavioral techniques that included strategies to interrupt or delay bingeing and the collection of weekly symptom diaries. At the time Ms. A entered the program, studies suggesting that nondepressed bulimic patients might respond to antidepressants were as yet unpublished. Moreover, she was not considered to be sufficiently depressed to require antidepressants.

After 1 year in the treatment group Ms. A's Beck Depression Inventory scores had fallen from the high teens (mildly to moderately depressed) to less than 10 (normal). Her binge-purge frequency had decreased from daily to several times weekly, and her eating had improved. She was not skipping meals and had learned to eat breakfast, but we (and she) were unsatisfied with the residual bingeing and purging.

We introduced imipramine, but quickly switched to desipramine when she became constipated. Because of the high cost of desipramine, however, she chose to discontinue it and resumed taking imipramine together with a bulk-forming fiber (psyllium hydrophilic mucilloid) to promote elimination. Her bulimia remitted completely after several weeks. She was successfully weaned from medication 8–9 months later.

Case 2: Normal-weight bulimia nervosa in a healthy outpatient with moderate mood symptoms

Ms. B was a 21-year-old recent college graduate, who had been treated intermittently over a period of 4 years for depression and bulimia nervosa. She presented at UCLA after a treatment hiatus because of depression.

Her initial evaluation, just after she completed high school, revealed a bright young woman who had done well in private school despite chronic procrastination and a somewhat alienated stance. She had experimented with street drugs, occasionally stolen small things, and was oppositional with her family, testing their limits on issues of curfew times and spending money. She binged and vomited daily and occasionally more often. Combined individual and group cognitive behavioral treatment led to only mild improvements after 2 months. Ms. B was moderately dysphoric (primarily irritable, self-critical, and pessimistic). We initially assessed this as situational (precollege anxiety) because she was leaving for a rather prestigious and competitive school in another city. We also assumed that anxiety related to this impending move was interfering with her response to treatment.

Home from college on vacation, Ms. B reported that she was not doing well; she was not studying, she was using cocaine, and she was still bingeing and purging. Adding imipramine at that point resulted in improved mood and concentration. Moreover, because the medication interfered with the cocaine high, Ms. B stopped using cocaine. Her class attendance increased and her binge and purge frequency decreased. Ultimately her eating symptoms ceased altogether. She was seen for occasional visits during college but had no further contact with us until many months after graduation. It was at this point that she presented once again, complaining that she was "crying all the time."

Reevaluation showed Ms. B to be depressed and actively bulimic. In addition to being plagued by tearfulness, she complained of problems concentrating and sustaining interest in her part-time job. She reported resuming cigarettes and street drugs, being obsessed with looks and weight, and daily bingeing and vomiting. As we reviewed the sequence of disappearance and reemergence of her mood and eating disorder symptoms, the interplay between the two could be clearly seen.

Some 8 months earlier, while she had been doing well, Ms. B's parents, who had never been comfortable with their daughter's requiring "psychiatric medications," urged her to stop taking imipramine. Initially, she felt well and remained free of eating symptoms. Three months after discontinuing the medication she started to feel unsure of herself and uncertain about the future, but she attributed these feelings to not knowing what she would be doing after graduation. She coped by increasing exercise and seeing friends.

Her feelings of uncertainty evolved into more pronounced depressed mood and stimulated a new round of acting-out behaviors. Although engaged to be married, she had an affair with another man. Seven months after discontinuation of imipramine she assessed herself as a failure, noted that she was hypersensitive with others, and felt she craved attention. She also decided that her slender body was "fat and disgusting." Eight months after discontinuation this rising tide of disordered mood and acting-out behaviors culminated in a return of binge eating and purging. At first this new episode of bulimic behaviors functioned as a form of self-treatment for the emergent depression: it made her thinner; reduced the depressive load of negative, body-centered ruminations; and gave her "something to do." However, the bulimic behaviors were clearly an ineffective treatment for her depression; if anything the return of bulimia nervosa made her depression even worse and exacerbated the full panoply of symptoms described above.

At this point Ms. B was treated with 40 mg/day of fluoxetine. Both mood and eating disorder symptoms improved rapidly. After 8 days she reported, with great relief, that she was no longer thinking about her body all the time. She had cried only once and binged and purged just twice since starting the medication. Her family and boyfriend remarked on her improved mood and obviously diminished hypersensitivity. This positive response, although welcome, still fell short of total remission since sleep disturbance and mildly restricted affect remained.

Ms. B's history of reactivated mood and eating disorder symptoms illustrates how bulimia can both be a response to depression and serve to intensify a depressive syndrome. In Ms. B's case—in contrast to the observations made by Keller et al. (1989)—bulimia and depression seem to be closely linked. Both of her syndromes were responsive to the antidepressant medication. When she stopped taking it, however, she first had a clear, step-by-step return of depression (with low mood, feelings of failure, and hypersensitivity) and then, as the depression became worse, a return of bulimia nervosa.

Bingeing and purging represented the last symptoms to reappear in a sequence of maladaptive coping efforts aimed at modifying her growing feelings of depression, uncertainty, and fearfulness. They capped Ms. B's previous efforts to feel better, which had included hyperexercise, drugs, alcohol, and an affair. The return of the bulimia nervosa heightened her affective instability, led to the unstoppable tears, and intensified her cognitive impairment to the point where she was unable to concentrate or work.

It should be noted that this case history represents only one possible interweaving of mood and eating disorder symptoms and that the response to treatment also represents only one of several possibilities. In terms of the evolution of symptoms, the cessation of antidepressant medication could have resulted in a stepwise return of mood disorder symptoms without bulimic symptoms, or her eating patterns could have deteriorated while her mood remained unimpaired. Next, when treatment was initiated, either mood or food symptoms might have abated, but not necessarily both. This patient fortunately experienced resolution of both disorders, but many cases are to be found where only one set of symptoms responds to medication.

Case 3: Alternating anorexia nervosa and bulimia nervosa in a graduate student with major mood disorder

Ms. C, a patient who both illustrates and confounds some of the conventional wisdom about eating disorders, was a 5'6" 30-year-old woman who had four distinct patterns of abnormal eating. Over a 6-year period, her weight fluctuated from 95 to 135 lb. At various points she met criteria (in ascending weight order) for pure anorexia nervosa, restricting subtype, while weighing as little as 96 lb; for bulimia with vomiting, while weighing 112–114 lb; and for severe bulimia nervosa with binges several times daily followed by vomiting and laxative abuse (up to 200 tablets daily of a docusate sodium/phenolphthalein combination available without prescription), while weighing as much as 135 lb. She also had periods of highly restrained "normal" eating, while weighing between 110 and 112 lb.

Chronologically, Ms. C's first episode at age 14 involved weight loss through self-starvation. Her bulimic symptoms began in college. Figure 2–3 illustrates her weight changes, key life events, episodes of depression, and various pharmacologic interventions over the 6 years. During this time, Ms. C was seen twice weekly in psychotherapy for the first 2 years and once weekly thereafter.

The depressive disorder chronicled in Figure 2–3 started in Ms. C's early teenage years. It involved two distinct periods characterized by feelings of inadequacy, hopelessness, guilt, and suicidal ideation; each occasioned a psychiatric hospitalization. Figure 2–3 shows only episodes of major mood disorder; in addition the patient met criteria for dysthymia from the outset of treatment and throughout the next 4 years. Only when she was successfully completing advanced degree work and gaining weight did her dysthymia lift. At this writing she has been free of depression for 2 years.

Ms. C's treatment began with individual insight-oriented psychotherapy. Antidepressant medications were soon added. Hopes of obtaining antibinge and antidepressant effects met with only moderate success. She was on 400 mg of imipramine at bedtime (with serum level monitoring) and 25 µg of L-triiodothyronine (LT$_3$) when she began feeling very suicidal, driving with her eyes closed. She was admitted to the hospital, where 1,500 mg/day of lithium was added and her dose of LT$_3$ was increased. She improved and was discharged but decompensated several months later after she began a new job. Imipramine was tapered in preparation for switching to an MAOI, but suicidal behaviors prompted readmission.

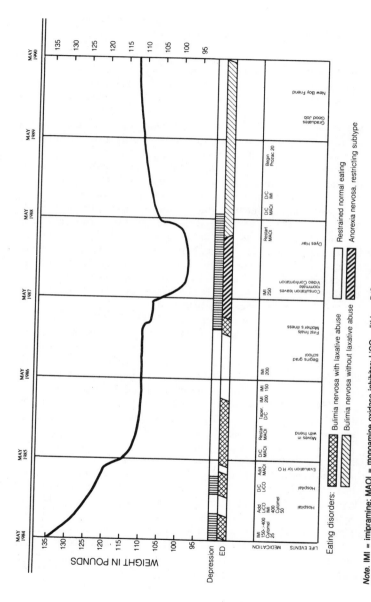

Note. IMI = imipramine; MAOI = monoamine oxidase inhibitor; LiCO = lithium; D/C = discontinue; R/O = rule out; ED = eating disorder.

Figure 2–3. Alternation eating disorder in a graduate student with mood disorder.

The ward team started phenelzine while her imipramine dose was still 200 mg/day and continued LT$_3$ at 50 μg. She improved considerably during this 3-week hospitalization, but it was never clear what occasioned her significant improvement: the auxiliary ego functioning provided by the milieu and structure of the hospital program, a normal nutritional intake, the MAOI, or meeting a friend with whom she roomed for the next 2 years (a mood disorders patient). During this first posthospital period, Ms. C intermittently attended Overeaters Anonymous (which had been her main form of therapy during college) and, in general, was unable to comply with the requirements of cognitive behavioral approaches when she was actively bulimic (although during her subsequent restricted normal eating phase she carefully kept food diaries). She also saw a nutritionist.

Treatment with the combination of tricyclic antidepressant (TCA) and MAOI was suspended when Ms. C had a probable seizure. Because she had begun full-time employment and was not actively depressed, the MAOI (only) was discontinued pending further evaluation. Although the neurologist consultant could not determine the reason for her seizure, in the light of a negative workup (which included magnetic resonance imaging and two electroencephalograms) and no recurrences after 4 months, toxicity from LT$_3$ was suspected (elevated blood levels had been found and she subsequently acknowledged overusing LT$_3$ to obtain weight loss benefits).

Alternatively, the neurologist thought that the combined TCA-MAOI medication regimen could have been associated with an orthostatic hypotensive episode, resulting in syncope and a seizure. Later on, as Ms. C's bulimic symptoms and dysthymia continued unabated, the MAOI was cautiously restarted, but side effects (muscle twitching) led to its discontinuation. She continued on the TCA without difficulty. A few months later, with strong urging from her family, she applied to graduate school and was admitted. During her first year of classes, Ms. C's anorexia nervosa, restricting subtype, reemerged, and she even became apprehensive about the hidden calories that might be present in the imipramine.

Consultation with a colleague was obtained during the following summer as her weight decreased and depression intensified. This consultation yielded several useful suggestions, among them the need to refocus the psychotherapy on her active role in making hoped for changes, the potential usefulness of an MAOI if required again, and the potential use of guided imagery and video confrontation with the patient clad in a bathing suit.

During her second year of graduate school, Ms. C constantly struggled with food obsessions and preoccupations that interfered with her studying. She also kept her weight at approximately 97–98 lb, negotiated separation from her roommate and the end of that friendship, and faced the major problems created when her mother fell seriously ill.

At this low point, using reserves we doubted were present, Ms. C made several decisions that ultimately led to her transformation from a virtual social isolate to one of the most popular and successful members of her class. She began by dyeing her hair and literally shedding her drab image. Soon she was befriended by a male student she admired. He told her that she was too thin and recommended lunch. So began a daily habit she had not practiced in over a decade. Other students joined them, and now Ms. C began to have a social life. She completed school with better grades over the next 18 months and obtained a desirable job. During this time, her weight rose to 116 lb, but at the price of resurgent bulimia.

Fluoxetine 20 mg/day was added but had no impact on her binge-purge behavior. However, with improved mood and stronger social supports she committed herself to using the tools of the cognitive behavioral approach, which resulted in decreasing binge-purge frequency from daily to 3–4 times a week. The fluoxetine dosage was increased to 40 mg/day but resulted in subjective restlessness and nervousness, occasioning a return to 20 mg/day.

At this writing, Ms. C was quite satisfied with her current, somewhat improved state and, although a trial at 30 mg/day of fluoxetine was recommended to her, as well as the adjunctive use of trazodone to diminish any side effects, she was not interested, for the moment, in any further medication changes.

This case raises questions regarding some current notions about eating disorders. As discussed earlier, Keller et al. (1989) found depressive and bulimic episodes to be unrelated, confounding those who argue that depression and bulimia may share a common pathophysiologic abnormality (Hudson and Pope 1990). In the case of Ms. C, depression and bulimia nervosa appeared closely related for some episodes (those that led to the two hospitalizations) but independent at other times (the third episode of bulimia with laxative abuse and the long period of bulimia without laxative abuse that occurred during the last 2 years of treatment). In addition, some of her most severe depressions were concurrent with periods of weight change, when she was in transition between different patterns of eating disorder.

This case also illustrates how one individual can meet criteria for different DSM-III-R eating disorders at different times. The fluidity of her shifts between diagnoses and the presence of near-normal respites demonstrate that these disorders do not always "breed true" and may be characterized by quickly shifting levels of severity.

Specific Guidelines

Anorexia Nervosa

The clinician's most difficult task in using medications with either bulimic or restricting anorexic patients is to educate the patients and their families. These patients are the least likely to want to take medication, and the literature is least optimistic about what medications can do for them (Herzog and Brotman 1987; Hudson et al. 1985). Although most reports consist of small series and the few placebo-controlled trials have not yielded robust beneficial results (Biederman et al. 1985; Halmi et al. 1986), informed opinion seems to hold that if medications are to be used, anorexia nervosa patients with concurrent affective disorder do better when the medication used is an antidepressant. Given this speculative conclusion, the clinician may wish to provide patients with the opportunity for a medication to potentially help improve mood and hopelessness and perhaps help the patient become more amenable to psychotherapy.

One myth that educational efforts must challenge is that anorexia nervosa patients who take medication will lose control. First, the very act of explaining a medication's likely primary effects and side effects and the clinician's rationale for using it may signal the clinician's desire and intention to share decision making with the patient and may lessen her fear of ceding control. Second, since patients and families are often denying both the degree of weight loss and its psychobiological impact, education about the biological effects of anorexia nervosa on mood is important. Some patients may have had previous abortive medication trials that were interrupted due to side effects and may therefore be reluctant to try medications again. Other patients may ascribe great powers to medications and fear that they will take away their anorexia nervosa and leave them without any coping strategies. Clearly, these issues must be discussed and reviewed at length, and any medication must be introduced slowly. Because side effects can always be disruptive, clinicians should fully prepare patients for these possibilities and back down to lower doses if necessary.

The best time to assess an anorexic patient for a medication trial is after weight restoration, when starvation effects are minimized. However, in the presence of severe major affective disorder, treatment should begin right away. Available literature does not yet strongly support any particular medication. Halmi et al.'s study (1986) of amitriptyline versus cyproheptadine (a serotonin and histamine antagonist associated with weight gain) versus placebo concluded that cyproheptadine was of some use in improving weight gain and mood in nonbulimic anorexia nervosa (restricting subtype) patients whose initial weights were quite low. However, it was less efficacious with bulimic anorexia nervosa patients. Table 2–2 summarizes studies of medication trials in anorexia nervosa.

The combined experiences of clinicians at UCLA suggest consideration of fluoxetine for low-weight anorexic patients (Gwirtsman et al. 1990). This medication has a low side effect profile. We have not seen low-weight patients lose additional weight while taking fluoxetine, but we have seen some patients gain weight on 20–40 mg/day. Furthermore, fluoxetine appears to have sometimes helped reduce obsessional thinking in anorexia nervosa patients. In an open trial with 22 anorexic patients (Gwirtsman et al. 1990), fluoxetine (average dose 36 mg) led to maintenance of near-normal body weights in 9 patients. These patients also had improvements in mood and obsessional symptoms and told the authors they had lost the urge to lose more weight. A second group of 9 patients had partial effects, but 2 patients had no effects and 2 patients dropped out. Most of the improvements were seen among the restricting patients, suggesting that vomiting losses may have reduced the amount of bioavailable fluoxetine in the bulimic patients (Weltzin et al. 1990).

In an earlier open study of 10 patients with anorexia nervosa (Hudson et al. 1985), frequent shifts of medications, some involving as many as four different medications with and without augmentation, led to improvements in weight and mood for 4 patients. Those who improved achieved their results on (respectively) trazodone, an MAOI plus L-tryptophan, and imipramine (2 patients).

Bulimia Nervosa

Because assessing whether a depression is historically primary or secondary to the eating disorder may be difficult with these patients, our first step with normal-weight bulimia nervosa patients is an attempt to tease out the "eating disorder component" of their affective symptoms, as discussed above. If intense dysphoria arises *only* immediately after binge eating but the patient enjoys periods of normal mood, good instrumental role functioning, and normal mood reactivity, we categorize the patient as predominately an abnormal eater and follow a nonmedication strategy, at least initially. Although such a patient should be educated about the potential usefulness of medications, our initial treatment for this patient consists of an individual cognitive behavioral approach that uses diaries, journals, commitment to regular meals, strong nutritional planning, and support. Group therapy is also made available. Ongoing screening for affective symptoms takes place as the patient's progress is monitored.

If pervasive depression is prominent, medications should be introduced early. We use an office self-rating test measure of depression (the Beck Depression Inventory, although several good measures are available) to provide relatively consistent ratings of cognitive and vegetative symptoms and to indicate the direction of changes. Keeping diaries and journals should also be introduced at the beginning of treatment with this group (Fairburn 1983; Yager and Edelstein 1985). Such procedures confront patients with the details of their eating behaviors, thus countering denial, setting the stage for cognitive behavioral work, and providing data for clinicians to develop strategies for normalized eating.

Bulimic patients also harbor beliefs, fears, and questions that must be articulated and addressed: "Are medications addictive?" "Will they make me fat?" "If I take medication will you think I'm crazy or weak and lacking in willpower?" "How can a pill change the way I eat?" When responding, clinicians must acknowledge that many unanswered questions remain regarding mechanisms of action, while they carefully review the generally positive medication studies with their patients. Copies of articles from both the lay press and medical journals should be collected and provided to patients and their families. In addition to clarifying concerns and addressing misconceptions, this process of educating patients and sharing the medical literature puts the treatment on a collaborative basis that is well suited to later cognitive behavioral work.

With which medication does one begin? Because there are several options and because it is not yet possible to predict which patient will best respond to which agent, thorough patient education should be undertaken before any medication is prescribed. This education should include discussion of the frequent need to change doses, switch medications, or augment with lithium to minimize surprise and disappointment if the initial choice of medication does not produce an optimum result. Also, because a significant percentage of patients will respond to a subsequent trial (Mitchell et al. 1989), careful preparation will maximize the chance that patients will capture all possible benefits.

In Mitchell et al.'s study (1989), 47% of the patients ($n = 15$) who had not responded to a previous trial of imipramine achieved remission on other drugs. Eight improved with MAOIs (four with tranylcypromine and four with phenelzine). Of these eight, four remitted completely. One of three who tried fluoxetine remitted and one improved. Two of three remitted on desipramine, whereas the one patient on nortriptyline remained unimproved.

In a report of two studies, Pope et al. (1989b) noted that many of the 20 patients in a 2-year follow-up required a series of different medications to achieve good results. Of the 65% of patients ($n = 17$) who achieved remission in a 9- to 19-month study, only 4 remitted with the first drug tried. The authors reported that 8 required a second trial, 3 required a third trial, and 2 had four trials. Sample regimens from the remitted group included fluoxetine (5 patients), nortriptyline (2 patients), trazodone (2 patients), tranylcypromine plus trazodone (1 patient), and tranylcypromine plus lithium (1 patient).

Although many medication changes and adjustments are designed to boost efficacy, some are prompted by side effects. Patients in the various reported trials complained of numerous side effects (Pope and Hudson 1989), except for those in the large study of two dosage levels of fluoxetine, in whom side effects were described as "mild" (Enas et al. 1989). The most troubling side effects were those commonly associated with the specific class of medication: sedative and anticholinergic effects with tricyclic antidepressants and insomnia and orthostasis with MAOIs. Problems with MAOIs caused defections even among responders.

Although 52% of the patients in a trazodone trial complained of drowsiness, none withdrew for this reason (Pope et al. 1989a). In the fluoxetine study, the dropout rate for both the 20 mg/day and the 60 mg/day groups did not differ significantly from that in the placebo group (Enas et al. 1989).

Therefore, because of the need for frequent medication adjustments, the key is not to choose a medication, but rather to choose a sequence. To do this the clinician should know which drugs have been shown to be effective (e.g., imipramine, desipramine, MAOIs, trazodone, and fluoxetine) (Table 2–1) and the clinical rules for sequencing and combining medications. For example, a 5-week washout is required *after* fluoxetine before beginning an MAOI, and a 2-week washout is required when a TCA is given after a course of treatment with an MAOI.

Thus one would probably not want to plan the sequence TCA→fluoxetine→MAOI because the lengthy washout between steps 2 and 3 could undermine the therapeutic alliance while the clinician and patient wait and wonder. However, TCA regimens (e.g., using imipramine) are less expensive than fluoxetine regimens, and for certain patients with good ego strengths and willingness to engage in a multiple-branched trial this choice may be wiser than starting with fluoxetine.

In contrast, Pope and Hudson (1989) recommend starting with fluoxetine. (Up to 60 mg/day is recommended for bulimia nervosa based on the superiority of that dose versus 20 mg/day in reducing the frequency of binge eating and vomiting.) If adequate response is not achieved in 4–5 weeks, lithium augmentation may increase the likelihood of improvement. Such augmentation can be used with TCAs as well. Although weight gain has been associated with lithium treatment (affecting 11–36% of patients and causing increases of more than 10 lb in the majority of patients who do gain [Silverstone 1985]), little is known of the weight effects of adding lithium as augmentation to the antidepressant medications of bulimic patients with depression. The one reported case of successful combined lithium and fluoxetine therapy in an eating-disordered patient did not mention effects on weight (Pope et al. 1988). Although dosing with lithium three times a day has been suggested, at UCLA we have always used and recommend once-a-day dosing at bedtime when lithium is used for augmentation. Prescribing divided doses for patients who frequently vomit may result in unknown fluctuations and may decrease clinical efficacy even when serum levels are monitored. Lithium serum levels of 0.8–1.0 mEq/L are recommended.

MAOIs are generally the medication of last choice because, although they are very effective in this disorder, their side effects cause frequent dropouts.

In summary, the most efficient (fastest) sequence is

fluoxetine→(augment with lithium)→TCA→(augment with lithium)→MAOI

A less expensive approach with substantial chance of success is to use the TCA first. TCA serum levels can be followed to assure compliance, guide increases in dosage, and establish the effect of any vomiting losses. In the sequence we recommend above, trazodone can be introduced before or after TCAs.

Trouble Shooting

If medications are being taken as prescribed but fail to help, the clinician should check for ongoing dietary restriction and review the patient's diaries to assess estimated nonpurged intake. Many patients are subclinically malnourished and have associated mood dampening. If treatment has persisted for a year or longer and appears to be less effective than desired, a consultation with an experienced colleague may help refocus and renew the treatment plan.

Psychotherapy for the Depressed Patient With an Eating Disorder

Anorexia Nervosa

Kalucy et al. (1984) noted that "severe dysphoria and disorganizing experiences are common in anorexia nervosa patients. . . . Within a predictable, supportive and well-controlled environment, most patients can work through these experiences without medication" (p. 467). They described an inpatient program and the elements involved in such an environment, including weight restoration with contractual goals, an eclectic theoretical orientation, emphasis on individual psychotherapy, a strong nursing staff, and limited use of medication (confined chiefly to concurrent major mood disorder).

Of interest, Kalucy and his group (1984) noted that major mood disorder is often not seen at initial presentation in anorexia nervosa. After the cheerful facade and denial of the anorexic patient is pierced, perhaps as weight gain occurs, fear and depression emerge. These authors view such affective developments as a sign of progress. This accords with Lacey's view (1990) that the goal of psychotherapy is to convert a behavioral (eating) disorder into the emotional disorder it truly is. If the supportive milieu cannot help a patient work through a bout of depression in Kalucy's program, intensive individual psychotherapy is tried along the theoretical and technical lines laid out by Kernberg (1984) for the treatment of severe psychopathology. Approximately 30% of patients are found to require such psychotherapy.

Cognitive behavioral approaches have been tried in depressed patients with anorexia nervosa with mixed results. Cooper and Fairburn's series of five case reports (1984) included three moderately depressed young students with the bulimic variant of anorexia nervosa who presented with weights ranging from 73 to 78% of normal. In these three patients mood normalized and eating and weight improved. However, two patients with weights that were 60 and 64% of normal (one who vomited and one who restricted intake) did poorly and required admission to a psychiatric hospital.

Bulimia Nervosa

Although depression is found frequently in bulimia nervosa patients, most current nonpharmacologic approaches to treatment have not focused on improving mood, per se, but have instead focused on the symptoms of abnormal eating, usually measured by binge, vomit, and laxative use frequencies. However, for patients in whom depression appears to be primarily related to abnormal eating, a wide variety of psychosocial treatments (behavior therapy [BT], cognitive behavioral treatment [CBT], and group therapy [GT]) have been shown to be effective in improving both mood and eating symptoms. Researchers using these approaches have found that depression scores, as measured by the Beck Depression Inventory or the Depression Scale of the HSCL-90, improve as eating symptoms improve.

In a controlled trial of CBT versus BT versus GT versus a waiting-list control condition, Freeman et al. (1988) found that all three therapy treatments led to significant decreases in rates of bingeing and self-induced vomiting. Improvements in depression and anxiety scores and increases in measures of self-esteem were also found. Although not expected, BT outperformed CBT, with BT patients having fewer drop-outs and an earlier response to treatment. BT patients had highly significant reductions in depression ratings on the Montgomery and Åsberg Depression Scale (MADS; Montgomery and Åsberg 1979), whereas CBT patients achieved only modestly significant reductions on this measure and GT patients had no significant changes. The patients treated in this study were carefully screened and had low rates of impulsive behaviors (e.g., shoplifting, drug use, self-mutilating behavior, and suicide attempts) and rates of alcohol use no greater than in the general population. This selection suggests that the sample treated in this study conforms quite closely to the group we earlier characterized as predominately abnormal eaters with dysphoria.

In a controlled study of cognitive restructuring with and without exposure and response prevention, Wilson et al. (1986) found that Beck Depression Inventory scores fell significantly in the 17 patients they treated with each approach. Fairburn et al. (1985) also concluded that behavioral control of bulimia will lead to reduction of depressive symptoms in bulimic patients.

In a comparison of a CBT group versus a nondirective group in which patients discussed eating behaviors but were not told how to modify these behaviors, Kirkley et al. (1985) found that both approaches led to significant reductions in symptoms of anxiety and depression as well as decreased vomiting frequencies. In Lee and Rush's study (1986) of a CBT group versus waiting-list controls, treated subjects had significant decreases in depression at follow-up. The focus of Lee and Rush's approach was drawn directly from CBT work with depressed patients, and it focused on helping patients develop improved coping with the negative affects presumed to lead to binge eating.

Several authors who have reviewed treatment outcome studies in bulimia nervosa support the conclusion that symptoms of psychological distress (which include depressive symptoms) are influenced by overall clinical state and hence are likely to diminish as the clinical state improves (Garner 1987). Taken together, available studies and reviews in the psychotherapy literature appear to conclude that the depressive affects associated with abnormal eating behaviors will generally lessen or disappear after resumption of normal eating. We would agree. However, the psychotherapy-oriented literature frequently does not address the issue of primary major mood disorder episodes, characterological depression, and the mood-impairing results of prolonged social isolation and withdrawal seen in the patient with a chronic, entrenched eating disorder whose social support network is weak or absent (Figure 2–1). Although these studies amply document the resolution of eating-related dysphoria, it would be a misreading of the psychotherapy research, based largely on very time-limited psychosocial treatments for bulimia nervosa, to assume that the remedy for the depressed mood of these patients is always to be found in strategies that aim to normalize eating through behavioral and cognitive behavioral interventions.

Reviews of methodological problems in the outcome literature (Garner 1987) and recent discussions of the high variability in outcomes seen at different research centers (Plenary Session, Fourth International Conference on Eating Disorders, New York, NY, April 1990) underscore the critical role of patient selection in interpreting results with depressed or nondepressed patients. Often psychotherapy research study samples contain few subjects with generalized problems of impulse control (the so-called multi-impulsive bulimic patient) whose poor overall functioning gives rise to low self-esteem and dysphoria. It is *not* clear how effective brief behavioral or cognitive behavioral approaches are in improving mood and eating either in such cases or in those with significant Axis I mood disorders.

In our view, and that of Lacey (1990), the more impulsive acting-out patient requires several modifications to the standard CBT approach. In Lacey's program (1990), such a patient's therapy will be longer term, will involve some mix of group and individual psychotherapy components, will include meal-planning consultations, and will contain written contracts specifying expectations about eating and self-injurious behaviors. Perhaps most important, given the theoretical construct that character difficulties and related dysphoria have origins in insecure attachments during childhood, the patient is assured that maintenance or follow-up treatment will be available indefinitely and will be provided at least once a month. In this program, medication also plays a role, but only a supporting one.

Johnson (1984) offered some recommendations for the treatment of character-disordered, eating-disordered patients whose labile affects fluctuate between surges of anger and empty depression. Patients such as these need to be managed via structured, directive, and supportive interventions aimed at improving life management skills. Johnson suggested that therapists avoid using abstract, insight-oriented therapy with these highly concrete and impulsive patients, but he did not specify how successful the direct approach was in ameliorating depression without the concurrent use of medication or other containment strategies such as increased frequency of sessions or change in venue from outpatient to day hospital or from day hospital to inpatient treatment.

Several conclusions emerge from this brief review of current approaches to the psychotherapy of depressed eating-disordered patients:

1. Where depression is related to eating disorder symptoms, any one of several well-described current modalities (e.g., BT, CBT, and GT) may result in improved mood.
2. Where depression is related to starvation effects at "normal" weight, modifying eating (including a nutritional counseling, meal planning component in treatment, and/or incorporating group eating events as in some outpatient or day hospital group treatment approaches) may improve depression.
3. Where depression is related to characterological disarray with prominent impulsivity and/or substance abuse, psychosocial treatments need to emphasize containment, long-term follow-up, and strategies aimed at enhancing coping and life management skills.
4. Where depression is related to any of the above and heightened by social isolation and withdrawal, or where depression is related to eating disorder chronicity with associated erosion of patients' social networks, strategies employing individual, group, and other structured social components may be useful.
5. Where depression is related to an independent, concurrent mood disorder, psychosocial strategies such as cognitive therapy or interpersonal psychotherapy aimed at alleviating depression may require supplementation with antidepressant medication.

In our view, medications are an essential treatment tool for many eating-disordered patients with depressed mood. However, we also believe that they should only be used as part of a comprehensive treatment program that includes active psychotherapy, most often designed to incorporate elements of a cognitive behavioral approach but flexible enough to include psychodynamic and interpersonal elements as well as to offer support and encouragement.

References

Agras WS, Dorian B, Kirkley BG, et al: Imipramine in the treatment of bulimia: a double-blind controlled study. International Journal of Eating Disorders 6:29–38, 1987

Altschuler KZ, Weiner MF: Anorexia nervosa and depression: a dissenting view. Am J Psychiatry 142:328–332, 1985

American Psychiatric Association: Diagnostic and Statistical Manual of Mental Disorders, Third Edition, Revised. Washington, DC, American Psychiatric Association, 1987

Andersen AE: Uses and potential misuses of antianxiety agents in the treatment of anorexia nervosa and bulimia nervosa, in The Role of Drug Treatments for Eating Disorders: Brunner/Mazel Eating Disorders Monograph Series, No 1. Edited by Garfinkel PE, Garner DM. New York, Brunner/Mazel, 1987, pp 59–73

Beck AT: Depression Inventory. Philadelphia, PA, Philadelphia Center for Cognitive Therapy, 1978

Biederman J, Herzog DB, Rivinus TN, et al: Amitriptyline in the treatment of anorexia nervosa. J Clin Psychopharmacol 5:10–16, 1985

Blouin AG, Blouin JH, Perez EL, et al: Treatment of bulimia with fenfluramine and desipramine. J Clin Psychopharmacol 8:261–269, 1988

Chaitin BF: The relationship of the eating and affective disorders, in The Eating Disorders: Medical and Psychological Bases of Diagnosis and Treatment. Edited by Blinder FJ, Chaitin BF, Goldstein RS. New York, PMA Publishing, 1988, pp 345–356

Cooper PJ, Fairburn CG: Cognitive behavior therapy for anorexia nervosa: some preliminary findings. J Psychosom Res 28:493–499, 1984

Cooper PJ, Fairburn CG: The depressive syumptoms of bulimia nervosa. Br J Psychiatry 148:268–274, 1986

Cooper JL, Morrison TL, Bignan OL, et al: Mood changes and affective disorder in the bulimic binge-purge cycle. International Journal of Eating Disorders 7:469–474, 1988

Derogatis LR, Lipman RS, Rickels K, et al: The Hopkins Symptom Checklist (HSCL): a self-report symptom inventory. Behav Sci 19:1–15, 1974

Edelstein CK, Yager J, Gitlin M, et al: A clinical study of antidepressant medications in the treatment of bulimia. Psychiatr Med 7:111–121, 1989

Enas GG, Pope HG, Levine LR, et al: Fluoxetine in bulimia nervosa: double blind study. Poster session presented at the annual meeting of the American Psychiatric Association, San Francisco, CA, May 1989

Fairburn CG: Bulimia: its epidemiology and management. Psychiatric Annals 13:953–961, 1983

Fairburn CG: What is the best treatment for eating disorders? Paper presented at the Fourth International Conference on Eating Disorders, New York, NY, April 1990

Fairburn CG, Cooper PT, Kirk J, et al: The significance of the neurotic symptoms of bulimia nervosa. J Psychiatric Res 19:135–139, 1985

Freeman CPL, Mundro JKM: Drug and group treatments for bulimia/bulimia nervosa. Psychosomatic Research 32:647–660, 1988

Freeman CPL, Barry F, Dunkeld-Turnbull J, et al: Controlled trial of psychotherapy for bulimia nervosa. Br Med J 296:521–525, 1988

Garner DM: Psychotherapy outcome research with bulimia nervosa. Psychother Psychosom 48:129–140, 1987

Gross HA, Ebert MH, Faden VB: A double-blind controlled trial of lithium carbonate in primary anorexia nervosa. J Clin Psychopharmacol 1:376–381, 1981

Gwirtsman HE, Guze BH, Yager J, et al: Treatment of anorexia nervosa with fluoxetine: an open drug trial. J Clin Psychiatry 51:378–382, 1990

Halmi KA, Eckert E, LaDu TJ, et al: Anorexia nervosa: treatment efficacy of cyproheptadine and amitriptyline. Arch Gen Psychiatry 43:177–181, 1986

Hamilton M: Development of a rating scale for primary depressive illness. British Journal of Social and Clinical Psychology 6:278–296, 1967

Hatsukami D, Eckert E, Mitchell JE, et al: Affective disorder and substance abuse in women with bulimia. Psychol Med 14:701–704, 1984

Herzog DB, Brotman AW: Use of tricyclic antidepressants in anorexia nervosa and bulimia nervosa, in The Role of Drug Treatments for Eating Disorders: Brunner/Mazel Eating Disorders Monograph Series, No 1. Edited by Garfinkel PE, Garner DM. New York, Brunner/Mazel, 1987, pp 36–55

Horne RL, Ferguson JM, Pope HG Jr, et al: Treatment of bulimia with bupropion: a multicenter controlled trial. J Clin Psychiatry 49:262–266, 1988

Hudson JI, Pope HG Jr: Affective spectrum disorder: does antidepressant response identify a family of disorders with a common pathophysiology? Am J Psychiatry 147:552–564, 1990

Hudson JI, Pope HG, Jonas JM: Treatment of bulimia with antidepressants: theoretical considerations and clinical findings. Psychiatric Annals 13:965–969, 1983

Hudson JI, Pope HG, Jonas JM, et al: Treatment of anorexia nervosa with antidepressants. J Clin Psychopharmacol 5:17–23, 1985

Hudson JI, Pope HG, Yugelun-Todd D, et al: A controlled study of lifetime prevalence of affective and other psychiatric disorders in bulimia outpatients. Am J Psychiatry 144:1283–1287, 1987

Hughes PL, Wells LA, Cunningham CJ, et al: Treating bulimia with desipramine: a placebo-controlled double-blind study. Arch Gen Psychiatry 43:182–186, 1986

Johnson C: Initial consultation for patients with bulimia and anorexia nervosa, in Handbook of Psychotherapy for Anorexia Nervosa and Bulimia. Edited by Garner DM, Garfinkel PE. New York, Guilford, 1984, pp 19–51

Kalucy RS, Gilchrist PN, McFarlene CM, et al: The evolution of a multitherapy orientation, in Handbook of Psychotherapy for Anorexia Nervosa and Bulimia. Edited by Garner DM, Garfinkel PE. New York, Guilford, 1984, pp 458–487

Katz JL: Eating disorder and affective disorders: relatives or merely chance acquaintances? Compr Psychiatry 28:220–228, 1987

Kaye WH, Gwirtsman H, George DT, et al: Altered feeding behavior in bulimia: is it related to mood and serotonin? in Eating Behavior in Eating Disorders. Edited by Walsh BT. Washington, DC, American Psychiatric Press, 1988, pp 199–216

Keller MB, Lavori PW, Herzog DB, et al: High rates of chronicity and rapidity of relapse in patients with bulimia nervosa. Arch Gen Psychiatry 46:480–481, 1989

Kennedy SH, Piran N, Garfinkel PE: A clinical trial of isocarboxazid in bulimia. J Clin Psychopharmacol 8:391–396, 1988

Kernberg OF: Severe Personality Disorder: Psychotherapeutic Strategies. New Haven, CT, Yale University Press, 1984

Keys A, Brozek J, Henschel A, et al: The Biology of Human Starvation. Minneapolis, MN, University of Minnesota Press, 1950

Kirkley BG, Schneider JA, Agras WS, et al: Comparison of two group treatments for bulimia. J Consult Clin Psychol 53:43–48, 1985

Lacey JH: Outpatient eclectic treatment program for normal weight bulimia. Paper presented at the Fourth International Conference on Eating Disorders, New York, NY, April 1990

Lacey JH, Crisp AH: Hunger, food intake, and weight: the impact of clomipramine on a refeeding anorexia nervosa population. Postgrad Med J 56:79–85, 1980

Laessle RG, Schweiger U, Pirke KM: Depression as a correlate of starvation in patients with eating disorders. Biol Psychiatry 23:719–725, 1988

Lee NF, Rush AJ: Cognitive-behavioral group therapy for bulimia. International Journal of Eating Disorders 5:599–615, 1986

Levin AP, Hyler SE: DSM-III personality diagnosis in bulimia. Compr Psychiatry 27:47–53, 1986

Levy AB, Dixon KN, Stern SL: How are depression and bulimia related? Am J Psychiatry 146:162–168, 1988

Luby ED, Marrazzi MA, Kinzie J: Case reports: treatment of chronic anorexia nervosa with opiate blockade. J Clin Psychopharmacol 7:52–53, 1987

Mitchell JE, Groat R: A placebo-controlled double-blind trial of amitriptyline in bulimia. J Clin Psychopharmacol 4:186–193, 1984

Mitchell JE, Hatsukami D, Pyle RL: Bulimia with and without a family history of depressive illness. Compr Psychiatry 27:215–219, 1986

Mitchell JE, Pyle RL, Eckert ED, et al: Response to alternative antidepressants in imipramine nonresponders with bulimia nervosa. J Clin Psychopharmacol 9:291–293, 1989

Mitchell P: Pharmacological management of bulimia nervosa: a critical review. International Journal of Eating Disorders 7:29–41, 1988

Montgomery SA, Åsberg M: A new depression scale designed to be sensitive to change. Br J Psychiatry 134:382–389, 1979

Norman DK, Herzog DB: Bulimia, anorexia nervosa, and anorexia nervosa with bulimia: a comparative analysis of MMPI profiles. International Journal of Eating Disorders 2:43–52, 1983

Perry S: Combining antidepressants and psychotherapy: rationale and strategies. Paper presented at the annual meeting of the American Psychiatric Association, San Francisco, CA, May 1989

Piran N, Kennedy S, Garfinkel PE, et al: Affective disturbance in eating disorders. J Nerv Ment Dis 173:395–400, 1985

Piran N, Lerner P, Garfinkel PE, et al: Personality disorders in anorexic patients. International Journal of Eating Disorders 7:589–599, 1988

Pirke KM, Pahl J, Schweiger U, et al: Metabolic and endocrine indices of starvation in bulimia: a comparison with anorexia nervosa. Psychiatry Res 15:33–40, 1985

Pope HG, Hudson JI: Antidepressant drug therapy for bulimia: current status. J Clin Psychiatry 47:339–345, 1986

Pope HG, Hudson JI: Pharmacologic treatment of bulimia nervosa: research findings and practical suggestions. Psychiatric Annals 19:483–487, 1989

Pope HG Jr, Hudson JI, Jonas JM, et al: Bulimia treated with imipramine: a placebo-controlled, double-blind study. Am J Psychiatry 140:554–558, 1983

Pope HG, Hudson JI, Jonas JM, et al: Antidepressant treatment of bulimia: a two-year follow-up study. J Clin Psychopharmacol 5:320–327, 1985

Pope HG, McElroy SL, Nixon RA: Possible synergism between fluoxetine and lithium in refractory depression. Am J Psychiatry 145:1292–1294, 1988

Pope HG, Keck PE, McElroy SL, et al: A placebo-controlled study of trazodone in bulimia nervosa. J Clin Psychopharmacol 9:254–259, 1989a

Pope HG, McElroy SL, Keck PE Jr, et al: Long-term pharmacology of bulimia nervosa. J Clin Psychopharmacol 9:385–386, 1989b

Rossiter EM, Agras WS, Losch M: Changes in self-reported food intake in bulimics as a consequence of antidepressant treatment. International Journal of Eating Disorders 7:779–783, 1988

Sabine EJ, Yonance A, Farrington AJ, et al: Bulimia related with imipramine: a placebo-controlled, double-blind therapeutic trial of mianserin. Br J Clin Pharmacol 15:1958–2028, 1983

Silverstone T: Psychotropic drugs, appetite, and body weight, in Psycho-Pharmacology and Food: British Association for Psychopharmacology Monograph, No 7. Edited by Sandler M, Silverstone T. Oxford, British Association for Psychopharmacology, 1985, pp 139–145

Strober M, Katz JL: Do eating disorders and affective disorders share a common etiology? a dissenting opinion. International Journal of Eating Disorders 6:171–180, 1987

Strober M, Katz JL: Depression in the eating disorders: a review and analysis of descriptive, family, and biological findings, in Diagnostic Issues in Anorexia Nervosa and Bulimia Nervosa: Brunner/Mazel Eating Disorders Monograph Series, No 2. Edited by Garner D, Garfinkel P. New York, Brunner/Mazel, 1988, pp 80–111

Szmukler GI: Some comments on the link between anorexia nervosa and affective disorder. International Journal of Eating Disorders 6:181–189, 1987

Vandereycken W, Pierloot R: Pimozide combined with behavior therapy in the short-term treatment of anorexia nervosa: a double-blind placebo-controlled crossover study. Acta Psychiatr Scand 66:445–450, 1982

Walsh BT, Gladis M, Roose SP, et al: Phenelzine vs placebo in 50 patients with bulimia. Arch Gen Psychiatry 45:471–475, 1988

Wamboldt FS, Kastow NJ, Swift WJ, et al: Short-term course of depressive symptoms in patients with eating disorders. Am J Psychiatry 144:362–364, 1987

Weltzin TE, Hsu LKG, Kay WH: An open trial of fluoxetine in anorexia nervosa: maintenance of body weight and reduction of obsessional symptoms. Paper presented at the Fourth International Conference on Eating Disorders, New York, NY, April 1990

Wilson GT, Lindholm L: Bulimia nervosa and depression. International Journal of Eating Disorders 6:725–732, 1987

Wilson GT, Rossiter E, Kleifield EI, et al: Cognitive-behavioral treatment of bulimia nervosa: a controlled evaluation. Behav Res Ther 24:277–288, 1986

Wing JK, Cooper JE, Sartorius N: The Measurement and Classification of Psychiatric Symptoms. New York, Cambridge University Press, 1974

Yager J, Edelstein CK: The outpatient management of bulimia, in A Comprehensive Approach to the Treatment of Normal-Weight Bulimia. Edited by Kaye WH, Gwirtsman HE. Washington, DC, American Psychiatric Press, 1985, pp 47–75

Chapter 3

Eating Disorders
and Personality Disorders

Stephen A. Wonderlich, Ph.D.
James E. Mitchell, M.D.

*R*ecently there has been considerable interest in the comorbidity of clinical syndromes and personality disorders (Stone 1980). The introduction of DSM-III (American Psychiatric Association 1980) and DSM-III-R (American Psychiatric Association 1987) stimulated research regarding this relationship, and the placement of personality disorders on a separate axis has been particularly influential in promoting the study of the covariation of these conditions (Docherty et al. 1986). Paralleling this growing interest in the relationship of personality and clinical syndromes, there has been an increase in studies examining the association of personality disorders and various eating disorders (Swift and Wonderlich 1988). However, the relationship of personality factors and eating disturbances intrigued clinicians and researchers long before the development of DSM-III.

For example, Janet (1919) provided an early description of hysterical and obsessive (psychasthenic) forms of anorexia nervosa. Later psychoanalytic writers emphasized the importance of primitive erotic and aggressive fantasies in the etiology of anorexia nervosa (Benedek 1936; Waller et al. 1940), while interpersonal and object relations theorists underscored the helplessness and submissiveness of the anorexic individual in relation to others (Bruch 1973; Selvini-Palazzoli 1978). Similarly, empirical personality trait studies have generally indicated that persons with anorexia nervosa are socially insecure, dependent, compliant, and

Thanks are expressed to Dr. Dennis Staton for his thoughtful comments on our earlier version of this chapter.

lack autonomy, whereas those with bulimia nervosa have been consistently characterized as having low self-esteem and impulsivity (Strober 1985; Swift and Wonderlich 1988)

In this chapter we examine evidence suggesting a higher than expected comorbidity between eating disorders and personality disorders. After briefly reviewing conceptual and methodological issues relevant to the study of personality disorder and clinical syndromes, we review the theoretical and clinical literature that addresses the relationship between these disorders. Finally, we examine the empirical literature relevant to the relationship of these disorders, with particular emphasis on studies of borderline personality in eating-disordered individuals.

Conceptual Issues in the Study of Personality Disorders

Study of the comorbidity of DSM-III-R Axis I syndromes and personality disorders is embedded in a multitude of theoretical issues associated with the scientific study of personality disorders. Historically, there has been considerable debate over the basic definition of a personality disorder (Millon 1988), over whether personality constructs have any validity (Mischel 1969), and over whether they should be studied in psychiatry at all (Schwartz and Schwartz 1976). More recently, however, there has been increased acceptance of the relevance of personality disorders to the study of major psychiatric syndromes (Akiskal 1988; Millon and Frances 1987), and a growing awareness that personality disorders are best conceptualized as theoretical constructs with fallible indicators rather than as discrete and tangible disease entities (Millon 1988; Widiger 1989).

There continues to be considerable uncertainty regarding which conceptual level of analysis best captures the essence of personality disorders. Personality can be meaningfully studied from a biophysical, intrapsychic, phenomenologic, behavioral, or sociocultural perspective, and to simplify the concept by choosing one level of analysis ignores the inherent complexity of personality as a phenomenon (Millon 1981, 1988). Thus the historical dichotomy suggesting that personality disorders are psychosocial in origin and should be treated psychotherapeutically, whereas psychiatric syndromes are biogenetic in nature and should be treated with somatic therapy, has come under increased scrutiny and criticism (Gunderson and Pollack 1985; Widiger 1989). Another conceptual issue concerns the nature of the relationship between clinical syndromes and personality disorders. Several possible explanations for the presence of such comorbidity have been advanced (Docherty et al. 1986; Widiger 1989).

Predispositional. This perspective posits that personality factors may predispose individuals to develop clinical syndromes. In the area of eating disorders, this model is illustrated by the work of Bruch (1973), who proposed that premorbid personality traits are critical etiological factors in the development of anorexia nervosa. Casper (1990) provided empirical support for this perspective in relationship to anorexia nervosa, reporting that recovered anorexic patients (restricting subtype) scored higher on measures of risk avoidance, restraint in emotional expression, and conformity than controls at 8–10 year follow-up. Similarly, the recovered anorexic patients appeared more controlled and less spontaneous than their sisters. The author suggested that a disposition toward emotional and behavioral restraint along with strong traditional values may be a risk factor for anorexia nervosa.

Complication. Personality disturbance in this perspective is a complication or consequence of the syndrome. For example, Strober (1985) reported that after weight restoration, anorexic patients became less introverted and obsessed, suggesting that these personality traits may be complications or consequences of the eating disorder and may have minimal or no predispositional significance.

Coeffect. In this perspective, personality disorders and clinical syndromes are considered psychobiologically distinct entities that are both caused by a third factor. For example, particular family structures and processes might give rise to both anorexia nervosa and dependent personality disorder.

Interaction. This perspective also proposes that the clinical syndromes and personality disorders may arise independently, but that both interact to alter the features of each. For example, the impulsivity and interpersonal chaos of the borderline personality may create life circumstances that independently precipitate a bulimic episode. Also, the continual interaction of the borderline personality and bulimia will demonstrate strong pathoplastic influences that color and shape each disorder.

Forme fruste.   This perspective posits that the personality disorder is simply a subclinical version of a clinical syndrome. For example, schizotypal personality disorder may represent an attenuated form of schizophrenia (Akiskal 1984). However, it is difficult to imagine a personality disorder that might simply present as an attenuated form of anorexia or bulimia nervosa. The specificity and instrumentality of the behaviors associated with eating disorders leave the *forme fruste* hypothesis least applicable to the eating disorders (Swift and Wonderlich 1988).

Overlapping criteria.   This perspective implies that the appearance of comorbidity may be artificially produced by the presence of overlapping criteria sets between clinical syndromes and personality disorders. For example, there is considerable overlap between the criteria sets for borderline personality disorder and bulimia nervosa in DSM-III. Persons with bulimia meet the impulsivity and affective instability criteria of borderline personality (Levin and Hyler 1986). (This overlap has been reduced somewhat in DSM-III-R because of the deletion of the affective instability item [depression and self-deprecating thoughts following eating binges] from the DSM-III criteria set for bulimia.) Thus overlapping criteria sets could lead to overestimates of such comorbidity (Pope and Hudson 1989). Widiger (1989) argued that conceptualizing borderline personality and bulimia as two co-occurring disorders is misleading and that, in fact, there may be only one disorder present, borderline personality, that manifests itself partially through bulimic symptoms. This perspective underscores the idea that distinctions between Axis I and Axis II disorders in DSM-III and DSM-III-R are clearly paradigmatic and not reflective of a true distinction in nature between clinical syndromes and personality disorders (Gunderson and Elliot 1985; Widiger and Frances 1989).

Clearly five of these six perspectives are relevant to the study of the comorbidity of personality and eating disorders. While the predispositional perspective has been discussed for some time (Bruch 1973), only recently have the complicating, interactional, and overlapping perspectives been recognized as to how personality disorder may relate to the phenomenology, course, and treatment response of eating disorders

(Garfinkel and Garner 1982; Johnson and Connors 1987). The question of which perspectives are most relevant to the comorbidity of eating and personality disorder becomes even more complex when we realize that a given comorbid relationship (e.g., borderline personality and bulimia) may have more than one valid explanation across different patients (Docherty et al. 1986).

Methodological Issues in the Study of Personality Disorders

The methodological controversies and advancements associated with Axis II will continue to impact comorbidity research using DSM-III-R. Space limitations preclude a thorough examination of these developments, but a few key issues should be discussed.

Classical Versus Prototypal Categories

Although there continues to be debate about whether psychiatric disorders are best classified as points on a continuum or discrete categories, categorical systems continue to prevail in modern psychiatry. However, the absence of clear boundaries between various personality disorders and the heterogeneity within personality categories have seriously challenged the use of a classical categorical typology for Axis II (Frances and Widiger 1986; Widiger and Kelso 1983). Such a classical categorical system conceives of disorders as qualitative, discrete entities and implies that the defining features of the category are singly necessary and jointly sufficient, and also that individuals within a category are homogenous with respect to defining features (Widiger and Kelso 1983).

Some argue that if a categorical system is to prevail, it will need to be prototypal in nature, as opposed to classical, with categories defined by polythetic criteria sets (i.e., membership involves meeting five of eight criteria rather than eight of eight). This approach relies on definitional features that are not singly necessary or jointly sufficient and recognizes that members of a category may be relatively heterogenous, but will resemble that category's prototype more than the prototype of another category. Movement toward polythetic diagnostic criteria was seen in the changes from DSM-III to DSM-III-R, as all personality disorder criteria sets on Axis II are now polythetic (Widiger et al. 1988). Other approaches that follow from a prototypal perspective would include a measure of prototypality (i.e., the number of personality disorder criteria satisfied by an individual) or weighting schemes, with specific diagnostic criteria weighted differentially, but these options need further validating research (Frances and Widiger 1986).

Dimensional Classification

The problems inherent in a categorical typology have led some writers to recommend adopting a dimensional model of personality classification (Frances 1986; Frances and Widiger 1986). Such models tend to be more flexible and comprehensive and minimize classification dilemmas when an individual falls at the boundary of categories. Because two-thirds of patients meeting criteria for one personality disorder also meet criteria for at least one other personality diagnosis (Frances 1986), there is empirical evidence supporting the use of dimensional schemes.

Dimensional systems are complex, however, and may be less descriptively vivid than categorical systems (Frances 1986). Moreover, which dimensions to use in such typologies is unclear. Several models have been suggested, including dimensionalizing the current Axis II categories and various circumplex models (McLemore and Benjamin 1979; Wiggins 1982).

Reliability

Continued concerns regarding the poor reliability of Axis II diagnoses have resulted in greater efforts to reduce inference in the psychodiagnosis of personality disorders. Efforts to identify multiple and specific behavioral indicators representing particular personality disorders have increased (Buss and Craik 1987) as has the development of reliable structured interviews and self-report measures of personality disorder (Reich 1987). Concerns over a loss of validity through the creation of clinically sterile but reliable and operationally defined constructs remain.

Clinical and Theoretical Descriptions

Numerous clinical and theoretical reports have suggested an association between personality disorders and eating disorders (Garfinkel and Garner 1982; Herzog et al. 1987; Johnson et al. 1984; Swift and Stern 1982). These reports generally refer to eating-disordered patients with borderline personality organizations and their associated self-regulatory deficits, impulsivity, and interpersonal chaos. Garfinkel and Garner (1982) hypothesized that persons with anorexia nervosa, bulimic subtype, were more likely to display borderline personality organization than were persons with other eating disorder subtypes and that their dietary restriction was a reflection of underlying separation and individuation failure from parents. Swift and Stern (1982) emphasized the range of personality functioning among anorexic patients. In addition to the chaotic and turbulent borderline type of anorexic, they defined a group of "empty understructured" anorexic patients, who were externally focused, emotionally bland, and unaware of internal states, as well as a group of "emotionally confused, identity conflicted" anorexic patients, in whom prominent identity confusion appears to exist in an otherwise relatively healthy personality structure.

In the most detailed theoretical formulation of the relationship of personality disorders and the eating disorders, Johnson and Connors (1987) proposed two categories of character disorder in individuals with eating disorders (borderline and false self/narcissistic) and explained differences between restricting anorexic and bulimic patients within each of these categories (Table 3–1). The authors suggested that borderline patients with anorexia nervosa, restricting subtype, experienced their parental relationships as malevolently intrusive and developed obsessive-paranoid defenses to protect and distance themselves from this hostile control. Body fat became a threatening paranoid object, against which the patient organized her defensive system to maintain a sense of personal control. In contrast, borderline patients with bulimia nervosa are thought to have experienced their parental relationships as malevolently neglectful and to utilize impulsive, hysterical defenses to promote attachment and gain nurturance. The authors also described a group of patients presenting a false self/narcissistic adaptation devised to compensate for, or hide, interoceptive deficits. Although quite impaired, these individuals, like Swift and Stern's empty understructured anorexic patients (1982), appear to possess greater ego resources than borderline patients. Restricting false self patients purportedly experienced nonmalevolent parental overinvolvement and adapted to this control by becoming submissive "parent pleasers," similar to Bruch's description (1973) of classic restricting patients. Bulimic false self patients, like borderline bulimic patients, also experienced parental neglect, but as a nonmalevolent action. They adapt to this circumstance through pseudomature behavior that provides a sense of control. Because they feared that their pseudomaturity would be revealed, these individuals adopted a rather avoidant posture that is described as a "distant closeness."

Overall, there is a paucity of theoretical explanation on the reported relationship between personality disorders and the eating disorders. The initial efforts to identify theoretically distinct subgroups of eating disor-

Table 3–1.   Variations in character pathology for bulimic and anorexic patients

	Borderline **Malevolent**	False self/Narcissistic **Nonmalevolent**

Restrictor
 	
**Over-
involvement**
	Malevolent intrusiveness
	(Intentional)
	Attachment—Hostile,
	  controlling enmeshment
	Separation—Retaliation by
	  other, injury to self
	Self—Repeatedly
	  overwhelmed, in danger
	Other—Punitive, controlling,
	  harsh, critical
	Defenses—Paranoid defenses
	  used to establish and
	  protect boundaries, splitting
		Nonmalevolent intrusiveness
		(Unintentional)
		Attachment—Controlling but
		  less hostile and punitive
		  enmeshment
		Separation—Depletion of
		  both self and other, injury
		  to other
		Self—Extension of other
		  without identity, ineffective,
		  reactive
		Other—Fragile
		Defenses—Less paranoid,
		  more obsessive, phobic

Bulimic
 	
**Under-
involvement**
	Malevolent neglect
	(Intentional)
	Attachment—Hostile
	  disengagement resulting in
	  clingy dependence
	Separation—Abandonment,
	  emptiness, fragmentation
	Self—Worthless, unlovable
	Other—Withholding, punitive
	Defenses—Hysterical/
	  impulsive used in effort to
	  introject, projective
	  identification
		Nonmalevolent neglect
		(Unintentional)
		Attachment—Less hostile
		  disengagement; wish for
		  intimacy versus fear of
		  disappointment, discovery,
		  rejection; injury to other
		Separation—Protective of self
		  and other,
		  pseudoautonomy, distant
		  closeness
		Self—Fraud, inadequate,
		  destructively needy
		Other—Incapable of adequate
		  holding
		Defenses—Schizoid defenses,
		  avoidance, denial, isolation
		  of affect, intellectualization,
		  suppression

ders based on personality (Johnson and Connors 1987; Swift and Stern 1982) need to be empirically tested. Additionally it remains unclear how terms such as false self presentation or empty understructured anorexic, although descriptively interesting, may translate into DSM-III-R Axis II terminology.

Empirical Studies

The number of studies examining the relationship of DSM-III and DSM-III-R personality disorders to anorexia nervosa and bulimia nervosa has grown considerably in recent years. It is now possible to discuss the implications of studies that used objective diagnostic criteria and reasonably large sample sizes. In this section we examine first the relationship of borderline personality to the eating disorders and then the studies reporting relationships of other personality disorders and the eating disorders.

Borderline Personality Disorder

As in the clinical and theoretical literature, empirical research has focused more on the prevalance of borderline personality among eating-disordered patients than on that of any other personality disorder. However, only recently have researchers started describing the clinical features and course of eating disorders when accompanied by borderline personality disorder.

Prevalence. Reports of the prevalence of borderline personality disorder in eating-disordered populations have ranged from 2 to 75% depending on the research setting, eating disorder subtype studied, and personality disorder measure used. Studies using self-report measures of borderline personality have varied markedly in the discerned prevalence rates among both bulimic and anorexic subjects (Table 3–2). For example, Johnson et al. (1989) administered the Borderline Syndrome Index (BSI; Conte et al. 1980) to 95 consecutive patients seeking treatment for an eating disorder. Although eating disorder diagnoses and inpatient or outpatient status were not specified, 41% of their mixed sample met criteria for borderline personality on this measure. When using the Personality Diagnostic Questionnaire (PDQ; Hyler et al. 1983), Yager et al. (1989) also found high rates of borderline personality among anorexic

Table 3–2. Prevalence rates of borderline personality disorder in patients with eating disorders

Study	Criteria for borderline personality disorder	Sample size	Eating disorder subtype	Patient status	%
Self-report					
Johnson et al. 1989	BSI	94	NS	Outpatient	41
Kennedy et al. 1990	MCMI	44	Mixed	Inpatient	32[a]
	BSI		(AN/R, BN, AN/B)		43[b]
Wonderlich and Swift	MCMI	10	AN/R	Mixed	50
(June 1989, unpub-		11	AN/B		63
lished observations)		16	BN		50
		10	BN/A		60
Yager et al. 1989	PDQ	15	AN/B	NS	33
		300	BN		47
		313	Sub ED		29
Yates et al. 1989a	PDQ	30	BN	Outpatient	13
Unstructured interviews					
Levin and Hyler 1986	DSM-III	24	BN	Outpatient	25
Piran et al. 1988	DSM-III	30	AN/R	Inpatient	7
		38	AN/B		55
Semistructured interviews					
Gartner et al. 1989	PDE	6	AN/R	Inpatient	33
		21	AN/B		33
		8	BN		38

Study	Instrument	n	ED subtype	Setting	%
Levendusky and Herring (1989)	DIB-R	12	NS	Inpatient	75
Piran et al. 1988	DIB	30	AN/R	Inpatient	37
		38	AN/B		42
Pope et al. 1987	DIB-R	52	BN	Outpatient	2
Powers et al. 1988	SCID-II	30	BN	Outpatient	23
Sansone et al. 1989	DIB	6	AN/R	Mixed	50
		17	BN		18
		3	Atypical		0
Wonderlich et al. 1990	SCID-II	10	AN/R	Mixed	20
		10	AN/B		20
		16	BN		19
		10	BN/A		40

Note. Eating disorder subtypes: AN/B = Anorexia nervosa, bulimic subtype. AN/R = Anorexia nervosa, restricting subtype. BN = Normal-weight bulimia nervosa. BN/A = Normal-weight bulimia nervosa with a history of anorexia nervosa. Sub ED = Subclinical eating disorder. NS = Not specified. Criteria for diagnosing borderline personality disorder: PDQ = Personality Diagnostic Questionnaire (Hyler et al. 1983); BSI = Borderline Syndrome Index (Conte et al. 1980); MCMI = Millon Clinical Multiaxial Inventory (Millon 1982); DIB = Diagnostic Interview for Borderlines (Kolb and Gunderson 1980); DIB-R = Diagnostic Interview for Borderlines, Revised (Zanarini et al. 1989); SCID-II = Structured Clinical Interview for DSM-III-R-Axis II (Spitzer et al. 1990); DSM-III = Diagnostic and Statistical Manual of Mental Disorders, 3rd Edition (American Psychiatric Association 1980); PDE = Personality Disorder Examination (Loranger et al. 1987).

[a]MCMI discharge.

[b]BSI discharge.

patients with bulimic tendencies and normal-weight bulimic patients (33% and 47%, respectively). In contrast, Yates et al. (1989a) found that only 13% of their outpatient bulimic sample met criteria for borderline personality when using the PDQ.

Two studies using the Millon Clinical Multiaxial Inventory (MCMI; Millon 1982) revealed high rates of borderline personality disorder across several eating disorder subtypes. S. A. Wonderlich and W. J. Swift (unpublished observations, June 1989) reported MCMI borderline personality prevalences of 50–63% for restricting anorexic, bulimic anorexic, and normal-weight bulimic patients. The MCMI borderline and schizoid scales were found to be significant predictors of overall eating disturbance. Similarly, D. K. Norman, D. B. Herzog, and J. Stasior (June 1989, unpublished observations) found that more than half of their sample of 87 eating-disordered patients showed severe personality deficits on the MCMI and that among the patients with deficits, 89% had elevations on the borderline scale. Although self-report measures are easy to administer and offer the advantage of dimensional scales of measurement, their utility in diagnosing personality disorder is limited by low positive predictive power (Dubro et al. 1988; Edell 1984; Widiger and Frances 1989). Furthermore, the test-retest reliability of the MCMI and BSI has recently been brought into question with eating-disordered subjects; Kennedy et al. (1990) found that the prevalence of personality disorders among inpatient anorexic and bulimic individuals decreased significantly over the course of hospitalization. They reported that 79% of their sample met criteria for borderline personality on the MCMI and BSI at admission, but this rate dropped to 32% (MCMI) and 43% (BSI) at discharge. The authors suggested that the assessment of personality disorder with self-report measures may be greatly influenced by state-related eating pathology. Thus the prevalence rates of borderline personality reported in these studies may be overestimated and should be interpreted with caution.

Two studies have relied on clinical interviews and DSM-III criteria to assess the prevalence of borderline personality among patients with eating disorders. Levin and Hyler (1986) interviewed 24 outpatient bulimic patients and identified six (25%) as having borderline personality disorder. This finding is particularly noteworthy because the authors had excluded subjects who exhibited suicidal behavior in the previous 2 years and drug or alcohol abuse in the previous year, thereby probably limiting the estimated prevalence. Piran et al. (1988) used a clinical interview based on DSM-III to obtain discharge diagnoses for samples of restricting anorexic ($n = 30$) and bulimic anorexic inpatients ($n = 38$). They found that 55% of the bulimic anorexic patients, but only 7% of the restricting anorexic patients, met criteria for a borderline diagnosis. They suggested that this difference reflects bulimic anorexic patients' propensity to discharge conflicts actively, which is consistent with the DSM-III borderline criteria, unlike the reliance by restricting anorexic patients on defenses such as overcontrol and inhibition. These studies suggest a relatively high prevalence of borderline personality among bulimic and bulimic anorexic patients.

Although both of these studies reported adequate levels of interrater reliability, clinical interviews lack the rigorous levels of operationalization and replicability characteristic of structured or semistructured personality disorder interviews that have recently been applied in studies of eating disorders. Furthermore, there is evidence that studies of personality disorder among eating-disordered subjects using semistructured interviews may produce different prevalence estimates than those using clinical interviews (Powers et al. 1988).

The enhanced reliability associated with structured interviewing has led to an increase in the number of structured or semistructured interviews available for the assessment of personality disorders (Reich 1987). Seven recent studies have utilized such interviews to examine the prevalence of borderline personality in eating disorder samples. For example, Gartner et al. (1989), used the Personality Disorder Examination (PDE; Loranger et al. 1987) to study the prevalence of personality disorders in an inpatient sample of 6 patients with anorexia nervosa, restricting subtype; 21 patients with anorexia nervosa, bulimic subtype; and 8 patients with bulimia nervosa. The PDE has well-documented interrater and test-retest reliabilities and assesses all 11 DSM-III-R personality disorders. The authors reported that two restricting anorexic patients (33%), seven bulimic anorexic patients (33%), and three of the bulimic patients met criteria for borderline personality disorder (38%).

Similarly Wonderlich et al. (1990) used the Structured Clinical Interview for DSM-III-R Axis II (SCID-II; Spitzer et al. 1990) to assess personality disorders in a mixed inpatient and outpatient sample of 46 subjects including restricting anorexic, bulimic anorexic, and bulimic patients with and without a history of anorexia. The SCID-II covers the full range of DSM-III-R personality disorders, and the authors reported adequate interrater reliability in the study. Prevalence rates of borderline personality varied from 19% of the bulimic patients with no history of anorexia to 40% of those with a history of anorexia, but the difference between eating disorder subtypes was not statistically significant. Powers et al. (1988) found a comparable rate of SCID-II borderline personality diagnoses in a sample of bulimic volunteers; however, because their study used only one interviewer, reliability estimates for their personality diagnoses are unknown.

Two studies reported the prevalence of borderline personality in eating-disordered samples using the Diagnostic Interview for Borderlines (DIB; Kolb and Gunderson 1980). The DIB has become the standard of comparison for new measures of borderline personality and has shown reasonable psychometric properties, although it may incorrectly identify certain other personality disorders as borderline (Reich 1987). Sansone et al. (1989) administered the DIB to 28 eating-disordered individuals, including restricting anorexic ($n = 7$), normal-weight bulimic ($n = 17$), and atypical eating-disordered patients ($n = 4$). Six (21%) subjects met criteria for borderline personality on the DIB and 5 of these individuals also met borderline criteria on the MCMI and BSI, providing some degree of convergent validation for the DIB diagnoses.

In the previously described clinical interview study by Piran et al. (1988), the bulimic and restricting anorexic subjects also received the DIB. Forty-two percent of the bulimic anorexics and 37% of the restricting anorexics met the DIB criteria for borderline personality. The latter figure is considerably higher than that found when the authors used their clinical interview based on DSM-III (i.e., 37% versus 6%). They suggested that the DIB placed less emphasis on active discharge of impulses, which may lead to a higher prevalence estimate of borderline personality among restricting anorexic patients than when DSM-III criteria are used.

Collectively, the studies described to this point indicate that borderline personality disorder is present in a sizable minority of both bulimic and anorexic patients. Pope and his colleagues (Pope and Hudson 1989; Pope et al. 1987) have challenged this conclusion, criticizing most of these studies on the grounds that nonspecific measures of borderline personality disorder were used. They suggested that because of the overlap between the symptoms of depression and borderline personality, these measures may produce false-positive diagnoses of borderline personality in eating-disordered patients who have comorbid mood disorders. To test their hypothesis, Pope et al. (1987) administered a revised, more specific version of the DIB (DIB-R; Zanarini et al. 1989), to 34 bulimic outpatients, 18 recovered bulimic individuals recruited through a newspaper advertisement, 22 depressed controls, and 13 nonpsychiatric control subjects. It is important to note that this is the only interview-based study that was conducted with controls under blind interviewing conditions. The authors found the prevalence of borderline personality to be only 2% among their bulimic sample and 5% among the depressed controls. Bulimic subjects with current or past major affective disorder displayed significantly higher scores on the DIB-R than did bulimic subjects without major affective disorder. The authors concluded that their data provided little support for the relationship of bulimia and borderline personality disorder. Although these findings seriously challenge the suggested relationship between bulimia and borderline personality, a more recent study clarified the findings by Pope et al. (1987) and suggested that the setting of the study also exerts a significant influence on borderline prevalence estimates.

Levendusky and Herring (1989) administered the DIB-R to 12 consecutive eating-disordered patients admitted to a behaviorally oriented inpatient unit. Importantly, the interviewer for this study was trained by the interviewer from the study by Pope et al. (1987), and this study was conducted at the same institution, thereby limiting method and context variance. The authors reported that 75% of the subjects met the DIB-R criteria for borderline personality. Although this study used a small sample, lacked control groups, and was not conducted under blind conditions, it suggests that the conclusions reached by Pope et al. (1987) need further examination and that the relationship of eating disorders and borderline personality may be significantly influenced by the setting of the study (i.e., inpatient versus outpatient).

Conclusions about the prevalence of borderline personality disorder among eating-disordered individuals are plagued by the methodological limitations of the available studies, including considerable subject and instrumentation variability across studies and questions about the validity of these instruments. Most of the interview studies lacked adequate controls and blind interviewing techniques. Prevalence estimates may be particularly influenced by the severity of illness represented in inpatient versus outpatient settings. Inpatient samples generally show higher frequencies of borderline diagnoses than do outpatient samples, a finding well known in personality disorder research (Docherty et al. 1986).

The most troublesome factor influencing the variability of prevalence estimates across studies is the conceptual controversy surrounding the construct of borderline personality. Pope and Hudson (1989) suggested that depression is often misdiagnosed as borderline personality disorder and that this accounts for the relatively high prevalence estimates in samples of eating-disordered patients. Although such misdiagnosis no doubt occurs in practice, such an explanation relies on a clear distinction in nature between affective disorders and personality disorders that may not be warranted (Gunderson and Pollack 1985; Widiger 1989). As Gunderson and Elliot (1985) suggested, the signs and symptoms of both affective disorder and borderline personality disorder arise from multiple sources that may cluster to represent depression, borderline personality, or both, depending on environmental and temperamental factors. Widiger (1989) further emphasized the fluidity of the boundary between affective and characterological disturbances and proposed that borderline personality simply represents a characterological form of affective disturbance. When a boundary between these disorders is appreciated as theoretically useful but not real, it becomes plausible to imagine a subgroup of eating-disordered patients with severe impulsivity, identity disturbance, tumultuous interpersonal relationships, and affective disturbance who meet criteria for borderline personality, affective disorder, and eating disorder (Wonderlich et al. 1990). Whether such persons should be construed as borderline patients who express their character disturbance through mood and eating disturbance (Widiger 1989) or as patients who manifest distinct but interacting comorbid disorders is an issue requiring future research.

Clinical features.   A few recent studies have attempted to characterize the eating behaviors and associated clinical features of borderline eating-disordered individuals. These studies indicate that borderline patients do not differ from other eating-disordered patients in body weight, binge frequency, or age at onset of the eating disorder (Johnson et al. 1989; Wonderlich and Swift 1990). Johnson et al. (1989) did find that patients in the borderline group used laxatives more often than those in the nonborderline group, but Wonderlich and Swift (1990) failed to replicate this finding and reported that their borderline sample vomited more often than eating-disordered patients without a personality disorder. Johnson et al. (1989) also reported that their borderline patients scored higher than nonborderline patients on six of eight scales of the Eating Disorders Inventory (EDI; Garner et al. 1983). However, Wonderlich and Swift (1990) failed to find differences between border-

line patients and other personality-disordered controls on any EDI subscale, even though both groups scored higher on four of eight EDI scales
than did eating-disordered subjects without a personality disorder. The
authors concluded that heightened eating attitude disturbance was not
reflective of borderline personality specifically, but was associated with
personality disorder in general.

Taken together, three studies (Cooper et al. 1988; Johnson et al.
1989; Wonderlich and Swift 1990) indicate that borderline patients with
eating disorders report more emotional distress, more sexual abuse, more
self-mutilation, more suicidal gestures, and greater perceived family
disturbance (heightened hostility, decreased cohesion, and greater neglect) than other eating-disordered groups. Reports of drug and alcohol
abuse in this population vary, noting both increased prevalence of substance abuse (Johnson et al. 1989) and no difference compared with
nonborderline eating-disordered subjects (Wonderlich and Swift 1990).
Many of these features can be seen in the following case example.

Case 1

Ms. A was a 35-year-old, white, single mother of one child. Her
medical history was significant for the presence of childhood
asthma, which appeared to substantially interfere with normal childhood and adolescent development. She perceived her parents as
extremely strict, religious individuals who were "overprotective"
due to her asthma. At age 14, Ms. A developed a mild anorexic
episode that was treated on an inpatient basis with partial response.
Her anorexia persisted for approximately 4 years, and she then
showed a general lessening of anorexic symptoms. She enrolled in
college briefly, but dropped out and has not since returned to school
or held steady work. After leaving college she began a series of
tumultuous relationships with men that were characterized by physical and emotional abuse, excessive drug and alcohol use, sexual
promiscuity, and an incident in which she was raped. Throughout her
many relationships with men, Ms. A's mood was extremely labile
with considerable dysphoria and wrist-cutting behavior after rejection or abuse by her boyfriends. Her relationship to her parents
deteriorated markedly because of her interpersonal chaos. Furthermore, her identity confusion intensified as she attempted to maintain
her family's strict religious beliefs but continued her interpersonal
and sexual impulsivity. With the birth of her child, she resumed
dieting, began bingeing and purging two to three times a day, and

abused laxatives. Precipitants for bingeing were often related to a sense of loneliness or fear of rejection. She continued to be sexually promiscuous, indicating that sexual contact helped her to feel calmer. However, continued disappointments in these relationships often precipitated suicidal threats or gestures by drug overdose and consequent brief hospitalizations. Ms. A was seen by a psychiatric resident who tried numerous antidepressants, with minimal to moderate effects. Treatment was characterized by extreme difficulties in goal setting and disruptions due to crisis. Furthermore, Ms. A was extremely resistant to attempting to modify her bulimic behaviors.

Course. There has been only one study of the effect the presence of borderline personality has on the course of eating disorders. Johnson et al. (1990) compared 21 borderline bulimic and 19 nonborderline bulimic subjects at the beginning of treatment and again at 1-year follow-up. The two groups did not differ in specific bulimic behaviors at initial evaluation, but the borderline sample did express greater eating attitude disturbance and emotional distress than did the nonborderline group. At follow-up, only 21% of the nonborderline group continued to meet DSM-III-R criteria for bulimia, compared to 62% of the borderline subjects. The borderline group also continued to display clinically significant elevations in eating attitude disturbance and emotional distress.

Treatment. There is virtually no empirical data examining the treatment of borderline patients with an eating disorder, although it is generally accepted that the presence of such personality features significantly complicates and lengthens treatment of the eating disturbance (Garfinkel and Garner 1982; Johnson and Connors 1987; Swift and Wonderlich 1988). Johnson et al. (1990) found that borderline eating-disordered patients, identified with the BSI, received significantly more therapy sessions than did nonborderline patients and that the borderline patients who received the greatest number of sessions showed the most improvement. They suggested that borderline patients need frequent therapeutic contact during the first year of treatment.

Recently, two psychodynamic theories of the treatment of borderline individuals with eating disorder have been offered. Johnson and Connors (1987) recommended that treatment for borderline bulimic patients should differ from that for borderline patients with anorexia nervosa, restricting subtype. They suggested that because the borderline bulimic patient has experienced significant underinvolvement with significant others the therapist should err on the side of overinvolvement, offering a highly engaged and active but stable therapeutic relationship. To support the therapist in managing the borderline patient's neediness and everyday chaos, a team approach is recommended, with the therapist serving as case manager.

In contrast to the treatment of the borderline bulimic patient, the authors suggested that treatment of the borderline patient with anorexia nervosa, restricting subtype, should be characterized by less activity and involvement. The restricting borderline patient's intense fear of engulfment requires a therapeutic relationship that is interdependent, but clearly not characterized by therapist control or dominance. The authors suggested that a split treatment team be utilized in which the therapist serves as an advocate for the patient, but is not involved in weight management decisions.

Dennis and Sansone (1991) offered another dynamically oriented treatment of the borderline individual that included four stages: establishing the therapeutic milieu, stabilizing transference, resolving internal themes (promoting object constancy and managing self-destructive behaviors), and preparing for termination. The authors focused most extensively on treating the patient's underlying personality structures and actively discouraged attempts to directly alter eating behavior until the therapeutic relationship had been established. In the service of promoting object constancy, they encouraged the development of enhanced evocative memory and resolving splitting defenses with specific therapeutic techniques. Management of self-destructive behavior was attained through cognitive behavioral and psychodynamic techniques that assisted in containing and exploring the meaning of such behavior. In every phase of the treatment careful attention was paid to transference-countertransference phenomena in the therapeutic relationship.

It is clear that the treatment of the borderline eating-disordered patient, like that of all borderline patients, will be arduous and difficult. Although some high-functioning borderline patients may respond to treatments targeting eating symptoms, many will not. For these individuals, treatment will require a strong and explicit contract detailing the structure, expectations, and limitations of treatment (Benjamin 1987; Kernberg 1984; Linehan 1987). The therapeutic relationship will need to be highly differentiated (Benjamin 1987; Kernberg 1975), but validating and supportive of the patient, even when symptomatic or dynamic progress is stalemated (Linehan 1987). Benjamin (1987) underscored the importance of focusing therapy for the borderline individual on destructive interpersonal patterns oriented around using hostile control to attain stability and affection from others. Destructive and counterproductive behaviors need to be gently but firmly confronted in terms of motivations for and consequences of such actions (Klein 1989). The therapist must vigilantly attend to and confront the borderline patient's distortions of reality associated with primitive defenses such as projective identification and splitting (Kernberg 1975, 1984; Masterson 1976). A major arena for examining such defenses will be the therapeutic relationship, in which working through transference and countertransference reactions will be a considerable focus of treatment (Kernberg 1984). As the therapeutic relationship stabilizes, borderline individuals are likely to benefit from learning problem-solving and coping skills (Linehan 1987), as well as from an increased focus on symptom control (Dennis and Sansone 1991). An emphasis on teaching dialectical reasoning to borderline patients may also prove a useful strategy in managing the splitting defenses surrounding food, weight, and shape in the eating-disordered individual (Linehan 1987).

Recent studies have also suggested that certain pharmacological agents may be useful in the treatment of borderline patients. Although no drug appears effective in treating borderline personality disorder as a syndrome, several drugs appear effective in reducing the effects of comorbid states (affective and anxiety disorder) or particular symptoms (behavioral dyscontrol and affective instability) (Cowdry 1987; Gorton and Akhtar 1990). Cowdry (1987) suggested that if there is evidence of significant affective comorbidity, lithium with the possible addition of a monoamine oxidase inhibitor (MAOI) should be considered. Similarly, heterocyclics or possibly MAOIs are recommended for treatment of unipolar endogenomorphic depressive presentations.

The presence of highly reactive depressive symptoms, mood lability, and dysphoric reactions—especially with overeating, oversleeping, loss of energy, and withdrawal—may be an indication for an MAOI. If there is prominent cognitive dysfunction (disorganization, mild thought disorder, and suspiciousness), a trial of low-dose antipsychotics may be beneficial (Cowdry 1987; Gorton and Akhtar 1990). Leibenluft et al. (1987) also suggested that carbamazepine may be useful in reducing behavioral dyscontrol.

In spite of these numerous drug treatment options, Cowdry (1987) pointed out that monopharmacy is preferable to polypharmacy with borderline patients. Also, the risk of overdose is substantial for this population, and the treating physician must be careful not to provide these patients with a lethal supply of medication. Although not formally tested in this population, drugs such as fluoxetine and trazodone, which are less toxic when taken in large amounts, should be considered in the management of depressive symptoms. Finally, it is important to recognize that even in relatively successful treatments of borderline eating-disordered patients, abstinence from eating symptoms may be unrealistic (Johnson and Connors 1987; Dennis and Sansone 1991). It may be useful to keep in mind that eating-related symptoms may be the least destructive of the borderline patient's numerous acting-out and tension-reducing behaviors (Johnson and Connors 1987).

Other Personality Disorders

Several studies have examined the comorbidity of eating disorders and a full range of DSM-III-R personality disorders (Gartner et al. 1989; Kennedy et al. 1990; Levin and Hyler 1986; Piran et al. 1988; Wonderlich et al. 1990; Yates et al. 1989a). These studies suggest that 53–93% of eating-disordered individuals display at least one personality disorder and that 37–56% meet criteria for two or more personality disorders (Gartner et al. 1989; Powers et al. 1988; Wonderlich et al. 1990). These studies indicate that the prevalence of DSM-III-R Axis II personality clusters and individual personality disorders varies considerably among the various eating disorder subtypes and that the presence of a concurrent personality disorder is associated with a greater overall level of psychopathology (Yates et al. 1989b). These personality disorders are reviewed below under the rubric of the personality disorder clusters outlined in DSM-III-R (Table 3–3). These three clusters—the odd-eccentric (Cluster A), dramatic-emotional-erratic (Cluster B), and anxious-fearful (Cluster C)—were introduced to represent symptomatic similarities between specific disorders. Recent factor-analytic studies have provided some support for the validity of the DSM-III-R personality disorder clusters in samples of eating-disordered patients (Yager et al. 1989).

Cluster A: the odd-eccentric personality disorders. Generally, the prevalence of Cluster A personality disorders—paranoid, schizoid, and schizotypal—has been quite low (less than 10%) in samples of

Table 3–3.   Personality disorders by DSM-III-R clusters

Cluster A *(odd-eccentric)*
Paranoid
Schizoid
Schizotypal

Cluster B *(dramatic-emotional-erratic)*
Antisocial
Borderline
Histrionic
Narcissistic

Cluster C *(anxious-fearful)*
Avoidant
Dependent
Obsessive-compulsive
Passive aggressive

---

eating-disordered patients (Table 3–4). There have been exceptions, however, particularly in studies using the MCMI or the PDQ, such as those by Kennedy et al. (1990), Yates et al. (1989a), and Yager et al. (1989), who found that schizoid or schizotypal personalities were prominent in their eating-disordered samples. However, Kennedy et al. (1990) reported that reductions over time in schizoid and schizotypal scales on the MCMI were significantly correlated with similar reductions in depression. Thus the high rates of Cluster A personality disorders may reflect the state effects of a comorbid mood disturbance on self-report measures of personality disorder.

Yet, two other studies using semistructured interviews also reported moderate rates of Cluster A disorders in eating-disordered samples. Gartner et al. (1989) found that 16% of their restricting anorexic group met criteria for schizotypal personality disorder and 16% also were diagnosed as having paranoid personality disorder when using the PDE, although this only represented one subject for each diagnosis. Similarly, when using the SCID-II, Powers et al. (1988) found that 8 of 30 (27%) outpatient bulimic subjects met criteria for paranoid personality disorder. Although further studies are needed to clarify these findings, the more generally reported low-prevalence estimates from Cluster A are consistent with clinical descriptions of the premorbid personality of eating-disordered individuals as compliant, anxious, dramatic, or labile.

Table 3–4. Prevalence rates of most common personality disorders in patients with eating disorders

Study	Criteria for personality disorder	Sample size	Eating disorder subtype	Most prominent eating disorders
Self-report				
Kennedy et al. 1990	MCMI[a]	44	Mixed (AN/R, BN, AN/B)	Dependent (43%) Passive-aggressive (41%)
Wonderlich and Swift (June 1989, unpublished observations)	MCMI	10	AN/R	Dependent (70%) Passive-aggressive (60%)
		11	AN/B	Dependent (64%) Avoidant (60%)
		16	BN	Dependent (63%) Borderline (44%) Passive-aggressive (44%)
		10	BN/A	Passive-aggressive (80%) Borderline (60%)
Yager et al. 1989	PDQ	15	AN/B	Schizotypal (53%) Dependent (53%)
		300	BN	Schizotypal (55%) Borderline (47%)
		313	Sub ED	Schizotypal (34%) Borderline (29%)
Yates et al. 1989a	PDQ	30	BN	Compulsive (37%) Histrionic (33%) Dependent (33%) Schizotypal (33%)
Unstructured interviews				
Levin and Hyler 1986	PDQ and interview	24	BN	Histrionic (40%) Borderline (25%)
Piran et al. 1988	Clinical interview DSM-III	30	AN/R	Avoidant (60%) Compulsive (16%) Dependent (16%)
		38	AN/B	Borderline (55%) Histrionic (18%)
Semistructured interviews				
Gartner et al. 1989	PDE	6	AN/R	Borderline (33%) Avoidant (33%)
		21	AN/B	Compulsive (38%) Borderline (33%) Avoidant (33%)
		8	BN	Dependent (38%) Borderline (38%)

Table 3–4 *(continued)*

Study	Criteria for personality disorder	Sample size	Eating disorder subtype	Most prominent eating disorders
Powers et al. 1988	SCID-II	30	BN	Histrionic (53%) Obsessive-compulsive (33%)
Wonderlich et al. 1990	SCID-II	10	AN/R	Obsessive-compulsive (60%) Dependent (40%)
		10	AN/B	Avoidant (60%) Dependent (40%)
		16	BN	Histrionic (31%) Borderline (19%) Avoidant (19%) Dependent (19%)
		10	BN/A	Borderline (40%) Histrionic (40%)

Note. Eating disorder subtypes: AN/B = Anorexia nervosa, bulimic subtype. AN/R = Anorexia nervosa, restricting subtype. BN = Normal-weight bulimia nervosa. BN/A = Normal-weight bulimia nervosa with a history of anorexia nervosa. Sub ED = Subclinical eating disorder. Criteria for diagnosing borderline personality disorder: PDQ = Personality Diagnostic Questionnaire (Hyler et al. 1983); MCMI = Millon Clinical Multiaxial Inventory (Millon 1982); SCID-II = Structured Clinical Interview for DSM-III-R-Axis II (Spitzer et al. 1990); DSM-III = Diagnostic and Statistical Manual of Mental Disorders, 3rd Edition (American Psychiatric Association 1980); PDE = Personality Disorder Examination (Loranger et al. 1987).
[a]At discharge.

Cluster B: the dramatic-emotional-erratic personality disorders.
Swift and Wonderlich (1988) speculated that the action-oriented personality disorders of Cluster B (antisocial, borderline, histrionic, and narcissistic) are likely to be associated with eating disorders, particularly bulimic subtypes. Although borderline personality is comparably prevalent among patients in both restricting and bulimic eating disorder subtypes, there is some evidence that histrionic personality disorder shows a greater affinity to bulimia nervosa than to anorexia nervosa, restricting subtype. Studies have reported prevalence rates for histrionic personality disorder in normal-weight bulimic samples ranging from 25 to 53% (Levin and Hyler 1986; Powers et al. 1988; Wonderlich et al. 1990;

Yates et al. 1989a). Estimates of the prevalence of histrionic personality disorder in samples of restricting and bulimic anorexic patients are considerably lower, ranging from 0 to 20% (Piran et al. 1988; Wonderlich et al. 1990). Even though one study found a low prevalence of histrionic personality disorder across all eating disorder subtypes (Gartner et al. 1989), there appears to be an association between histrionic personality and normal-weight bulimia.

Narcissistic and antisocial personality disorders appear to be uncommon among eating-disordered patients (Table 3–4). Therefore only two of the Cluster B personality disorders of DSM-III-R seem to be associated with the eating disorders. Borderline personality shows a moderate level of comorbidity across all eating disorder subtypes, particularly among inpatients. Histrionic personality disorder is fairly common in samples of bulimic patients and shows greater comorbidity with bulimia nervosa than with anorexia nervosa. Further studies of histrionic personality disorder among eating-disordered individuals are needed to further clarify this apparent comorbid relationship. The case of Ms. W highlights certain features of a bulimic individual with a Cluster B personality disorder, specifically histrionic personality.

Case 2

Ms. W was a 22-year-old college student with a 6-year history of bingeing and purging. Her bulimic symptoms waxed and waned, often depending on the status of her relationship with her boyfriend. She was exquisitely aware of others' perception of her physical presentation, and, in spite of her impeccable appearance, often believed others viewed her as unattractive. She felt that her parents (particularly her father) had difficulty expressing affection or interest in her, and she was typically concerned that others did not approve of her. She excelled in academic and extracurricular activities, but was despondent if she thought others did not view her as clearly outstanding. The perception of not being "special" was generally followed by impulsivity (bingeing), increased depression, and social withdrawal.

Ms. W also displayed periods of excessive spending and flirtatious sexual behavior, which provided some sense of heightened self-esteem. The treatment was characterized by her substantial dependency and eagerness to please her male therapist, alternating with periods of anger when she felt he did not care about her. She expressed considerable uncertainty about how much she could rely on the therapist without "expecting too much from him" and generally displayed considerable confusion over intimacy. Although she was able to significantly reduce her bingeing and purging with treatment, her difficulties maintaining self-esteem and developing mature and realistic interpersonal relationships persisted.

Cluster C: the anxious-fearful personality disorders. In an early report, Levin and Hyler (1986) found a much lower prevalence of Cluster C personality disorders (avoidant, dependent, obsessive-compulsive, and passive aggressive) than of Cluster B personality disorders in a sample of outpatients with bulimia nervosa. Other recent studies, however, have found higher rates of Cluster C than Cluster B disorders among eating-disordered patients (Gartner et al. 1989; Wonderlich et al. 1990), particularly when anorexic subtypes were included. In samples including both anorexic and bulimic patients, avoidant personality disorder has been diagnosed in from 30 to 35% of the cases. Although some researchers have reported that avoidant personality appears more commonly in anorexic subtypes (Piran et al. 1988; Wonderlich et al. 1990), there is some evidence that the prevalence rates among normal-weight bulimic patients are equally high (Gartner et al. 1989).

The prevalence of avoidant personality does appear to vary across anorexic subtypes. Piran et al. (1988) reported a much higher rate of avoidant personality among restricting anorexic patients than among bulimic anorexic patients (60% versus 16%), whereas Wonderlich et al. (1990) found the opposite relationship, with bulimic anorexic patients displaying a higher, although statistically nonsignificant, frequency of avoidant personality than restricting anorexic patients (60% versus 20%). Although these discrepant findings may be accounted for by differences in instrumentation and subject sample characteristics (e.g., binge frequency and weight), variation in the diagnostic criteria used may also be a significant factor.

Piran et al. (1988) used DSM-III criteria for avoidant personality whereas Wonderlich et al. (1990) used DSM-III-R criteria, which rely less on social avoidance and more on fear of risk taking and embarrassment than do the DSM-III criteria set (Widiger et al. 1988). Although this may partially explain the discrepancy, the issue is confused further by a recent finding in which patients in both restricting and bulimic anorexic subtypes displayed a 33% prevalence rate for avoidant personality when DSM-III-R criteria for personality disorders were used (Gartner et al.

1989). Additional studies are required in order to clarify the magnitude and direction of the relationship between avoidant personality disorder and subtypes of anorexia nervosa.

Obsessive-compulsive personality disorder has shown a modest comorbid relationship with eating disorders. Reports of its prevalence have ranged from 4 to 37% in samples of anorexic and bulimic patients. With the exception of studies by Yates et al. (1989a) and Powers et al. (1988), examination of normal-weight bulimic subjects has revealed low rates (0–13%) of concurrent obsessive-compulsive personality disorder.

As is the case with avoidant personality, however, the relationship of obsessive-compulsive personality to anorexic subtypes is presently unclear. Whereas one study reported high frequencies of obsessive-compulsive personality among restricting anorexic patients and low frequencies among bulimic anorexic patients (Wonderlich et al. 1990), another suggested that the magnitude of the difference was smaller (Piran et al. 1988). Still another study found the opposite relationship, with a trend toward obsessive-compulsive personality diagnoses in bulimic rather than in restricting subtypes (Gartner et al. 1989). Once again variability in measures of personality disorder and patient characteristics complicate interpretation of these findings. Thus, although restricting anorexic individuals have been characterized as obsessional in personality trait studies (Strober 1980, 1981), the nature of the relationship of true obsessive-compulsive personality disorder and subtypes of anorexia nervosa remains uncertain and in need of further study.

Dependent personality disorder has consistently shown a comorbid association with various eating disorders. With the exception of Levin and Hyler (1986) and Powers et al. (1988), studies have reported frequencies of dependent personality ranging from 16 to 33% in eating disorder samples (Gartner et al. 1989; Piran et al. 1988; Wonderlich et al. 1990). These studies also suggest that dependent personality is equally represented across eating disorder subtypes. Wonderlich et al. (1990) reported that dependent personality disorder, along with borderline personality, was the best predictor of degree of self-reported dysthymic mood, regardless of eating disorder subtype.

Passive-aggressive personality disorder has not been shown to have a significant relationship with the eating disorders. Prevalence rates in mixed samples have been consistently low (from 0 to 9%). Although there are some data to suggest that rates may be higher in normal-weight bulimic than in anorexic subtypes (Gartner et al. 1989), this finding is based on a very small sample and needs further study.

Overall, the personality disorders of Cluster C appear to be nearly as prevalent among eating-disordered individuals as are the disorders of Cluster B, suggesting that anxiety in bulimia nervosa and particularly in anorexia nervosa deserves greater attention. Avoidant and obsessive-compulsive personality appear to be most common among anorexic individuals, which is consistent with Casper's recent personality trait findings (1990) in recovered anorexic patients. However, differences between restricting and bulimic subtypes continue to be inconsistently reported. Dependent personality disorder shows a moderate but consistent relationship to all eating disorder subtypes. The influence of a concurrent Cluster C personality disorder, specifically avoidant personality, can be seen in the case of Ms. G, who showed a history of anorexia nervosa and bulimia nervosa.

Case 3

Ms. G was a 20-year-old college student with a 4-year history of eating disorder. At age 16 she developed an anorexic episode and reached a low weight of 70 lb (5'5"). She received psychiatric treatment and responded with significant weight restoration.

Shortly after attaining her previous weight, she began bingeing and purging, reaching a peak frequency of eight binge-purge episodes a day. She displayed extreme perfectionism and nearly constant ruminations about food and dieting.

Although she was able to refrain from bingeing and purging on occasion, her abstinence typically was short lived. A return of her symptoms most often appeared to be associated with prolonged periods of isolation in which she would spend her time alone studying in her dormitory. She indicated she had no close friends at college, but would engage in superficial conversation or activities with other students. She stated she had always felt uncomfortable in her relationships to other people, especially males. Although she wished to develop closer relationships, she expressed considerable concern about relying on others.

Ms. G was treated in a group therapy format, where she initially was extremely inhibited and restrained. With time, however, she became more invested in the group, and occasionally sought feedback from others about interpersonal issues. Her avoidance continued to be a major impediment to recovery, however, with periods of isolation serving as prominent cues for bulimic episodes.

Treatment. Literature addressing the treatment of eating-disordered patients with nonborderline personality disorders is virtually nonexistent. Although space limitations prevent a review of the treatment issues involved in the full range of DSM-III-R personality disorders, several general comments can be made. It is likely that many of the principles derived from the treatment of borderline patients will be relevant to eating-disordered patients with other personality disorders, particularly those in Cluster B (narcissistic, histrionic, and antisocial). Masterson (1989) suggested that his theoretical conceptualization and treatment of borderline patients actually encompassed six DSM-III-R personality disorders: borderline, histrionic, dependent, avoidant, passive aggressive, and obsessive-compulsive. It is interesting that five of these personality disorders (all but passive aggressive) show high prevalences in eating disorder samples. The possibility that these five personality disorders share some underlying feature that increases the risk of eating disorder and hence may all be responsive to a particular treatment strategy deserves further study.

It may be, however, that a patient's general level of functioning, rather than the specific personality disorder, has the most significance for treatment (Liebowitz et al. 1986). Thus a histrionic patient who is somewhat decompensated may do worse in treatment than a schizoid patient, even though a histrionic personality would be expected to do better. Nonetheless, specific personality disorders are often associated with varying expectations about response to treatment that may have clinical validity. Liebowitz et al. (1986) suggested that the DSM-III personality disorders may be regrouped according to prognosis into subgroups that often attain a good outcome with psychotherapy (histrionic, obsessive-compulsive, dependent, avoidant, and passive aggressive), occasionally attain a good outcome (narcissistic, schizoid, borderline, and schizotypal), and almost never attain a good outcome (antisocial).

As with borderline personality disorder, adjunctive drug therapy for symptomatic and behavioral treatment in other personality disorders appears useful for some patients. Gorton and Akhtar (1990) listed several behaviors or symptoms often seen in personality disorders and associated drugs that have been shown to be of some benefit in treatment. For example, transitory psychotic states, paranoia, cognitive distortion, derealization, and depersonalization all may show some response to antipsychotics. They also suggest that lithium, carbamazepine, and antipsychotics may prove useful in the treatment of impulsivity, behavioral dyscontrol, and affective lability. Anxiety-related symptoms, such as panic, compulsions, social phobia, and agoraphobia, have been shown to respond to a host of agents including tricyclic antidepressants, MAOIs, alprazolam, clonazepam, clomipramine, fluoxetine, and trazodone. Depressed states or atypical "hysteroid dysphoria" may respond to tricyclics, MAOIs, or lithium, whereas acute conversion disorder has shown a response to benzodiazepines. However, reports on the effectiveness of these agents in personality-disordered individuals are anecdotal, and controlled trials are distinctly needed. Gorton and Akhtar (1990) also highlighted the need for clinicians to avoid presenting these drugs to personality-disordered patients as panaceas and recommended maintaining concurrent alternative treatments, given the rarity of a global effect of drug therapy in cases of significant personality disorder.

Although certain psychotherapeutic treatment techniques, such as confrontation, are likely to be effective for a broad range of personality disorders, specific interventions used in treatment of eating disorders may be differentially effective for particular personality types. For example, certain personality types may benefit particularly from self-monitoring and structured meal planning (histrionic and dependent), others from assertion training (dependent, passive aggressive, and avoidant), and still others from labeling of emotional states (obsessive-compulsive, schizoid, and dependent). Matching specific treatment techniques to personality types clearly deserves more attention in future studies.

Summary

It should be clear to the reader that the study of the comorbidity of personality and eating disorders is in its infancy. Few statements can be made about this relationship with certainty, and the literature may be characterized more by its inconsistencies than by valid generalizations or conclusions. Methodological and conceptual problems plague the research to date, including the effects of subject state on personality assessment, psychometric limitations of the many personality measures, and inadequate research designs. Many of these problems reflect the relatively short time that these issues have been systematically studied.

Nonetheless, several tentative conclusions and working hypotheses may be offered.

First, there does appear to be a relationship between the eating disorders and personality disorders. The majority of eating-disordered patients meet criteria for at least one personality disorder, most commonly borderline, avoidant, histrionic, dependent, or obsessive-compulsive. Second, particular types of eating disorders may be associated with specific personality disorders although all eating disorder subtypes show a moderate prevalence of borderline and dependent personality disorders. Normal-weight bulimia appears to be associated with histrionic personality disorder, whereas avoidant and obsessive-compulsive personality disorders may be associated with anorexia nervosa. In general, there appears to be an association between DSM-III-R Cluster C (anxious-fearful) personality disorders and anorexia nervosa.

Finally, although there is substantial comorbidity between personality and eating disorders, the meaning of this relationship remains uncertain. The presence of concurrent borderline personality is associated with heightened emotional distress, family disturbance, abusive histories, and social dysfunction, but not with atypically elevated levels of eating-related symptoms. Furthermore, there is preliminary evidence indicating that the presence of borderline personality has a negative impact on response to treatment for an eating disorder, and necessitates more intensive treatment. More studies are needed that examine both the prevalence of borderline and nonborderline personality disorders in eating disorder samples, and the impact of these personality disorders on symptom formation, clinical course, and response to treatment.

References

Akiskal HS: Characterologic manifestations of affective disorders: toward a new conceptualization. Integrative Psychiatry, May/June, 1984, 83–88

Akiskal HS: Personality as a mediating variable in the pathogenesis of mood disorders: implications for theory research and prevention, in Depressive Illness: Prediction of Course and Outcome. Edited by Helgason T, Daly RJ. Berlin, Springer-Verlag, 1988, pp 131–146

American Psychiatric Association: Diagnostic and Statistical Manual of Mental Disorders, 3rd Edition. Washington, DC, American Psychiatric Association, 1980

American Psychiatric Association: Diagnostic and Statistical Manual of Mental

Disorders, 3rd Edition, Revised. Washington, DC, American Psychiatric Association, 1987

Benedek T: Dominant ideas and their relation to morbid cravings. Int J Psychoanal 17:40–56, 1936

Benjamin LS: An interpersonal approach (commentary on a borderline self-mutilator). Journal of Personality Disorders 1:334–340, 1987

Bruch H: Eating Disorders: Obesity, Anorexia and the Person Within. New York, Basic Books, 1973

Buss D, Craik K: Act criteria for the diagnosis of personality disorders. Journal of Personality Disorders 1:73–81, 1987

Casper R: Personality features of women with good outcome from restricting anorexia. Psychosom Med 52:156–170, 1990

Conte HR, Plutchik R, Karasn TB, et al: A self-report borderline scale: descriptive validity and preliminary norms. J Nerv Ment Dis 168:428–435, 1980

Cooper JL, Morrison TL, Bigman OL, et al: Bulimia and borderline personality disorder. International Journal of Eating Disorders 7:43–49, 1988

Cowdry RW: Psychopharmacology of borderline personality disorder: a review. J Clin Psychiatry 48 (suppl):15–22, 1987

Dennis AB, Sansone RA: The clinical stages of treatment for the eating-disordered patient with borderline personality disorder, in Psychodynamic Treatment of Anorexia Nervosa and Bulimia Nervosa. Edited by Johnson C. New York, Guilford Press, 1991, pp 128–164

Docherty JP, Fiester SJ, Shea T: Syndrome diagnosis and personality disorder, in American Psychiatric Association Annual Review, Vol 5. Edited by Frances AJ, Hales RE. Washington, DC, American Psychiatric Press, 1986, pp 315–355

Dubro AF, Wetzler S, Kahn MW: A comparison of these self-report questionnaires for the diagnosis of DSM-III Personality Disorders. Journal of Personality Disorders 2:256–266, 1988

Edell WS: The borderline syndrome index: clinical validity and utility. J Nerv Ment Dis 168:428–435, 1984

Frances AJ: Introduction to personality disorders, in Psychiatry, Vol 1: Personality Disorders and Neurosis. Edited by Frances AJ, Sacks MH. New York, Basic Books, 1986

Frances AJ, Widiger T: The classification of personality disorders: an overview of problems and solutions, in American Psychiatric Association Annual Review, Vol 5. Edited by Frances AJ, Hales RE. Washington, DC, American Psychiatric Press, 1986, pp 240–257

Garfinkel P, Garner D: Anorexia Nervosa: A Multidimensional Perspective. New York, Brunner/Mazel, 1982

Garner DM, Olmsted MP, Polivy J: Development and validation of a multidimensional eating disorder inventory for anorexia nervosa and bulimia. International Journal of Eating Disorders 2:15–34, 1983

Gartner AF, Marcus RN, Halmi K, et al: DSM-III-R personality disorders in eating disorder patients. Am J Psychiatry 146:1585–1591, 1989

Gorton G, Akhtar S: The literature on personality disorders, 1985–88: trends, issues, and controversies. Hosp Community Psychiatry 41:39–51, 1990

Gunderson JG, Elliot GR: The interface between borderline personality disorder and affective disorder. Am J Psychiatry 142:277–288, 1985

Gunderson J, Pollack W: Conceptual risks of the Axis I–II division, in Biologic Response Styles: Clinical Implications. Edited by Klar H, Siever L. Washington, DC, American Psychiatric Press, 1985, pp 82–95

Herzog DB, Hamburg PA, Brotman AW: Psychotherapy and eating disorders: an affirmative view. International Journal of Eating Disorders 62:651–657, 1987

Hyler SE, Reider RD, Spitzer RL: Personality Diagnostic Questionnaire (PDQ). New York, New York State Psychiatric Institute, 1983

Janet P: Les obsessions et la psychosthenic. Paris, Felix Alcan, 1919

Johnson C, Connors ME: The Etiology and Treatment of Bulimia Nervosa. New York, Basic Books, 1987

Johnson C, Lewis C, Hagman J: Bulimia: review and synthesis. Psychiatr Clin North Am 7:247–273, 1984

Johnson C, Tobin D, Enright A: Prevalence and clinical characteristics of borderline patients in an eating-disordered population. J Clin Psychiatry 50:9–15, 1989

Johnson C, Tobin D, Enright AB: Differences in treatment outcome between borderline and nonborderline bulimics at one year follow-up. International Journal of Eating Disorders 9:617–627, 1990

Kennedy SH, McVey G, Katz R: Personality disorder in anorexia nervosa and bulimia nervosa. J Psychiatr Res 24:259–269, 1990

Kernberg OF: Borderline Conditions and Pathological Narcissism. New York, Jason Aronson, 1975

Kernberg OF: Severe Personality Disorders: Psychotherapeutic Strategies. New Haven, CT, Yale University Press, 1984

Klein R: The art of confrontation, in Psychotherapy of the Disorders of the Self. Edited by Masterson JF, Klein R. New York, Brunner/Mazel, 1989, pp 215–230

Kolb JE, Gunderson JG: Diagnosing borderline patients with a semistructured interview. Arch Gen Psychiatry 37:37–41, 1980

Leibenluft E, Gardner DL, Cowdry RW: The inner experience of the borderline self-mutilator. Journal of Personality Disorders 1:317–324, 1987

Levendusky PH, Herring J: Therapeutic contract program for treatment of severe eating disorders. Paper presented at the 97th American Psychological Convention, New Orleans, August 1989

Levin AP, Hyler SE: DSM-III personality diagnosis in bulimia. Compr Psychiatry 27:47–53, 1986

Liebowitz MR, Stone MH, Turkat ID: Treatment of personality disorders, in American Psychiatric Association Annual Review, Vol 5. Edited by Frances AJ, Hales RE. Washington, DC, American Psychiatric Press, 1986, pp 356–393

Linehan MM: Dialectical behavior therapy: a cognitive behavioral approach to parasuicide. Journal of Personality Disorders 1:328–333, 1987

Loranger AW, Susman VL, Oldham JH, et al: The personality disorder examination: a preliminary report. Journal of Personality Disorders 1:1–13, 1987

Masterson JF: Psychotherapy of the Borderline Adult. New York, Brunner/Mazel, 1976

Masterson JF: The Masterson approach: application to the personality disorders (DSM-III-R), in Psychotherapy of the Disorders of the Self. Edited by Masterson JF, Klein R. New York, Brunner/Mazel, 1989, pp 5–8

McLemore CW, Benjamin LS: Whatever happened to interpersonal diagnosis? a psychosocial alternative to DSM-III. Am Psychol 34:17–34, 1979

Millon T: Disorders of Personality: DSM-III: Axis II. New York, John Wiley, 1981

Millon T: Millon Clinical Multiaxial Inventory, 3rd Edition. Minneapolis, MN, National Computer Systems, 1982

Millon T: Perspectives on the nature of the personality disorders. Journal of Personality Disorders 2:323–325, 1988

Millon T, Frances A: Editorial. Journal of Personality Disorders 1:i–iii, 1987

Mischel W: Continuity and change in personality. Am Psychol 24:1012–1018, 1969

Piran N, Lerner P, Garfinkel PE, et al: Personality disorders in anorexic patients. International Journal of Eating Disorders 7:589–599, 1988

Pope HG, Hudson JI: Are eating disorders associated with borderline personality disorder? a critical review. International Journal of Eating Disorders 8:1–9, 1989

Pope HG, Frankenburg FR, Hudson JI, et al: Is bulimia associated with borderline personality disorder? a controlled study. J Clin Psychiatry 48:181–184, 1987

Powers PS, Coovert DL, Brightwell DR, et al: Other psychiatric disorders among bulimic patients. Compr Psychiatry 29:503–508, 1988

Reich JH: Instruments measuring DSM-III and DSM-III-R personality disorders. Journal of Personality Disorders 1:220–240, 1987

Sansone RA, Fine MA, Seuferer S, et al: The prevalence of borderline personality symptomatology among women with eating disorders. J Clin Psychol 45:603–610, 1989

Schwartz RA, Schwartz IK: Are personality disorders diseases? Diseases of the Nervous System 86:613–617, 1976

Selvini-Palazzoli M: Self Starvation. New York, Jason Aronson, 1978

Spitzer RL, Williams JBW, Gibbon M, et al: Structured Clinical interview for DSM-III-R: Personality Disorders (SCID-II, Version 1.0). Washington, DC, American Psychiatric Press, 1990

Stone MH: The Borderline Syndromes: Constitutions, Personality and Adaptation. New York, McGraw-Hill, 1980

Strober M: Personality and symptomatological features in young nonchronic anorexia nervosa patients. J Psychosom Res 24:353–359, 1980

Strober M: A comparative analysis of personality organization in juvenile anorexia nervosa. Journal of Youth and Adolescence 10:285–295, 1981

Strober M: Personality factors in anorexia nervosa. Pediatrician: International Journal of Child and Adolescent Health 12:134–138, 1985

Swift WJ, Stern S: The psychodynamic diversity of anorexia nervosa. International Journal of Eating Disorders 2:17–36, 1982

Swift WJ, Wonderlich SA: Personality factors and diagnoses in eating disorders: traits disorders and structures, in Diagnostic Issues in Anorexia Nervosa and Bulimia Nervosa. Edited by Garner DM, Garfinkel PE. New York, Brunner/Mazel, 1988, pp 112–165

Waller JV, Kaufman MR, Deutsch F: Anorexia nervosa: psychosomatic entity. Psychosom Med 2:3–16, 1940

Widiger TA: The categorical distinction between personality and affective disorders. Journal of Personality Disorders 3:77–91, 1989

Widiger TA, Frances AJ: Epidemiology diagnosis and comorbidity of borderline personality disorder, in American Psychiatric Press Review of Psychiatry, Vol 8. Edited by Tasman A, Hales RE, Frances AJ. Washington, DC, American Psychiatric Press, 1989, pp 8–24

Widiger TA, Kelso I: Psychodiagnosis of Axis II. Clinical Psychology Review 3:491–510, 1983

Widiger TA, Frances A, Spitzer RL, et al: The DSM-III-R personality disorders: an overview. Am J Psychiatry 145:786–795, 1988

Wiggins JS: Circumplex models of interpersonal behavior in clinical psychology, in Handbook of Research Methods in Clinical Psychology. Edited by Kendall PC, Butcher JN. New York, John Wiley, 1982

Wonderlich SA, Swift WJ: Borderline versus other personality disorders in the eating disorders: clinical description. International Journal of Eating Disorders 9:629–638, 1990

Wonderlich SA, Swift WJ, Slotnick HB, et al: DSM-III-R personality disorders in eating disorder subtypes. International Journal of Eating Disorders 9:607–616, 1990

Yager J, Landsverk J, Edelstein CK, et al: Screening for Axis II personality disorders in women with bulimic eating disorders. Psychosomatics 30:255–262, 1989

Yates WR, Sieleni B, Reich J, et al: Comorbidity of bulimia nervosa and personality disorder. J Clin Psychiatry 50:57–59, 1989a

Yates WR, Sieleni B, Bowers WA: Clinical correlates of personality disorder in bulimia nervosa. International Journal of Eating Disorders 8:473–477, 1989b

Zanarini MC, Gunderson JG, Frankenberg FR, et al: The revised diagnostic interview for borderlines: discriminating BPD from other axis II disorders. Journal of Personality Disorders 3:10–18, 1989

Chapter 4

Males With Eating Disorders

Arnold E. Andersen, M.D.

*I*n 1694 Richard Morton, a London physician and a Fellow of the College of Physicians, published his comprehensive work on consumptions. In the section now considered to describe the first well-documented cases of anorexia nervosa in the English language, Morton described with rich clinical detail two patients: Mr. Duke's daughter, who went on to die of her illness, and the son of the Reverend Minister Steele, who showed improvement with treatment. It should be noted that at this historical moment of publication of the first two accounts of anorexia nervosa in English, half of the cases were male, and the outcome of treatment in the male was satisfactory. These two points remain pertinent to any discussion of the subject of eating disorders among males today.

Silverman (1990) amplified the chronology of early male cases with Whytt's report of a 14-year-old lad having a condition much like modern anorexia nervosa. A third case reported in the medical literature before 1800 was that of Robert Willan's young Englishman who fasted for 78 days and then died (Silverman 1990). Gull (1874), in his detailed monograph on anorexia nervosa in the mid-19th century, included mention of males suffering from this disorder.

If these early clinicians included males with anorexia nervosa in their reports, why was there so little mention made of them in the century after Gull? Several reasons may help to explain the subsequent decreased notice of males with anorexia nervosa. First, some psychodynamically based theories of anorexia nervosa required the presence of a particular motif of "fear of oral impregnation" which would, a priori, exclude males. Other criteria required the presence of amenorrhea, thereby implicitly restating a gender bias. The DSM-III (American Psychiatric Association 1980) criteria did not mention amenorrhea, but DSM-III-R (American Psychiatric Association 1987) requires that, if present in a female, the disorder must include the absence of at least three consecutive menstrual cycles. There is no mention of a comparable requirement for males, bringing up the question of the validity of this requirement.

On a less theoretical level, males may have presented to clinicians so infrequently in the past that sometimes the fact that they could develop anorexia nervosa was lost sight of because of their statistical rarity. Finally, there exist socioculturally determined stereotypes on the part of both patients and clinicians that males do not develop eating disorders, with the result that this diagnostic possibility may simply be overlooked whereas similar symptoms in a female would prompt a correct diagnosis.

Beginning in the 1960s, Crisp (1967) and others noted the occurrence of anorexia nervosa among male patients. A number of systematic studies have followed, including reviews by Vandereycken and Van der Broucke (1984) and Sterling and Segal (1985). The material in this chapter is drawn from experience at The Johns Hopkins Hospital with almost 100 males with eating disorders, as well as a review of the literature. The format of this chapter is a series of questions with answers that will vary greatly in their degree of empirical certainty.

Questions and Some Possible Answers

Do Males Develop Eating Disorders?

The answer to this question is an unequivocal yes. Russell's three essential requirements for the diagnosis of anorexia nervosa (1979)—substantial self-induced weight loss, a morbid fear of becoming fat, and an abnormality of reproductive hormone functioning—pertain equally well to males and females. Similarly, using DSM-III-R criteria, a diagnosis of anorexia nervosa can be easily made in males.

The diagnosis of bulimia nervosa, drawn from the Greek words for *ox* and *hunger,* can likewise be as equally applied to males as to females. The history of men and boys with bulimia nervosa has not been as widely discussed in the literature as that of anorexia nervosa because bulimia was not formalized as a separate diagnostic entity until the late 1970s (Russell 1979). It almost certainly existed in its conceptually inchoate form long before that time as a companion to anorexia nervosa. The essential diagnostic features are compulsive binge eating followed by remorse or physical distress, a fear of fatness, and a variety of compensating efforts to avoid weight gain.

How Many Males Have an Eating Disorder?

The answer to this question devolves to a review of the adequacy of the methodologies of epidemiological studies completed to date and to an examination of the nature of their defining criteria. A few general principles are worth stating. First, cases presenting to a tertiary care facility do not necessarily represent, qualitatively or quantitatively, the cases of a disorder actually present in the community. Second, studies differ in the rigor of their definitions of anorexia nervosa and bulimia nervosa, and therefore results cannot always be strictly compared with each other. Halmi et al. (1981) found, for example, that 5% percent of male college students experienced binge eating but not all purged or had fear of fatness. Studies with stricter criteria (e.g., Fairburn and Beglin 1990) have found lower percentages of males with eating disorder behavior. As reported in studies on patients seen at the Eating and Weight Disorders Clinic of The Johns Hopkins Hospital, almost exactly 10% of the cases presenting were males (Andersen 1988). While recognizing the validity of the caution that university hospital samples may not accurately represent community samples, it is interesting to note that a study from Sweden (Rastam et al. 1989) found an almost identical incidence of 10 females to 1 male having an eating disorder in a community-based study.

Why Do So Few Males Develop Eating Disorders?

Hippocrates noted several millennia ago that it is more difficult for boys to withstand fasting. Males clearly differ from females in a number of basic biological parameters. Parameters that may be pertinent to understanding the differential incidence of eating disorders include differential response to tryptophan and other precursors of neurotransmitters, differences in hypothalamic functioning, differences in levels and ratios of testosterone to estrogen, and differences in percentage of stored body fat.

Recent studies have suggested that males may respond differentially compared with females to intravenous doses of L-tryptophan, with implications for serotonin synthesis and the consequent effects of serotonin on neuroregulatory processes including prolactin (Goodwin et al. 1987). These changes appear to be incidental rather than etiological, however.

The male hypothalamus is organized early in fetal life to produce a steady state rather than a cyclical gonadotropin interaction with peripheral sex hormones. The cyclical gonadotropin response inherent in the female rat brain can be converted to the male steady-state response through the injection of testosterone on a single day before birth. Testosterone during the critical developmental phases of life clearly has an organizing effect on brain morphology, whereas later in life it has an eliciting effect on various behaviors. The high ratio of testosterone to estrogen in the developing male appears to contribute to the increased ratio of lean muscle mass to body fat. The enhancing effect of illegal androgen preparations on lean muscle mass has been used by many athletes to attempt to increase performance in competition.

Finally, men have a substantially lower percentage of body fat than do women. Frisch (1988) drew the implication that females utilize this additional body fat to nourish a pregnancy and furnish a subsequent period of lactation. By this reasoning, gender specific functions determine the difference in amount of stored body fat.

Having given due obeisance to these four well-documented biological differences between males and females, it can still be stated that current evidence weighs heavily in favor of a psychosocial rather than biological origin to explain the differential rate of eating disorders in males and females. Indeed, Hsu (1989) examined the "gender gap" in eating disorders and concluded that "eating disorders are more prevalent in the female because more of them are dieting to lose or control weight" (p. 402).

Other support in this direction comes from studies by DiDomenico and Andersen (1990). When the 10 popular magazines most frequently read by men were compared with the ten most often read by women, the authors found a ratio of 10.5 to 1 in women's versus men's magazines for articles and advertisements concerning weight loss. This ratio duplicates almost exactly the ratio of women to men with eating disorders found both in community samples and in hospital-based referral populations. What is cause and what is effect remains to be determined, but the proportionality between the sociocultural emphasis on weight loss in women to men is more clearly correlated with the ratio of cases of eating disorders than any biological differences.

The second line of argument in favor of a primary initiating role for sociocultural factors is the fact that in vulnerable subgroups of males there is indeed an increased incidence of eating disorders proportional to the emphasis of that subgroup on weight loss. Males in sports for which regular cycles of weight loss are required, such as wrestling, have documented eating abnormalities with possible significant long-term metabolic consequences (Steen et al. 1988). Jockeys are another group in which food avoidance or self-induced vomiting may be used to attain the advantage for that sport of lowered weight (King and Mezey 1987). This increased frequency of eating disorders in vulnerable subgroups of males mirrors the increased rate in comparable subpopulations of females where weight loss is even more emphasized than in the general female population, such as ballet or modeling. In summary, whenever weight loss is required for a particular group of individuals, male or female, there is an increased incidence of eating disorders. If our society placed as much pressure on men as it did on women to lose weight, there would predictably be a comparable increase in the incidence of eating disorders among males.

The hypothesis that sociocultural reinforcement for weight change is the primary source of the gender-related differential frequency of dieting behavior is supported additionally by examining a research finding in which the pressures to change a different aspect of the body, body shape rather than weight, are equally distributed between the sexes. In the study on popularly read magazines, DiDomenico and Andersen (1990) reported an almost exactly equal emphasis in the male and female magazines for change of body shape. Therefore, it may be concluded that there is no significant, unexplained difference in gender-related frequency of behaviors related to body weight or shape change that cannot be correlated with existing sociocultural values. Where a sociocultural norm is equally distributed between the sexes, the behavioral response is roughly equal in both sexes. It appears that these behavioral disorders represent primarily socioculturally triggered behavioral mechanisms, not neurological mechanisms in their genesis and maintenance, with the recognition that there may possibly be important secondary biological contributions to perpetuation of illness.

Additional psychodynamic reasoning has been advanced to explain the decreased incidence of males with eating disorders. Sours (1980) noted that girls reach puberty about 2 years earlier than boys and experience radically disruptive changes in body shape and functioning as a result of their secondary sex characteristics. The male counterpart to menstruation, ejaculation, is less frightening or "dirty" to the male. For boys, there appears to be less conflict regarding self-assertion at the onset of puberty compared with girls, who are more often caught in conflict between passive and receptive fears versus aggressive drives. Sours (1980) reasoned that the more conflicted and traumatic onset of puberty in girls may be the cause of the higher incidence of anorexia nervosa as a defense against these conflicts in sexual emergence.

Why Do Particular Males Develop an Eating Disorder?

The Framingham studies (Dawber 1980) on coronary disease described a multifactorial model that best predicts the onset of coronary disease, with contributions to the development of the illness potentially coming either from several smaller etiological sources or from a few larger sources. In a somewhat similar manner, Andersen (1990) suggested that the probability of developing an eating disorder is proportional to the number and severity of risk factors. For example, in a group of college wrestlers, there will be a greater tendency toward voluntary weight loss and compensatory bulimic behavior than in a group of athletes of the same age and sex whose sport does not require weight loss on a regular basis.

The major risk factors that have been associated in general with the development of an eating disorder are

1. Living in an industrialized country in which attaining slimness and avoiding fatness are sociocultural norms.
2. An increased incidence of affective disorders in the family.
3. A vulnerable personality, either from the Cluster B disorders (narcissistic, histrionic, antisocial, or borderline) or Cluster C (avoidant, dependent, obsessive-compulsive, or passive aggressive).
4. Dieting behavior, especially during the critical adolescent and early adult years.
5. Dysfunctional family patterns in which eating disorders produce a stabilizing effect.
6. Membership in a vulnerable subgroup for which weight loss is required.
7. A history of sexual abuse, the emergence of sex disgust during adolescence, or other issues in sexuality that are ameliorated by weight loss.

Beyond these general factors, there may be several additional reasons why males undergo dieting that do not appear to be equally shared by females. In a recent study (Andersen 1988), three major dieting factors were found in which males were overrepresented compared with females: the presence of actual pre-illness obesity rather than the above average but normal weight range of females before anorexia nervosa, weight loss related to greater sports attainment or to fear of gaining weight because of a sports injury, and weight loss in order to avoid weight-related medical illnesses found in other family members. These factors may be elaborated as follows.

First, in contrast to women who, in general, "felt" fat before they dieted, males who went on to develop eating disorders were, in general, medically obese at some time (usually in the mild to moderate range), especially if the eating disorder included any bulimic features. To a greater degree than in women who went on to develop anorexia nervosa or bulimia nervosa, men experienced negative social consequences of teasing and criticism from being overweight during critical phases of preadolescent and pubertal development. This experience, when associated with a sensitive personality, led to dieting, weight loss, and a determination never to be fat again. The threshold among males for a negative social response to excess weight may simply be set at a higher level relative to ideal norms than that among females and may be less likely to lead to dieting except in association with personality or psychodynamic vulnerability. Second, more often than women, men dieted either to attain certain goals in sports or to avoid the possible weight gaining effects of a sports-related injury that caused them to decrease in their physical activity for a while. Finally, more men than women in the study dieted to avoid potential medical complications, especially ones they had seen develop in their parents or heard their parents warned about. No young women in the series dieted to avoid future medical illness, and only one older woman (in her 40s) did so.

Father-son issues relating to the onset and maintenance of eating disorders have not been fully explored. These issues may influence the dynamics associated with weight loss. Of the male eating-disordered patients seen at the Eating and Weight Disorders Clinic at The Johns Hopkins Hospital, some have reported losing weight to avoid appearing like an overweight father with whom they were conflicted and wished to avoid any similarity. They also have occasionally reported that their motive for weight loss was to become more attractive to homosexual partners. Similar motivation among female patients has not been noted; relatively few of the clinic's female patients endorsed a homosexual orientation. These factors need to be confirmed in more detailed studies.

Table 4–1 summarizes the weight history features of a series of male patients with eating disorders seen at the Johns Hopkins Hospital. Table 4–2 identifies in relative order the frequency of common reasons for dieting among males who developed eating disorders. The following are case examples of two males who developed eating disorders, with comments about their onset of dieting.

Case 1: Gender-related risk factors

Mr. S was a 23-year-old dental student referred for treatment of binge eating and self-induced vomiting. As an overweight child, he was teased and criticized by family and friends. In the ninth grade, he decreased his weight from 211 to 148 lb, still in a normal weight range for his height (5'11"). He underwent cycles of increasing his weight up to 175 and then dieting back down to 150, but finally decided that he did not want to appear excessively thin. "I want to be big, but not too big." His primary goal became, instead of thinness, fitness and avoidance of appearing overweight or underweight.

In addition to avoiding being teased or criticized any longer for his weight, Mr. S wished to become fit to be more attractive to his homosexual partners, especially a current boyfriend. As a result, he trained strenuously until he had sharply defined his upper body musculature and achieved a low total body fat. He worried, however, that his generalized lymphadenopathy was symptomatic of acquired immunodeficiency syndrome (AIDS). Family history included a father with active alcoholism and an abstinent, formerly alcoholic mother. He initially followed his father's pattern of dominating and devaluing women, but then stopped dating women and developed a

Table 4–1. Weight history of 76 male patients with eating disorders by diagnostic subgroup

Diagnosis	n	Mean age (yrs)	Maximum weight[a]	Minimum weight[a]
Anorexia nervosa, restricting subtype	14	24.0	123	72
Anorexia nervosa, bulimic subtype	13	26.6	130	74
Bulimia nervosa, with a history of anorexia nervosa	14	27.7	146	76
Bulimia nervosa	25	30.4	155	103
Eating disorders, not otherwise specified	10	27.5	135	84

[a]Percent of ideal weight.

Table 4–2. Most common reasons for dieting among males with
eating disorders

---

1. History of obesity and being teased, criticized, or picked on for being overweight.
2. To change a specific body part, especially to remove "flab" and promote muscle definition.
3. Sports: advised by coach, to prevent weight gain after injury, or to make required weight for specific sport (e.g., wrestling).
4. To be more attractive to female or another male.
5. To avoid medical illness observed in relatives.
6. To look less like father.
7. To counteract iatrogenic weight gain.
8. In association with vegetarianism.
9. To develop the appearance of a model in magazines.
10. Concern about a particular weight on scale or size of clothing (infrequently noted).

---

homosexual orientation with a promiscuous lifestyle. Diagnoses were bulimia nervosa and mixed personality disorder with obsessive compulsive and impulsive features. Mr. S did well in treatment, learning to avoid cycles of weight change and to interrupt binge urges. He developed a more adult relationship with his parents and decreased his promiscuity.

Mr. S's case illustrates the frequent finding of a male with bulimia nervosa having a past history of obesity and the experience of being teased and criticized during crucial developmental periods. He also illustrates the primary emphasis by males on shape change, rather than attainment of extreme thinness. Finally, a major motivation for his change in body physique, to be more attractive to a homosexual partner, has not been found among females in my clinical experience.

Case 2: Weight loss related to sports

Mr. Z was a 16-year-old high school student referred for treatment for anorexia nervosa without bingeing or purging. Mr. Z had felt overweight since age 5, being called "fatty," among other names. At his highest weight of 180 lb, he was chosen for the football team but was dissatisfied with body shape and felt he did not have enough energy due to his pudgy condition. Through food restriction and exercise, he decreased his weight to a low of 129 lb, hoping he would not be teased anymore about his former slightly obese weight, and that he would have more energy for athletics. He found, however, that at his low weight he was also dissatisfied with his body, but feared becoming fat if he ate normally. He wished to increase to an in-between weight of about 150 lb, but only if he could be guaranteed having a well-defined muscular shape and be able to play a different, more glamorous position in football, such as quarterback, that would lead to more respect by girls and his classmates.

On mental state examination, Mr. Z met criteria for anorexia nervosa, restricting subtype. He also had vulnerable features of personality including obsessive-compulsive, anxious, and self-critical traits. In treatment, he was able to follow a program of nutritional rehabilitation and directed weight training, along with a primarily cognitive behavioral psychotherapy and some dynamic psychotherapy toward the end of treatment. At a final weight of 155 lb, with good muscle development, he felt he had achieved his goals of being able to play several sports and to be respected by both boys and girls around him. He stopped being the mediator in his parents' marriage. He developed more realistic expectations of himself and began to accept his artistic and sensitive side.

Mr. Z's case illustrates weight loss in the context of wanting to play sports more effectively and to gain more self-esteem. It also shows how often young men who develop eating disorders are not seeking to achieve extremely low weight, but prefer to be in a normal-weight range providing they can achieve some degree of muscular definition. Mr. Z has done well now after several years and has not needed additional treatment.

Are There Differences in the Natural History of Males and Females Who Develop Eating Disorders?

Strictly scientific studies have not been completed comparing the natural history of weight loss or binge-purge behavior among males and females. As noted above, males have a higher frequency of actual obesity before the onset of their eating disorder. Tables 4–3 and 4–4 suggest a series of stages through which anorexia nervosa and bulimia nervosa, respectively, appear to progress among both males and females. The process of development from relatively normal behavior (and dieting behavior in this society cannot be considered not abnormal in and of itself) to a

Table 4–3.   Stages of development of anorexia nervosa

Stage I: *Normal dieting behavior*
               Normal, voluntary dieting behavior.
Stage II: *A diagnosable disorder*
               Dieting not under personal control and/or dieting has
               serious medical, social, psychological consequences.
               Characterized by morbid fear of fatness. DSM-III-R
               criteria met (American Psychiatric Association 1987).
Stage IIIA: *Autonomous behavior*
               The disorder does not resolve even if conditions stimulating
               its origin have resolved. Behavior not susceptible to any
               degree of personal control. Secondary mechanisms
               frequently present.
Stage IIIB: *Illness becomes an identity*
               The patient identifies with being the illness, not only having
               the illness (I *am* anorexic). Prospect of loss of illness leads
               to existential fears of nothingness.

clinically recognizable eating disorder appears to progress in a regular stepwise fashion.

There are numerous advantages to an appreciation of the stepwise development of behaviors into disorders. First, it suggests that there is a regular pattern of development that can be anticipated. Second, it suggests that the stage at which a person presents may have some implications for treatment and prognosis. Third, it suggests that there may be some commonality between different disorders of the motivated behaviors in terms of shared, overarching features of illness development. Finally, it suggests that there may be different mechanisms underlying different stages of treatment.

In anorexia nervosa, the initial stage of development (stage I) is the dieting behavior itself (Table 4–3). Until this behavior becomes associated with the relentless pursuit of thinness and the phobic avoidance of fatness, however, clinical anorexia nervosa is not present even though some weight loss may be induced. When the twin psychopathological motifs of phobic fear of fatness and relentless pursuit of thinness are firmly established, then the clinical anorexia nervosa syndrome (stage II) is present. Anorexia nervosa goes on to develop further consolidating stages. In stage IIIA, the self-starvation becomes autonomous and may be now sustained by secondary biological mechanisms that cause dis-

Table 4–4. Stages of development of bulimia nervosa

Stage IA:	*Normal dieting behavior* Normal, voluntary dieting behavior.
Stage IB:	*Involuntary binge behavior* Dieting behavior and weight loss lead to involuntary binge behavior, based on response to hunger.
Stage II:	*A diagnosable disorder* The trigger for binge behavior generalizes from hunger to a variety of painful mood states. Marked fear of fatness is present. Meets DSM-III-R criteria (American Psychiatric Association 1987). May have serious medical, social, and psychological consequences.
Stage IIIA:	*Autonomous behavior* Binges are autonomous, frequent, and large. Secondary mechanisms are often present.
Stage IIIB:	*Illness becomes an identity* The thought of living without bulimic behavior provokes great fear, leading to an existential lack of identity and fear of inability to cope.

comfort when normal eating is attempted. Finally, in stage IIIB, the illness becomes an existential identity. Woodall et al. (1990) suggested that the more chronically ill anorexic patients have a much greater likelihood of developing a personal sense of identity equated with the presence and continuance of the eating disorders. They come to fear a life apart from the eating disorders and, in a sense, become "professional" anorexic patients.

In a similar manner, bulimia nervosa progresses through a series of predictable phases (Table 4–4). Patients with bulimia nervosa begin much like anorexic patients in that they generally wish to pursue a lower body weight (stage IA). In the context of anything from brief- to long-term weight loss after mild to strenuous dieting, bulimic individuals experience a "breakthrough" of hunger, leading to binge eating (stage IB), rather than the sustained food restriction of anorexia nervosa. For reasons that are currently being widely explored but not yet understood, it appears that both the psychology and the biology of these patients who go on to develop bulimia nervosa differ from those of patients who go on to develop anorexia nervosa. Bulimic patients appear to be less tolerant of hunger, more impulsive, and perhaps more sensitive to the experience of hunger. In this context, the initial binge can be understood as essentially a physiological response to some degree of food deprivation and weight loss.

What establishes stage II of bulimia nervosa as a clinical entity different from stage IB is the transition of binge eating from primarily a physiological response to hunger to a modulator of dysphoric affect. When binge eating is no longer a response to hunger from food restriction but becomes a short-term, partially effective treatment of low mood, anxiety, and anger, it then develops a "life of its own." In association with the morbid fear of fatness, the psychopathological and pathognomonic features shared with anorexia nervosa, the transition of bulimic behavior from hunger-driven to mood-stabilizing function establishes its illness roots firmly.

Finally, in stage IIIA bulimia nervosa may also become a self-sustaining state whereby attempts to interrupt the now autonomous binge-purge behavior cause medical discomfort and distress. The final stage (IIIB), akin to IIIB of anorexia nervosa, is the development of "professional" bulimia nervosa: the firm identification of self with the continued presence of the eating disorder symptoms and the inability to picture a life apart from the availability of bulimic behavior.

What Is the Nature of Sexuality Among Eating-Disordered Males?

The nature of sexuality among eating-disordered males depends to some extent on the age of the patient and the subtype of the eating disorder, whether anorexic or bulimic. I have not had much clinical experience with males below age 12, but others have described these patients in more detail (Gislason 1988). However, if patients above age 12 are divided into those with teenage-onset versus those with adult-onset eating disorders, there appear to be more issues in sexual identity associated with the teenage-onset group, whereas later life issues, such as marital and work-related conflicts, dominate the picture for those in the adult-onset group.

Herzog et al. (1990) noted that "anorexic males display a considerable degree of anxiety with regard to sexual activities and relationships" (p. 41). A large number of males with teenage-onset eating disorders, especially anorexia nervosa, manifest sex disgust similar to that found by King (1963) among girls with primary anorexia nervosa. Low levels of sexual activity have been noted among anorexic males before and during the illness by Fichter and Daser (1987). How much this decrease in sexual activity relates to psychological conflicts about sexuality and how much from either delayed onset of normal testosterone or a return to low, prepubertal hormone levels needs to be determined. Crisp and Burns (1990) also noted the presence of restricted pre-illness sexual activity among anorexic males.

Bulimic males, like bulimic females, are generally more sexually active both before illness and at the time of their illness. However, a study using the Derogatis Sexual Functioning Inventory (Derogatis and Melisaratos 1979) found that all hospitalized patients with eating disorders, of any diagnostic subgroup (anorexic or bulimic), had substantially diminished sexual activity and interest except for relatively normal fantasy levels in patients with bulimia nervosa (Rothschild et al., in press). Burns and Crisp (1990) have associated the outcome of anorexia nervosa in males with the frequency of pre-illness sexual activity. The worst outcome occurred in those with the least pre-illness sexual activity.

Although some studies suggest there is an increase in gender identity conflict and sexual orientation among males with eating disorders, there is lack of agreement about the degree to which these findings are present. Some studies suggest that homosexuals are overrepresented in samples of males with eating disorders. In contrast to a general population estimate of approximately 3–5%, Fichter and Daser (1987) found that 25% of eating-disordered males had some degree of homosexuality. Males with homosexual orientation may be under- or overrepresented, however, among patients who come to a referral clinic. The actual incidence of homosexuality among males with eating disorders in the community and not presenting for treatment is not known. Psychodynamically, however, conflicts over sex role and sexual identity are found with some frequency in the course of psychodynamic treatment of males with eating disorders. As with females, the presence of a self-starved state may serve as a defense against sexual conflicts through the mechanism of asceticism leading to lowered body weight, with a subsequent return to preadolescent hormone status, and decreased activation of sexual thoughts, feelings, and behaviors (Fagan and Andersen 1990).

Studies (e.g., Crisp and Burns 1990) have documented that anorexia nervosa among males is associated with a decrease in plasma testosterone. In contrast to the "on-off" phenomenon of amenorrhea in females, the decreased testosterone in males is more linearly proportional to the decrease in the male's weight. Andersen et al. (1982) found that testosterone returns to normal as weight is restored to a healthy range.

Two males admitted to the eating disorders clinic at The Johns Hopkins Hospital in the past year were human immunodeficiency virus (HIV) seropositive, the first such finding in the clinic's series of males with eating disorders. No females, despite the larger numbers admitted, shared this diagnosis. In one patient, the seropositivity was acquired through bisexual activity during the manic phase of bipolar illness that presented as a comorbidity along with bulimia nervosa. In the other male (who also had bulimia nervosa), the seropositivity was contracted during reportedly heterosexual activity, but the patient had low self-esteem and had experimented with bisexual activities. Whether this finding represents the tip of an iceberg remains to be seen. In general, males with eating disorders might be at increased risk for HIV seropositivity as well as for developing AIDS because males generally have a higher frequency of sexual interaction than females and, especially if bulimic, often have associated bipolar features or impulsive features of personality. The combination of Cluster B impulsive personality disorder traits with a bipolar mood disorder and the higher sexual frequency associated with the male sex may lead to increased high-risk sexual activity.

Mickalide (1990) noted that with the onset of AIDS as a widespread phenomenon, the image of the thin male as desirable may be decreasing because of the possibility of being confused with AIDS patients. Although a subgroup of males may still be pursuing extreme thinness, in general, the stereotypical male physique is still that of some degree of mesomorphic habitus, with a V shape for the upper body.

What Are the Psychological Characteristics of Males With Eating Disorders?

Assessment of comorbidities. Both males and females with eating disorders appear to have an increase in the presence of Axis I and Axis II comorbidities, in addition to their primary diagnosis of an eating disorder. In a study of males at Johns Hopkins, only 25% did not have an associated comorbidity in Axis I (Simpson et al. 1988). The most common associated Axis I codiagnoses are mood disorders, drug and alcohol abuse, and anxiety syndromes. Simpson et al. (1988) found a substantial increase in the incidence of bipolar II mood disorders associated with anorexia nervosa or bulimia nervosa. Winokur et al. (1980), Gershon et al. (1984), and Strober and Humphrey (1987) found an increase in the frequency of mood disorders in the families of individuals with eating disorders.

An unsolved argument continues as to whether eating disorders are a *forme fruste* of mood disorders or a separate entity. Pope and Hudson (1984) at least implied that eating disorders are a kind of mood disorder and that treatment with imipramine or another antidepressant is the quintessential treatment for bulimia nervosa. Other studies (e.g., Mitchell et al. 1990) found that a cognitive behavioral group approach was equally effective in treatment and argue against equating eating disorders with mood disorders.

Why Do Families of Patients With Eating Disorders Have an Increased Incidence of Mood Disorders?

Andersen (1990) argued that there has been an increased incidence of mood disorders among individuals with eating disorders and their families because the behaviors of the eating disorders bring stability and temporary improvement to abnormal mood states that occur for a variety of reasons. Approximately 70% of young women, and a smaller percent of young men, diet between the ages of 14 and 21 as a result of their perception of being overweight (Nylander 1971). This means that a substantial percentage of those who do have abnormalities of mood for whatever clinical reason (genetics, personality features, or psychodynamic vulnerabilities) will also experience dieting behavior, and a subgroup of these dieters will go on to binge-purge behavior. On the whole, the preponderance of evidence suggests that eating disorders "breed true" (Beumont 1970) and are not simply a subset of mood disorders in disguised form. It is possible to understand the increased frequency of these two psychiatric disorders on the basis of an operant conditioning model, whereby self-starvation, and more often, binge behavior, stabilize and ameliorate the abnormalities of mood.

Numerous studies have shown an increase in the frequency of personality disorders with eating disorders as well as some differential frequency of the type of personality disorders with subtype of eating disorder. King (1963) and Smart et al. (1976) noted an increase in the frequency of personality disorders among patients with anorexia nervosa. Piran et al. (1988) documented, with careful studies, an association that many clinicians have noted anecdotally, namely, that there is a higher probability among bulimic patients of having abnormal personality features from Cluster B (narcissistic, borderline, or histrionic), compared with anorexic patients. In contrast, food-restricting anorexic patients have a higher probability of deriving their personality disorder, when present, from Cluster C, with the characteristic obsessional, sensitive, perfectionist, and obsessive-compulsive features.

Standard psychological testing. Edwin and Andersen (1990) examined 76 males with eating disorders with a variety of standard psychological tests. In intelligence, they scored in the average to high-average range, except for normal-weight bulimic males who scored in the lower average range. On the General Health Questionnaire (GHQ; Goldberg and Hiller 1978), all subgroups of males with eating disorders exceeded the cutoff point for clinical distress, which is more than four positive responses. On the revised Hopkins Symptom Checklist (SCL-90-R; Derogatis 1983), all groups of males were "quite troubled," being more than two standard deviations above the average on the Global Severity Index summary. All groups were abnormal on the obsessive-compulsive scale. Many also showed anxiety features, impulsivity, resentfulness, and avoidance. On the Minnesota Multiphasic Personality Inventory (MMPI; Hathaway and McKinley 1943), all the diagnostic subgroups of males with eating disorders were elevated in their profiles, the mean profile being 278/287. On the Eating Attitude Test (EAT; Garner et al. 1982), all subgroups of male eating-disordered patients were above the threshold of 30, whereas patients presenting with secondary weight loss from other disorders were well below the threshold. The Eating Disorders Inventory (EDI; Garner et al. 1983) also documented typical subscale elevations among males, especially in the Drive for Thinness and Body Dissatisfaction, although scores for these two clinically relevant subscales were somewhat lower among males than among females, probably reflecting the greater sociocultural pressure toward thinness for women. Finally, Woodside et al. (1990) found similar abnormalities among males and females on the EAT and found on the EDI that scores for males were significantly elevated, but not as much as for females, in their Drive for Thinness subscale.

Central psychodynamic characteristics. Definitive, detailed studies need to be completed before the central psychodynamic characteristic of males with eating disorders can be confidently identified. Males with eating disorders share many features with females in regard to the central dynamic aspects of their illness but also have some important separate issues reflecting male vulnerabilities and social pressures in our society. Table 4–5 summarizes some of the most common psychodynamic features found among male eating-disordered patients presenting at Johns Hopkins. The experience of males with actual obesity, rather than feared obesity, especially males with sensitive features of personality during critical phases of development, forms a major predisposition to psychodynamic vulnerability. The retreat from narcissistic injury and the determination never to be exposed again to similar situations may lead them to achieve thinner weights as a means of psychological safety and as a means of avoiding repetition of painful experiences.

Second, low self-esteem, whether from personality vulnerabilities or from crucial family interactions, can lead males to attempt to attain through dieting a stereotypical V shape, which they fantasize will make them feel more masculine, implicitly in greater control of themselves, and more commanding in respect from those around them. The attainment of a particular masculine stereotype in physique as a way to deal with inner inadequacy points out the vulnerability of many of these individuals toward having an external locus of control and their sensitiv-

Table 4 – 5. Some psychodynamic themes frequently found among males with eating disorders

---

1. Avoidance of repetition of narcissistic injury experience as a result of obesity or body shape.
2. Enhancement of low self-esteem.
3. Attainment of an ego ideal.
4. Individuation and separation from parent(s).
5. Gaining a sense of control when life feels out of control due to unrealistic internal or external expectations.
6. Gaining mastery over sense of mortality.
7. Dealing with dysphoric mood state from affective disorder or adjustment disorder.
8. Regression to a safer or more youthful time in life.
9. Competition with sibling for parent attention or for increased sense of power.

---

ity to environmental responses and demands. As the search for thinness in women often represents a search for fantasized gold at the end of the weight-reduction rainbow, so the driven attempts of males toward a hypermasculine body image represent a kind of modern Faustian quest for achieving goals that are inherently not attainable through change in body size and shape.

Father-son and mother-son issues remain to be defined for male patients with eating disorders. Often there may be present an ineffective or distant father, in contrast to whom the male patient wishes to differentiate himself, plus an intrusive or emotionally unavailable mother against whom he seeks protection. Often they suffer a loss of play in childhood from the role of "reversed parent." It is not uncommon, however, to have demanding and verbally or physically abusive fathers who sow the mental seeds in their sons for the later desperate attempt to change in body size and shape as a way to protect themself from repeated physical or emotional injury from the father. The incidence of sexual abuse among males with subsequent eating disorders also needs to be investigated. Issues of sexual identity and conflict have been noted above. They may play a major role in the psychodynamic contribution to the development of eating disorders in adolescents.

With some male patients, when adequate transference takes place early in the psychological treatment, the clinician does not have to wait long for the emergence of central dynamic issues. The central dynamic formulation should ideally come from the transference relationship with the patient and not from textbook formulations. In general there are a cluster of half a dozen or so themes that keep repeating themselves as large numbers of patients are seen. In many ways, the essential goal of psychological treatment is to "work the eating disorders out of a job" by resolving the central dynamic issues, by treating the associated comorbidities stabilized by the eating disorders, and by interrupting features of anorexia nervosa and bulimia nervosa that have acquired lives of their own as independent behaviors or conferred an illness-based sense of identity.

Treatment of Males With Eating Disorders

Table 4–6 summarizes the essential steps of treatment of males with eating disorders. Treatment involves working with a series of interactive methods and multiple foci and appreciating the shared and the unique

Table 4 – 6. Steps in treatment of eating disorders

1. Decision regarding inpatient versus outpatient treatment.
2. Accurate diagnosis and exclusion of differential diagnoses (e.g., swallowing disorders, primary medical illness, or primary mood disorder).
3. Medical evaluation and stabilization.
4. Diagnosis of Axis I and Axis II comorbidities and comprehensive treatment plan.
5. Nutritional rehabilitation to restore healthy body weight, including weight reduction if needed.
6. Interruption of binge-purge behavior and identification of "triggers."
7. Psychological testing.
8. Appropriate psychopharmacology.
9. Sequence of psychotherapy according to patient's needs.
10. Identification and treatment plan for unique male issues.
11. Behavioral practice (e.g., choosing meals, purchasing clothing, and planning everyday activities).
12. Extended follow-up.

features of males and females; the biological, psychological, and socio-cultural contributions to illness; and the need for individual, group, and family methods.

Decision making: inpatient or outpatient treatment? Most of the males with bulimia nervosa can be treated out of hospital, and most patients meeting criteria for anorexia nervosa need to be treated in hospital, with numerous exceptions. When males experience substantial weight loss after dieting from some level of pre-illness obesity, an anorexic-like physiological state may actually occur at a body weight that seems normal on medical charts specifying desirable body weight but may, in fact, represent a state of starvation for that particular individual relative to his "set point." Anorexic males who can be treated out of hospital generally are acutely rather than chronically ill and less severely lowered in weight, with fewer associated psychiatric comorbidities, healthier personality features, and helpful family and community resources.

Bulimia nervosa patients who need to come into hospital are generally those who have a chronic course of illness; significant medical complications, such as hypokalemia; suicide intents (or who have made suicide threats); severe personality disorders; or a history of having not done well in organized outpatient treatment programs.

Medical stabilization. Medical assessment, as described in Chapter 5, should be followed by prompt medical stabilization. The most pressing initial issues are usually treatment of severe starvation, with its associated medical dangers, and treatment of the systemic effects of hypokalemia and other metabolic derangements secondary to vomiting and purging behavior. Other less common but potentially serious medical problems, such as osteoporosis, may also need to be identified and treated. In general, the slower the patient's history of weight loss is, the less urgent is its immediate reversal, except at very low weight. After stabilizing weight loss and supporting lowered vital signs, a program of gradual refeeding, with attention to the complications of weight gain, should be started. A major goal of the clinician experienced with treating eating disorders is to keep overly aggressive consultants from doing unnecessary invasive procedures. A slow heart rate, in the high 30s or low 40s, will generally not need cardiac pacing, for example, but will respond to supportive and nutritional care. Likewise, liver abnormalities and anemia usually do not need biopsies or bone marrows. Waldholtz and Andersen (1990) noted that most gastrointestinal (GI) symptoms in a series of 16 patients with anorexia nervosa improved by refeeding without the need for specialized GI testing except for preexisting GI disorders or severe persisting reflux. More than a century ago, Sir William Gull (1874) said that the essence of treatment was to keep patients warm, feed them frequent but small meals, persuade them to think and behave differently, and remove them temporarily from their distressed family situations.

Nutritional rehabilitation. A variety of approaches to nutritional rehabilitation have been tried without definitive studies to confirm that one particular method is clearly superior. In general, hyperalimentation is to be avoided whenever possible. At Johns Hopkins, we have not needed to use this procedure despite treating more than 500 patients over the last 14 years, including adult patients with weights as low as 48 lb. In general, the preferable approach is "normal food eaten normally," although an argument can be made, on the basis of efficiency and conservation of staff time and resources, for refeeding programs with balanced liquid preparations. An approach to nutritional rehabilitation is described in Chapter 5 and in separate publications (Andersen et al. 1984). A weight restoration of 2.5–3.5 lb a week can usually be accomplished safely. Formerly anorexic patients may at least temporarily require large number of calories, 3,000–4,000 a day, simply to maintain their goal weight once it is achieved.

Interruption of binge-purge behavior. Close supervision of patients during the vulnerable phase after admission to inpatient care will promptly interrupt bingeing and purging behavior. Incidentally, it should be remembered that subgroups of patients may separately practice only binge behavior or only purge behavior. Low-weight anorexic patients who would never think of bingeing may however purge after taking in small amounts of normally eaten food. In analogous fashion, bulimic patients may, at times, binge without inducing vomiting or effecting other means of weight loss.

Although an initial interruption of binge-purge behavior through staff supervision is almost always immediately effective, the next and considerably more difficult goal is to translate this externally determined restraint of illness behavior into the internal volitional state of the patient so that response inhibition becomes a self-governed, rather than other-governed, practice. For many patients, this transition requires identifying clearly the triggers for binge behavior and learning to choose alternative or incompatible behaviors. It is my impression that many patients with bulimia nervosa may be exquisitely sensitive to certain dysphoric moods and may be consciously insensitive (alexithymic) toward other distressing moods that may progress quickly into a dysphoria-alleviating behavior of bingeing rather than into a conscious "processing" and dealing with the distressing affect.

In addition to identifying the triggers for their binges, patients also find it helpful to learn to "wait them out." In some ways this process is similar to the treatment of patients with panic disorder who learn to become observers, rather than responders, of their distressing anxiety. Waiting for a painful mood to crescendo and then watching it decline involves inhibiting features of impulsivity in the personality and delaying the perceived need for immediate relief.

A requisite to progress in interrupting binge-purge behavior is altering the patient's all-or-none reasoning, helping him to accept that even a reduced frequency or reduced quantity of binges represents a substantial improvement. All-or-none reasoning tends to lead patients to think that any relapse, or an occasional binge, is a sign of failure and dissuades them from persevering. They often feel, because of this cognitive error, that once a binge is started, "why bother stopping" since they have already "failed." At Johns Hopkins we encourage the approach of "shaping" binge-related behaviors toward decreased frequency, recognizing that progress often occurs in a "saw-tooth" manner, rather than by the less achievable "gone for good" belief that leads to demoralization if relapse occurs.

Alternatives to binge behavior include practicing muscle relaxation, calling on staff or a "buddy" for help, and waiting out the urge as an observer of the impulse. As patients receive psychoeducation, they learn that purging efforts are ineffective and dangerous (Garner et al. 1985).

Treatment of comorbidities.   Axis I and Axis II psychiatric disorders are present more often than not in addition to an eating disorder. They need to be diagnosed and treated because they often have a sustaining role in the perpetuation of the self-starvation or binge-purge behavior. Treatment of mood disorders, the most common comorbidity on Axis I, involves the full range of psychiatric care including antidepressants, cognitive methods of psychotherapy, and dealing with underlying psychodynamic issues. A similar array of methods may help with anxiety states. Concomitant drug and alcohol problems often elevate treatment requirements to an additional level of difficulty, necessitating a decision as to whether treatment should begin with the eating disorder or with the drug and alcohol abuse.

Patients with personality disorders generally benefit from an approach that helps them to increase their strengths and decrease their vulnerabilities. Identifying and working with those aspects of personality that are functioning effectively in order to deal with those features that are problematic and vulnerable remain the essence of treating a personality disorder.

The rich and complex literature on treatment of personality disorder is too large to reference adequately. Basically, however, decisions need to be made between an "uncovering" and a "sealing over" approach. Patients with borderline features, for example, usually do best in a "here-and-now" relationship kind of therapy rather than one in which uncovering work or an interpretation of transference is a central features. Skilled and sophisticated efforts have been made to deal with borderline patients psychodynamically, but this is not generally for the beginner.

Psychotherapeutic treatment. A reasonable argument can be made that the fundamental center of treatment of the eating disorders is psychotherapeutic work, persuading people to understand the origin and course of their eating disorder, the purpose it serves, how to "trade in and trade up," how to act sanely in a weight- and shape-preoccupied culture of narcissism and densely packed calories, and how to deal in a healthy way with their life's development, issues, and relationships. As Bruch (1974) warned, manipulating people to "eat their way out of the hospital" does not accomplish much in the long run. To arrive at the beginning of effective psychotherapeutic work, however, many hurdles need to be overcome.

First of all, starvation needs to be treated so thinking can be freed from the nonspecific apathy and food-focused attention it causes. Metabolic abnormalities need to be corrected. Comorbidities that interfere with psychotherapy, such as a mood disorder, anxiety states, and drug and alcohol abuse, need to be effectively treated. Where many treatments end—with weight restoration, medical stabilization, and antidepressant medications—is where, in a sense, real treatment should begin. Table 4–7 suggests a 4-stage approach to psychological treatment. In general, very ill, starved, or actively bulimic patients are best started in the process of psychological treatment with psychoeducational and supportive efforts. The initial goal of supportive therapy is simply to reintegrate existing defense mechanisms and to give a sense of hope to individuals who often are demoralized. Frank noted (1974) that the essential features of all psychotherapy programs are the same: restoration of morale and dealing with specific problems.

The second stage of psychological treatment is logically a cognitive or cognitive behavioral approach as outlined by Garner and Bemis (1985) for anorexia nervosa and Fairburn (1984) for bulimia nervosa. These are effective methods that can be learned in a relatively brief time by psychiatric practitioners. There are virtually always cognitive distortions in the thinking of eating-disordered patients, including distorted perception of their bodies, beliefs about excessive demands by society or their own conscience on them, and fears about their ability to live successfully without the presence of an eating disorder. Patients often have characteristic vulnerabilities in thinking, such as all-or-none reasoning and "catastrophizing," that can be identified, refuted, and "upgraded" to more adaptive, age-appropriate, and healthier defense mechanisms.

Table 4–7. Sequence of psychotherapy methods for most eating-disordered males

Method	Comments
1. Supportive and psycho-educational work (first 2 weeks)	For restoration of morale, reintegration of existing defenses, and education about nature of illness.
2. Cognitive behavioral methods (several weeks to months)	For identification and replacement of abnormal cognition leading to painful mood states and self-defeating or dysfunctional behaviors.
3. Psychodynamic psychotherapy (several months to 1–2 years)	To make "connections" and bring resolution of central dynamic conflicts.
4. Existential psychotherapy (several months to 1 year)	To explore issues in meaning, values, and suffering. To develop purpose and spiritual dimensions.

The third stage of psychotherapeutic treatment involves the development of a central dynamic formulation and working through that formulation with psychodynamic methods. These methods may be pluralistic and may involve a variety of rich psychodynamic traditions rather than specifically psychoanalytic methods. But the essential component of this phase of treatment is to help patients make "connections" between the onset and maintenance of their disorder and crucial features of their early development, significant relationships, abiding personality traits, and characteristic beliefs. Here is where there are both unique issues and shared issues concerning males and females. Both male and female patients with eating disorders usually have an overvalued belief in the virtues of weight reduction or change in body shape. They often hold, uncritically, beliefs that essentially magical changes will occur in their lives as a result of these behaviors. Many vague fears are projected onto the dreaded higher weights or feared flabby or imperfect body shapes, whereas impossible fantasies are projected into the vision of a slimmer appearance or the chiseled features desired.

The unique dynamic features of males with eating disorders remain to be definitively described. A thorough case report of psychodynamic treatment of a male was described by Foehrenbach and Lane (1989). The experience of the prototypical male in our society is clearly, from birth, a different one than that for females. Particular stresses go with the male role that remain to be more completely identified among male patients. The tendency toward repression of emotions, the production of certain types of expected masculine activities, and braggadocio have been noted by others (Kearney-Cooke and Steichen-Asch 1990).

The male sexual experience often begins earlier than that of females with genital fondling due to the presence of more externally visible and accessible sex organs. A somewhat lower percentage of males appear to have experienced sexual abuse during development, and this observation may play a role in the differential frequency between men and women who develop eating disorders. Males who are sensitive and avoidant in personality may be conflicted in their development of inner traits because their personal desires do not coincide with stereotypical sociocultural expectations. In families that simply transmit unmodulated society's expectations for males or actually heighten and reinforce these stereotypes, sensitive, perfectionist males may be especially vulnerable toward receiving, full brunt, the demands of a macho culture that then need to be defended against with the anorexic stance or bulimic behavior.

Although methods of psychodynamic treatment vary, in general they involve frequent psychotherapy sessions using interpretation of the transference relationship and helping patients make connections between current behaviors and feelings and their crucial early life experiences and relationships. Psychodynamic work helps the patient move from a treatment phase of simply "fixing" internal thoughts that do not work accurately, as cognitive therapy does, toward a personal understanding of where these vulnerabilities come from and "working them through" in a meaningful way. Partisans on the extreme side of either devaluing psychodynamic psychotherapy or of worshiping psychodynamic psychotherapy will not be easily persuaded in the opposite direction. In general, however, the thoughtful clinician will appreciate that at least a substantial subgroup of eating-disordered patients need and benefit from psychodynamic psychotherapy.

Although psychodynamic treatment is a central aspect of long-term treatment for eating disorders, it does not have the methodology to deal with issues in meaning, values, and existence. The fourth and concluding phase of long-term treatment involves existential psychotherapy, coming to terms with suffering (with the sense of having misused or lost an important part of life past) and grappling with the meaning of life. In many ways, the pursuit of thinness has basic "spiritual" purposes: to give a focus to life, to give a sense of meaning and stability, and to provide a guide for the conduct of life by applying the ritual behaviors and abstract principles concerning fasting, and weight loss, that allow the individual to safely make his way in a world divided between "safe" and "dangerous" foods. Relieving symptoms of an eating-disordered patient is not like taking out an appendix. An unhealthy "vacuum" can be created by otherwise technically successful treatment. The therapist can help the patient become personally renewed, open to life and what it can realistically offer, in place of the pursuit of the fantasy and illusion of weight loss or shape change as a way to deal with fundamental issues. Patients may gain insight into these issues by reading works such as Martin Buber's *I and Thou* (1978), and Victor Frankl's account of existence in the concentration camps, *Man's Search for Meaning* (1959). The existential phase of psychotherapy can be accomplished within the patient's own world view without imposing the personal beliefs of the therapist.

Case 3: Example of treatment leading to good outcome

Mr. B was referred as a 14-year-old to the Eating and Weight Disorders Clinic for treatment of anorexia nervosa after a relapse following previous treatment elsewhere. In contrast to other young men with eating disorders, he had always been thin as a child. In fact, he developed a special sense of status at school from being the thinnest boy in his class. He also was a perfectionist young man, being devastated if he did not receive As in all of his courses.

His illness began at age 13 when he increased in weight to 110 lb at 5'2", no longer being the thinnest boy in his class. He restricted his food to only 300 calories a day and reached a low of 83.5 lb, but still did not feel thin enough. At a local psychiatric treatment center, his weight was increased to 100 lb through a strict behavioral program, but he relapsed after leaving the hospital.

Mr. B's family history included a father who was told to lose weight for medical reasons and a mother who was preoccupied with her own weight loss. His mother had been cautioning Mr. B since he was a child not to gain weight or to eat junk foods.

Mr. B did well in treatment, responding with appropriate weight gain, and achieving a discharge weight of 125 lb at 5'5". His depressive symptoms responded to a tricyclic antidepressant. During psychotherapy, he was able to develop a healthier basis for self-esteem than being the thinnest person in his class. He also began to separate the warnings he heard addressed to his father from health concerns that were relevant to himself.

After 3 months of treatment, he was scheduled for discharge but shortly before discharge became depressed again, felt overwhelmed, and was treated as an inpatient for an additional 4 weeks. During this time, he was able to make realistic plans for returning to his school and family. When he left, he was much more calm, without signs of significant depression or anxiety.

Three years later, Mr. B returned for a visit to the Clinic just before entering college. At this time, he was dressed in casual but sophisticated clothing, showing the staff a picture of his date at the high school prom. He had taken up weight lifting, but only to supplement his running rather than to develop a stereotyped weight lifter's physique. He still was somewhat anxious and self-doubting at times, but able to give himself reassurance and to turn to friends for support. He had stopped feeling he had to be the "standard bearer" for the family and instead was seeking to develop his own vocational plans as a recreational expert.

Mr. B is an example of a good outcome in a young man who originally dieted to avoid some of the medical consequences that he had heard addressed to his father because of being overweight and to maintain the prepubertal image of himself that was the basis for an outdated source of self-esteem. Treatment included a sequence of supportive, cognitive, behavioral, and psychodynamic psychotherapy. On the follow-up, he clearly had made substantial progress in developing a more wholesome self-view, reasonable expectations for himself, and age-appropriate behaviors, as well as a sense of humor.

Conclusions

Issues concerning males with eating disorders are just beginning to be reexplored. More questions than answers exist. As with other aspects of psychiatry, theoretical and experience-based concepts need empirical verification. In the meantime, adequate information is now available to allow clinicians to diagnose accurately eating disorders in male patients, and to organize comprehensive treatments that appreciate the multidimensional aspect of these illnesses. Treating eating disorders requires the ability to treat virtually every syndrome in psychiatry with the exceptions of dementia and schizophrenia. A practical approach to males with eating disorders will appreciate those aspects of illness that are shared with females as well as features of illness unique to males. There is no evidence currently that males with eating disorders have a worse prognosis than females (Andersen and Mickalide 1983). Virtually every aspect of these illnesses is treatable to some degree. A current stance of optimism tempered with realism, will guide current practice until well-designed research inquiries into etiology, mechanism, and treatment lead to more fundamental understanding in the future.

References

American Psychiatric Association: Diagnostic and Statistical Manual of Mental Disorders, 3rd Edition. Washington, DC, American Psychiatric Association, 1980

American Psychiatric Association: Diagnostic and Statistical Manual of Mental Disorders, 3rd Edition, Revised. Washington, DC, American Psychiatric Association, 1987

Andersen AE: Anorexia nervosa and bulimia nervosa in males, in Diagnostic Issues in Anorexia Nervosa and Bulimia Nervosa. Edited by Garfinkel PE, Garner DM. New York, Brunner/Mazel, 1988, pp 166–207

Andersen AE: A proposed mechanism underlying eating disorders and other disorders of motivated behavior, in Males With Eating Disorders. Edited by Andersen AE. New York, Brunner/Mazel, 1990, pp 221–254

Andersen AE, Mickalide AD: Anorexia nervosa in the male: an underdiagnosed disorder. Psychosomatics 24:1066–1076, 1983

Andersen AE, Wirth JB, Strahlman ER: Reversible weight-related increase in plasma testosterone during treatment of male and female patients with anorexia nervosa. International Journal of Eating Disorders 1:74–83, 1982

Andersen AE, Morse CE, Santmyer KKS: Inpatient treatment for anorexia nervosa, in Handbook of Psychotherapy for Anorexia Nervosa and Bulimia. Edited by Garner DM, Garfinkel PE. New York, Guilford, 1984, pp 311–343

Beumont PJV: Anorexia nervosa: a review. S Afr Med J 44:911–915, 1970

Bruch H: Perils of behavior modification in treatment of anorexia nervosa. JAMA 230:1419–1422, 1974

Buber M: I and Thou. Translated by Kaufmann W, Smith SG. New York, Macmillan, 1978

Burns T, Crisp AH: Outcome of anorexia nervosa in males, in Males With Eating Disorders. Edited by Andersen AE. New York, Brunner/Mazel, 1990, pp 163–186

Crisp AH: Anorexia nervosa. Hospital Medicine 1:713–718, 1967

Crisp AH, Burns T: Primary anorexia nervosa in the male and female: a comparison of clinical features and prognosis, in Males with Eating Disorders. Edited by Andersen AE. New York, Brunner/Mazel, 1990, pp 77–99

Dawber TR: The Framingham Heart Study: The Epidemiology of Atherosclerotic Disease. Cambridge, MA, Harvard University Press, 1980

Derogatis L: SCL-90-R Manual II. Towson, MD, Clinical Psychometric Research, 1983

Derogatis LR, Melisaratos N: The DSFI: a multidimensional measure of sexual functioning. J Sex Marital Ther 5:244–281, 1979

DiDomenico L, Andersen AE: Why so few males with eating disorders: a comparison of men's and women's magazines. Abstract presented at the Fourth International Conference on Eating Disorders, New York, NY, April 1990

Edwin DH, Andersen AE: Psychometric testing in 76 males with eating disorders, in Males With Eating Disorders. Edited by Andersen AE. New York, Brunner/Mazel, 1990, pp 116–130

Fagan PJ, Andersen AE: Sexuality and eating disorders in adolescence, in Atypical Adolescence and Sexuality. Edited Sugar M. New York, WW Norton, 1990, pp 108–126

Fairburn CCG: Cognitive-behavioral treatment for bulimia, in Handbook of Psychotherapy for Anorexia Nervosa and Bulimia. Edited by Garner DM, Garfinkel PE. New York, Guilford, 1984, pp 160–192

Fairburn CCG, Beglin SJ: Studies of the epidemiology of bulimia nervosa. Am J Psychiatry 147:401–408, 1990

Fichter MM, Daser CC: Symptomatology, psychosexual development, and gender identity in 42 anorexic males. Psychol Med 17:409–418, 1987

Foehrenbach LM, Lane RC: Bulimia: its dynamics and treatment: the case of an adolescent male. Journal of Contemporary Psychiatry 19:183–202, 1989

Frank JD: Persuasion and Healing, Revised. Baltimore, MD, Johns Hopkins University Press, 1974

Frankl VE: Man's Search for Meaning. New York, Pocket Books, 1959

Frisch RE: Fatness and fertility. Scientific American 258:88–95, 1988

Garner DM, Bemis KM: Cognitive therapy for anorexia nervosa, in Handbook of Psychotherapy for Anorexia Nervosa and Bulimia. Edited by Garner DM, Garfinkel PE. New York, Guilford, 1985, pp 107–146

Garner DM, Olmstead MP, Bohr Y, et al: The Eating Attitude Test: psychometric features and clinical correlates. Psychol Med 12:871–878, 1982

Garner DM, Olmsted MP, Polivy J: Development and validation of a multidimensional eating disorder inventory for anorexia nervosa and bulimia. International Journal of Eating Disorders 2:15–34, 1983

Garner DM, Rockert W, Olmsted MP, et al: Psychoeducational principles in the treatment of bulimia and anorexia nervosa, in Handbook of Psychotherapy for Anorexia Nervosa and Bulimia. Edited by Garner DM, Garfinkel PE. New York, Guilford, 1985, pp 513–562

Gershon ES, Schreiber JL, Hamovit JR, et al: Clinical findings in patients with anorexia nervosa and affective illness in their relatives. Am J Psychiatry 141:1419–1422, 1984

Gislason IL: Eating disorders in childhood (ages 4 through 11 years), in The Eating Disorders. Edited by Blinder BJ, Chaitin BF, Goldstein R. New York, PMA, 1988, pp 285–293

Goldberg DP, Hiller VF: A scaled version of the General Health Questionnaire. Psychol Med 8:1–7, 1978

Goodwin GM, Fairburn CG, Cowen PJ: Dieting changes serotonergic function in women, not men: implications for the aetiology of anorexia nervosa? Psychol Med 17:839–842, 1987

Gull WW: Anorexia nervosa. Transactions of the Clinical Society of London 7:22–28, 1874

Halmi KA, Falk JR, Schwartz E: Binge-eating and vomiting: a survey of a college population. Psychol Med 11:697–706, 1981

Hathaway SR, McKinley JC: Minnesota Multiphasic Personality Inventory. Minneapolis, MN, University of Minnesota, 1943

Herzog DB, Bradburn IS, Newman K: Sexuality in males with eating disorders, in Males With Eating Disorders. Edited by Andersen AE. New York, Brunner/Mazel, 1990, pp 40–53

Hsu LKG: The gender gap in eating disorders: why are the eating disorders more common among women? Clinical Psychology Review 9:393–407, 1989

Kearney-Cooke A, Steichen-Asch P: Men, body image, and eating disorders, in Males With Eating Disorders. Edited by Andersen AE: New York, Brunner\Mazel, 1990, pp 54–74

King A: Primary and secondary anorexia nervosa syndromes. Br J Psychiatry 109:470–479, 1963

King MB, Mezey G: Eating behaviour of male racing jockeys. Psychol Med 17:249–253, 1987

Mickalide AD: Sociocultural factors influencing weight among males, in Males With Eating Disorders. Edited by Andersen AE. New York, Brunner/Mazel, 1990, pp 30–39

Mitchell JE, Pyle RL, Eckert ED, et al: A comparison study of antidepressants and structured intensive group psychotherapy in the treatment of bulimia nervosa. Arch Gen Psychiatry 47:149–157, 1990

Morton R: Phthisiologica: Or a Treatise of Consumptions. London, Smith and Walford, 1694

Nylander I: The feeling of being fat and dieting in a school population. Acta Socio-Med Scand 1:17–26, 1971

Piran N, Lerner P, Garfinkel PE, et al: Personality disorders in anorexic patients. International Journal of Eating Disorders 7:589–599, 1988

Pope HG Jr, Hudson JI: New Hope for Binge Eaters: Advances in the Understanding and Treatment of Bulimia. New York, Harper & Row, 1984

Rastam M, Gillberg C, Garton M: Anorexia nervosa in a Swedish urban region: a population-based study. Br J Psychiatry 155:642–646, 1989

Rothschild BS, Fagan PJ, Woodall C, et al: Sexual functioning of female eating disordered patients. International Journal of Eating Disorders (in press)

Russell GFM: Bulimia nervosa: an ominous variant of anorexia nervosa. Psychol Med 9:429–448, 1979

Silverman JA: Anorexia nervosa in the male: early historic cases, in Males With Eating Disorders. Edited by Andersen AE. New York, Brunner/Mazel, 1990, pp 3–8

Simpson S, DePaulo JR, Andersen AE: Bipolar II affective disorders and eating disorders. Abstract presented at the annual meeting of the American Psychiatric Association, Montreal, Canada, May 1988

Smart DE, Beumont PJV, George CCGW: Some personality characteristics of patients with anorexia nervosa. Br J Psychiatry 128:57–60, 1976

Sours JA: Starving to Death in a Sea of Objects: The Anorexia Nervosa Syndrome. New York, Jason Aronson, 1980, p 356

Steen SN, Oppliger RA, Brownell KD: Metabolic effects of repeated weight loss and regain in adolescent wrestlers. JAMA 260:47–50, 1988

Sterling JW, Segal JD: Anorexia nervosa in males: a critical review. International Journal of Eating Disorders 4:559–572, 1985

Strober M, Humphrey LL: Familial contributions to the etiology and course of anorexia nervosa and bulimia. J Consult Clin Psychol 55:654–659, 1987

Vandereycken W, Van der Broucke S: Anorexia nervosa in males. Acta Psychiatr Scand 70:447–454, 1984

Waldholtz BD, Andersen AE: Gastrointestinal symptoms in anorexia nervosa: a prospective study. Gastroenterology 98:1415–1419, 1990

Winokur A, March V, Mendels J: Primary affective disorder in relatives of patients with anorexia nervosa. Am J Psychiatry 137:695–698, 1980

Woodall C, DiDomenico L, Andersen AE: Anorexia nervosa as a professional career identity: quantitative study and response to treatment. Abstract presented at the Fourth International Conference on Eating Disorders, New York, NY, April 1990

Woodside DB, Garner DM, Rockert W, et al: Eating disorders in males: insights from a clinical and psychometric comparison with female patients, in Males With Eating Disorders. Edited by Andersen AE. New York, Brunner/Mazel, 1990, pp 100–115

Chapter 5

Medical Complications
of Eating Disorders

Arnold E. Andersen, M.D.

Ever since Morton (1694) described the first two cases of anorexia nervosa in English, clinicians have appreciated the medical consequences of self-starvation. His first case, Mr. Duke's daughter, "fell into a total suppression of her monthly courses." In addition she experienced digestive problems, loose skin, paleness, fainting, and finally death. The second case, the son of the Reverend Minister Mr. Steele, had a more hopeful outcome, being partially improved as a result of nutritional rehabilitation, relaxation methods, and mild exercise. In the mid-19th century, Gull (1874) commented on patients' weight loss, amenorrhea, bradycardia, shrunken habitus, and paradoxical alertness. Although bulimia nervosa has been formally described only for the past 15 years (Russell 1979), there is increasing awareness of its medical complications as well.

A review of the medical complications of eating disorders may be helpful to the clinician for a number of reasons. First, these disorders present extremes in alteration of human physiology that may cause death or long-term consequences if not detected and treated. Second, several recent studies have uncovered new and unexpected medical complications of the eating disorders. Third, many eating-disordered patients are now treated by nonphysicians, such as psychologists, social workers, nurse-clinicians, and health educators. Even though the psychological treatment of these patients by nonphysicians may be satisfactory, these professionals may not be trained in the process of detecting and treating medical problems.

Fourth, anorexia nervosa and bulimia nervosa are among the "great pretenders" of the 20th century, often presenting to clinicians in a variety of forms affecting different organ systems, much as tuberculosis and syphilis did in the 19th century. Anorexia nervosa for example may present to internists as possible malabsorption, to endocrinologists as Addison's disease, to neurologists as suspected hypothalamic tumor, and to gynecologists as secondary amenorrhea. Bulimia nervosa, in a similar manner, may present to a gastroenterologist as irritable bowel syndrome, hematemesis, or melanosis coli.

Anorexia nervosa and bulimia nervosa each present their own diagnostic paradoxes. Anorexia nervosa is usually a publicly visible disease, but one which is often "ego-syntonic" to the sufferer, who many times does not willingly present for treatment. Bulimia nervosa, on the other hand, is a private disease whose medical complications are often not obvious, but which in most cases is "ego-alien" to the patient, who often hesitates out of embarrassment to come for help.

The goals of this review are to inform the clinician about the nature and recognition of the medical complications of eating disorders and to guide him or her in the treatment or referral of these problems. Although general medical articles suggest that virtually every organ system is affected by eating disorders, in practice it is important to know the most common medical consequences and complications of these disorders. There may even be legal implications in terms of timely recognition of medical problems and prompt treatment or referral. It is interesting that medically less serious but socially or personally sensitive medical complications may be the cause of a patient seeking treatment for an eating disorder. For example, loss of hair, feeling weak on the tennis court, soft nails, or prominent, "chipmunk-like" parotid glands may prompt treatment.

The discussion in this chapter stems from the experience of myself and my colleagues at The Johns Hopkins Hospital with approximately 650 inpatients and 1,000 outpatients, from specific studies in the literature, and from the principles illustrated by specific cases. Psychiatry and other branches of medicine are inductive, case-oriented methods that build up to general principles from specific cases. In addition, cases provide the vital and lively sense of the specialty in a way that the "skeleton" or bare bones of general precepts or statistical summaries do not supply.

Major Sources of Medical Symptomatology Among Patients With Eating Disorders

Table 5–1 summarizes nine sources of medical symptomatology among patients with anorexia nervosa or bulimia nervosa. Although it seems obvious that medical starvation is a major contributing factor to both the restricting and bulimic subtypes of anorexia nervosa, this point needs to be reinforced. In their classic study of experimental starvation, Keys et al (1950) noted that their volunteer subjects became anhedonic, apathetic, asocial, and preoccupied with food and displayed a number of abnormal behaviors toward food. Much of the behavioral and psychological symptomatology of eating disorders comes from starvation and does not reflect the primary pathognomonic psychopathology, such as the morbid fear of fatness.

First, anorexia nervosa and bulimia nervosa begin in a very similar fashion: by marching along the road to thinness, keeping pace to the sociocultural band playing the seductive musical theme of "thinner is

Table 5–1. Sources of medical symptomatology in patients with eating disorders

1. Self-starvation.
2. Other means of inducing weight loss including:
    a. Self-induced vomiting.
    b. Laxative abuse.
    c. Diuretic abuse.
    d. Ipecac abuse.
    e. Compulsive exercise.
3. Binge behavior.
4. Exacerbation of preexisting diseases, especially insulin-dependent diabetes mellitus.
5. Medical testing.
6. Treatment effects of nutritional rehabilitation and psychopharmacological agents.
7. Abuse of patient by frustrated family.
8. Passive starving of younger patients by a parent with anorexia nervosa.
9. Consequences of other Axis I comorbidities (such as mood disorders or substance abuse disorders) or Axis II disorders (such as borderline personality with impulsive behaviors).

happier; thinner is better." As the sirens of old lured Odysseus to the rocks, so these calls to weight loss lure individuals into either short bouts of illness or chronic careers as professional eating-disordered patients.

Among the patients presenting at Johns Hopkins, more than 90% of the time their bulimia nervosa begins with an attempt at weight reduction, just as anorexia nervosa does. Studies now just emerging or in progress suggest that bulimic patients have differences in physiology or psychology that lead them to respond to attempts at weight loss with binge behavior instead of sustained weight loss from pure food restriction. Appetite breaks through in the bulimic patient, causing a binge-eating episode, which then provokes compensatory responses. Even food restriction within the 24-hour period, for example, skipping breakfast and lunch, predisposes to binge eating later in the afternoon or evening.

Second, in addition to calorie limitation, eating-disordered patients practice various other means of lowering body weight, one of the foremost being self-induced vomiting. Self-induced vomiting is a common occurrence among bulimic individuals, but can be easily missed among anorexic patients, who may induce vomiting after ingestion of small amounts of food eaten slowly rather than after binge meals. Laxative abuse, diuretic abuse, and Ipecac (emetine) abuse damage both the gastrointestinal (GI) tract as well as initiate the systemic consequences of hypokalemia and other metabolic abnormalities of purging (Mitchell et al. 1987). Compulsive exercising may lead to fractures, hemoglobinuria, and aggravation of soft tissue injuries. Incidentally, clinicians at times mistakenly diagnose self-induced vomiting and other forms of purging by themselves as bulimia nervosa, without the requisite binge behavior being present.

Third, binge behavior, sometimes without purging but often preceding it, causes gastric distention, predisposes to reflux into the esophagus, and disturbs the regular feedback relationship between hunger and satiety. The normal signals to begin eating and to cease eating go awry. The amounts of food taken in during binge episodes may be enormous, from 10,000 to 15,000 calories many times a day. The stomach reservoir is put under a great stress by the large amounts of food that are so quickly consumed that occasionally gastric rupture occurs (Evans 1968).

Fourth, preexisting illnesses, especially diabetes mellitus, may be worsened by the presence of concomitant eating disorders. Although anorexic patients do not appear to have problems with immune function in their lowered weight, some bacterial and mycotic infections may prosper more readily in starved patients, or treatment of them may become more difficult. The body is surprisingly resistant to starvation—especially when it takes place slowly—having multiple, overlapping means of compensation.

Fifth, medical testing is not always a benign process. A physician concerned about not missing Crohn's disease may, for example, carry out a barium enema and an upper GI test and add extensive metabolic and endocrine investigations instead of searching directly for the symptoms of eating disorders. These and other medical tests may delay the diagnosis of an eating disorder, may worsen GI symptoms, and may produce medical complications of their own.

Sixth, treatment of the eating disorder may cause complications. Treatments for the eating disorders are now based on a combination of common sense and empirical experience but few rigorously controlled comparison methods. Certain treatment methods such as hyperalimentation have an intrinsic high rate of complications (Pertschuk et al. 1981). Even the time-honored methods suggested by Gull (1874) of keeping patients warm and feeding them frequent small meals may have inevitable, even if not serious, medical complications. The rates of food intake, kinds of food prescribed, and other aspects of nutritional rehabilitation may each cause milder serious medical complications.

A seventh and less obvious source of medical complications is the physical abuse sometimes carried out by frustrated family members. A starving anorexic patient can tax the most patient and thoughtful family members. At times, jaws have been broken by patients being forced to eat against their will. Stomachs have been perforated by tubes inserted to force food down. Lasègue (1873) noted more than a century ago that patients gain a sense of control by not eating and that attempts at forcing them to eat generally do not work. In addition to scolding bulimic patients, parents may lock the kitchen, lock the cabinets, and physically attempt to prevent them from their binge-eating episodes. General physical abuse from irritability and exasperation, rather than simply forced feeding, may also occur and is perhaps symptomatic of family dysfunction and parental personality disorder.

Eight, a more subtle form of family-induced medical symptomatology has emerged with the occasional finding that former anorexic patients starve their children out of fear that they will become fat. Occasionally children have had to be put under court protection to escape the effects of continued food deprivation by an anorexic mother. Although not the most common cause of failure to thrive, physicians who are treating children with growth and weight retardation should at least think of the possibility that these children are being passively starved by parents who project their fear of weight gain.

Finally, behaviors associated with the frequently co-occurring DSM-III-R (American Psychiatric Association 1987) Axis I diagnoses (mood disorders or substance abuse) and Axis II diagnoses (impulsive personality features) confer additional medical symptoms. We have seen an increase in human immunodeficiency virus seropositivity among male bulimic patients, for example, whose sexuality was altered in the setting of manic and impulsive personality features.

Medical Complications of Anorexia Nervosa and Bulimia Nervosa

Anorexia Nervosa, Restricting Subtype

Table 5–2 summarizes some of the major medical complications of anorexia nervosa, restricting subtype. Gross (1982), Silverman (1983), and Mitchell (1984) have all provided excellent overviews of medical complications of anorexia nervosa. Most of the consequences of anorexia nervosa are compensatory efforts by the body to adjust to the diminished food intake. The body acts as if there were true starvation in the environment by cutting down on nonessential functions, minimizing loss of tissue and heat, and eventually decreasing, on a priority basis, even vital functions. Table 5–3 lists clues to undiagnosed anorexia nervosa. Even though severely starved patients are often obvious, the decreased weight loss requirement by DSM-III-R of 15% may make mild cases of anorexia nervosa not as evident.

Two recent areas of study may be of sufficient interest to highlight: GI symptoms and osteoporosis. The general theme of the GI consequences of uncomplicated food-restricting anorexia nervosa is that they may be subjectively very uncomfortable but generally improve with conservative treatment. In contrast, osteoporosis may have no subjective discomfort but may present a serious, less obvious, risk.

Patients admitted for anorexia nervosa, restricting subtype, often feel bloated and distended and complain bitterly when nutritional rehabilitation is carried out at a brisk pace. Unless they have preexisting GI

Table 5−2. Medical consequences of anorexia nervosa, restricting subtype

Vital signs	Bradycardia
	Hypotension
	Hypothermia
Central nervous system	Generalized atrophy of brain and occasionally regional atrophy
Cardiovascular	Peripheral (starvation) edema
	Decreased cardiac diameter
	Narrowed left ventricular wall
	Decreased response to exercise demand
	Pericardial effusion
	Superior mesenteric artery syndrome
Renal	Prerenal azotemia
Hematologic	Anemia of starvation
	Leukopenia
	Hypocellular bone marrow
Gastrointestinal	Delayed gastric emptying
	Gastric dilatation
	Decreased intestinal lipase and lactase
Metabolic	Hypercholesterolemia
	Elevated serum carotene
	Hypoglycemia
	Elevated liver enzymes
Endocrine	Low luteinizing hormone
	Low follicle stimulating hormone
	Low estrogen or testosterone
	Low normal thyroxine
	Low triiodothyronine
	Increased reverse triiodothyronine
	Elevated cortisol
	Elevated growth hormone
	Partial diabetes insipidus

disease, however, the subjective complaints improve substantially by simply persisting with nutritional rehabilitation, by giving much psychological support, and by occasional symptomatic relief through antacids and continued reassurance (Waldholtz and Andersen 1990). Slowed gas-

Table 5−3.　Clues to undiagnosed anorexia nervosa

1. Weight loss of unknown origin.
2. Failure to grow at a normal rate.
3. Unexplained primary or secondary amenorrhea.
4. Unexplained hypercholesterolemia or hypercarotenemia in a younger person.
5. Medical complications of exercise abuse.
6. Membership in a vulnerable population subgroup (ballet, modelling, wrestling, and jockeying).
7. Osteoporosis in a younger person.

tric emptying appears to be a consequence rather than a cause of anorexia nervosa (Domstad et al. 1987). As a result, gastric functioning returns to normal in association with return to and maintenance of a healthy weight.

Osteoporosis on the other hand may not be at all apparent in anorexic patients. Studies by Rigotti et al. (1984) have shown that anorexia nervosa may be associated with substantial decreases in bone mineral density or failure to increase in density as normally would happen with growth. As a result patients may have multiple fractures from such simple activities as turning over in bed or slipping and falling. Multiple mechanisms have been suggested for osteoporosis associated with anorexia nervosa (Biller et al. 1989), including, of course, decreased estrogen. Other mechanisms include the calcium mobilization consequences of the elevated cortisol levels associated with both weight loss and depressive illness, and perhaps abuse of diet sodas, in addition to an abnormal metabolic milieu. Estrogen deficit does not explain the osteoporosis found in some males with eating disorders, but this may be associated with lowered testosterone levels.

Case examples.　The following case examples illustrate the clinical aspects of anorexia nervosa, restricting subtype: a "public" (visible) eating disorder.

Case 1: The woman who liked to draw dogs — death by starvation

Ms. A, a 29-year-old single white woman, was admitted for treatment of anorexia nervosa of 6 years duration. She had no family history of psychiatric disorder, and her childhood was normal except for temper tantrums, fearfulness, and extreme reactions to separation. In personality, Ms. A was described by her family as being self-critical and perfectionist. Her anorexic behavior had begun when, at age 16, she started dieting (at 110 lb and 5'2"), losing her periods and reducing her weight to 90 lb. Her weight was restored to 115 lb within a year, however, and she did well in her business career and in her avocation of painting dogs. Six years before admission, Ms. A again began losing weight, this time requiring several hospitalizations until finally she was admitted to The Johns Hopkins Hospital weighing 55 lb. She dated the onset of the present illness to the loss of a favorite dog who was shot by accident. In addition to restricting food, she abused laxatives but did not binge.

On mental status examination, Ms. A had low mood without hallucinations or delusions. She had fear of fatness and distortion of body image, being worried that she might need to take off a few more pounds despite being intellectually concerned about her low weight. On physical examination, her pulse was 46, and her blood pressure was obtainable only by palpation. She had moderate plus pitting edemas in her feet. She had a grade 2 (out of 6) holosystolic murmur and an enlarged liver, and her muscle strength was symmetrically decreased. On laboratory examination, her glucose level was 50 mg/dl (normal = 70–115), her phosphate level was 2.7 mg/dl (normal = 3.0–4.5), and her total protein level was 4.9 g/dl (normal = 6.0–8.5), with elevated liver enzymes, anemia, and elevated cholesterol levels. Her diagnoses included anorexia nervosa, restricting subtype; major depressive illness; and borderline personality disorder.

After 6 months of treatment, Ms. A was discharged at 107 lb without any essential change in her pursuit of thinness or feeling out of control of life around her. She lacked a sense of adult identity and was referred for follow-up close to her home. She relapsed after leaving the hospital and 12 months later was found dead in her room severely emaciated. No autopsy was performed.

Case 2: The young man I didn't recognize on follow-up—successful outcome

Mr. B, a 22-year-old single white man, was referred for treatment of anorexia nervosa, restricting subtype, with a 5-year history of weight loss and five previous hospitalizations. Mr. B grew up in a family characterized by constant hostility between his highly educated parents. He was distant and rejecting of his father. Since childhood, Mr. B had been a sensitive, worried child, fearful of change in routines and becoming anxious when new people or new situations came into his life. At age 17, he realized he did not want to be like his father in any way; he especially did not want to have a large "spare tire." He began a program of intensive exercise and food restriction (at 130 lb, 5'8"). During his first hospitalization, in addition to being severely starved, he experienced a life-threatening pneumonia with a positive culture for staph.

At the time of admission to Johns Hopkins, Mr. B weighed 69.75 lb. On mental status examination, he was low in mood and low in self-esteem. He also had a prominent fear of fatness and distortion of body image, fearing he would become fat again, but conversely wanting to achieve the stereotyped male physique of a slim mesomorph instead of being a "puny runt." His initial hematocrit was 20% (normal = 41–53), with low serum iron levels. X rays revealed infiltrates in his right upper lobe and right apex with positive cultures for several species of bacteria as well as *Candida* and *Aspergillus*. In addition, his testosterone level was 188 ng/dl (normal = 575 ± 150), and his plasma cortisol level was elevated. During treatment over 9 months, Mr. B almost doubled his weight, returned to an almost normal hematocrit, recovered from his pneumonia, and showed significant improvement in his psychosocial and psychosexual maturity as well as a decrease in his of fear of fatness. At the time of discharge, however, he still appeared very vulnerable psychologically and had unresolved family issues.

Approximately 2 years later, I was told that a former patient in the waiting room wished to see me. When I went out to greet this person, I saw no one I recognized and returned to my office. My secretary knocked on the door a minute later and said that Mr. B was still waiting for me. When I went out a second time, Mr. B introduced himself, saying his friends often did not recognize him either. In the interim, something had happened to make treatment "stick." He had begun a program of personal fitness, developing the classical, mesomorphic V shape of a weight lifter and increasing his weight to about 150 lb. Despite his return to relatively normal weight, he continued to have low testosterone levels, which had been treated by an endocrinologist with appropriate, not abusive, amounts of testosterone. He was holding a part-time job and going to school.

Comments.   At the depth of their illness, and at discharge, it was not possible to tell which of these chronically and severely ill patients would do well and which would do poorly. They both were medically and psychiatrically very ill. These cases point to the need for persistence in treatment, rehospitalization when necessary, and close follow-up. They mirror in a way the reports of Morton's first two cases (1694).

Bulimia Nervosa

The medical complications of bulimia nervosa include both the systemic affects of hypokalemia on heart, kidney, brain, and muscles and the local GI complications of binge and purge behaviors. In addition to the hypokalemia, other metabolic consequences may include alkalosis, acidosis, and hypochloremia (Table 5–4). Some clues to undiagnosed signs and symptoms of bulimia nervosa are listed in Table 5–5.

Case examples. The following case reports illustrate the clinical aspects of bulimia nervosa: the "private" eating disorder.

Case 3: The woman who dared her electrolytes to go lower

Ms. C was a 37-year-old divorced white woman, who was referred for treatment of bulimia nervosa of 17 years duration. She was always "daddy's girl" but had an up-and-down relationship with him. She consistently felt her privacy invaded by her perfectionist

Table 5–4. Medical complications of bulimia nervosa

Metabolic	Hypokalemic alkalosis or acidosis Hypochloremia Dehydration
Renal	Prerenal azotemia Acute and chronic renal failure
Central nervous system	Seizures Abnormal electroencephalogram
Cardiac	Arrhythmias Myocardial toxicity from emetine (Ipecac)
Dental	Lingual surface enamel loss Multiple caries
Gastrointestinal	Swollen parotid glands Elevated serum amylase levels Gastric distention Irritable bowel syndrome Melanosis coli from laxative abuse
Musculoskeletal	Cramps Tetany

Table 5 – 5. Signs and symptoms of secretive bulimia nervosa

1. Hypokalemia of unknown cause or complications of hypokalemia (cardiac, renal, and central nervous system).
2. Parotid gland or submandibular gland enlargement; esophagitis; esophageal bleeding or rupture.
3. Large unexplained weight fluctuations or weight loss.
4. Unexplained elevations of serum amylase levels.
5. Unexplained secondary amenorrhea.
6. Extensive loss of dental enamel or onset of many new caries.
7. Scars on the knuckles of the hand from induced vomiting.
8. Presence of juvenile diabetes mellitus.
9. Other disorders of impulse control (alcoholism, drug abuse, and borderline personality disorder).
10. Membership in predisposed vocational groups (modelling, ballet, wrestling, and jockeying).

mother. She was active in sports and went on to a graduate degree in marketing. Her marriage ended without children. Her personal habits included impulsive and excessive use of coffee, having 10 or more cups a day, as well as alcohol, at least six drinks a night. She began dieting (at 133 lb, 5'6") 17 years before admission and reached a low weight of 95 lb. Her weight was restored to a normal range but without alteration in the binge-purge behavior she began during her anorexic phase.

Although intellectually recognizing the danger of self-induced vomiting, Ms. C felt a "high" or thrill when she was told that her potassium was falling to dangerously low levels. She experienced an almost exhilarated feeling that alleviated her low mood when her potassium level got closer and closer to 2.0 mEq/L, finally achieving a level of 1.9 mEq/L (normal = 3.5–5.0). In the other areas of her life she felt ineffective, for example, in not setting boundaries on her mother's intrusions and in not obtaining relief from her own perfectionist standards at work. She focused instead on gaining exquisite control over her lowered potassium levels.

On mental status examination, Ms. C was alert, highly educated, and intellectualized, with a low mood and great ambivalence in giving up her binge-purge behavior. Her diagnoses included bulimia nervosa with a history of anorexia nervosa, major depressive illness, and personality disorder with mixed features from Cluster B (histrionic and borderline traits) and Cluster C (obsessional, sensitive, and perfectionist traits). She expressed disappoinment when told that her admission potassium level was normal, having been restored by outpatient potassium supplements; however, her thyrotropin level was elevated, and her bone mineral density was decreased at 0.97 g/cm^2 (normal = 1.20).

Treatment included desipramine (supplemented with thyroxine and augmented with lithium) and GI consultation for her esophageal reflux. Prolixin 1 mg bid brought further improvement in mood, while ranitidine decreased her reflux. Psychotherapy included helping her recognize her sense of ineffectiveness in critical areas of her life and the false sense of control and thrill that came from dangerous behaviors leading to low potassium levels. She was able to set boundaries on her mother's intrusiveness, develop a less perfectionist attitude toward her marketing job, and practice inhibiting her own impulsive behaviors.

Case 4: The woman hospitalized for an ulcer

Ms. D was a 22-year-old white woman admitted to the eating disorders service on transfer from internal medicine. Since childhood she had been characterized by having temper tantrums, violence against her younger sister whom she thought never should have been born, repeated attempts at self-harm through head banging and self-cutting, and other dramatic behaviors. She began dieting 7 years before admission (at 110 lb, 5'3") leading to a lowest weight of 90 lb associated with loss of periods. Gradually, Ms. D began to experience binges, followed by self-induced vomiting. Her weight increased gradually to 210 lb.

Ms. D's personal physician, unaware of the self-induced vomiting, which he did not inquire about and which she did not reveal, was not able to diagnose the source of her hematemesis, but evaluated her repeatedly for medical causes of vomiting blood. Finally, she was admitted to the medical service of The Johns Hopkins Hospital where gastroscopy noted tears in the lining of her stomach and the presence of esophagitis. When she did not respond to medical treatments, psychiatric consultation was requested. Psychiatric history and mental status examination confirmed bulimia nervosa.

In treatment on the eating disorders service, she was able to interrupt the binge-purge behavior but continued to cut her arms, requiring a total of three hospitalizations before this behavior was redirected into help seeking and relaxation. No acid-inhibiting or prokinetic agents were needed once her binge-purge behavior was interrupted.

Comments. At normal weights, patients with bulimia nervosa often suffer from "private" medical symptoms that may not be at all obvious. They may present to other specialists with medical complications. Unexplained low potassium levels or hematemesis in a younger patient should prompt an inquiry into the possible presence of an eating disorder.

Anorexia Nervosa, Bulimic Subtype

Anorexia nervosa, bulimic subtype, combines the medical consequences of starvation with the complications of both binge behavior and a variety of purging activities. These patients appear to suffer the most in terms of both medical symptoms and psychiatric symptoms (Mickalide and Andersen 1985), having neither the ego-syntonic benefits of food restriction (see *Golden Cage: The Enigma of Anorexia Nervosa* by Bruch [1978]) nor the rather private and almost normal appearing function of bulimia nervosa patients.

Case examples. These case examples illustrate the complications of anorexia nervosa, bulimic subtype: the worst of both worlds.

Case 5: The rabbinical student who ate late

Mr. E was a 35-year-old single white student at a seminary admitted at Johns Hopkins for treatment of low weight and binge-purge behavior. In contrast to his successful siblings, Mr. E had, since childhood, been a distant, suspicious person who struggled with compulsive urges that made him feel spiritually guilty. He struggled against allowing himself to have sexual thoughts by developing a variety of rituals. His increased interest in religious studies led him to take several trips to Israel and finally to study religion. His illness began 12 years before admission when he developed ascetic ideas that eating more than a very limited amount of food was wrong. Subsequent food restriction lowered his weight from 135 to 99 lb. He would resist eating breakfast or lunch and finally late in the evening give in to the overwhelming urge to eat, having a large binge episode that included eating food from garbage cans. His feeling of having lost control and given in to his "lower" instincts made him feel guilty and accentuated his depressive symptoms.

On admission, Mr. E was thin and anguished and wore a yarmulke, being fearful of revealing his symptoms to others. His mood was low but he described "ecstatic feelings" that occurred from time to time. He was suspicious that people around him would take away his religious faith and felt he would be punished for eating sweets. On medical examination, he had substantially lowered bone mineral density at L2 to L4 of 0.901 g/cm^2 (normal = 1.20). His white blood cell count, hematocrit, and triiodothyronine levels were lowered, his cholesterol level was elevated, and his testosterone level was low at 189 ng/dl. Diagnoses included anorexia nervosa, bulimic subtype; major depressive illness; and mixed personality disorder, having obsessional and schizoid features. Treatment included imipramine, lithium, fluphenazine hydrochloride, levothyroxine sodium, and calcium. At the time of discharge, Mr. E's weight had increased to a normal range and his mood had improved, but he was left with a quality of suspiciousness and a tendency toward asceticism and spiritualization of psychological issues.

Case 6: The saddest woman you ever saw

Ms. F, a 35-year-old divorced white woman, was referred for treatment of 18 years of anorexia nervosa with bulimic features. She had a family history of depressive illness and panic disorder. She had been preoccupied with weight since age 13 and had been amenorrheic since 18. A brief marriage ended in divorce. She had been ill with an eating disorder more than half of her life, falling as low as 59 lb and being admitted at 63 lb. Her hospitalizations were too numerous to count. Binge-purge behavior was frequent and severe.

On admission Ms. F was sad, cachectic, and frail, appearing apathetic and hopeless and stating she was too tired to even binge any more. Her mood was low, her speech was soft, and the content of her thought was self-critical. She felt fat at 63 lb and could not imagine life without her anorexic symptoms. She had chronic, severe GI symptoms, including abdominal distention, impaction, and persistent gastroesophageal reflux. On medical examination, she had anemia, severe osteoporosis, hypothyroidism, peripheral acrocyanosis, and an abnormal electrocardiogram, as well as hemoconcentration from dehydration.

Medical treatment involved coordination of teams of specialists from many medical services. The initial 1,200 calories a day that Ms. F could tolerate were gradually increased to 3,500 with a constant struggle to keep her GI symptoms under control. Omeprazole, despite its unknown effects for long-term use, finally helped with her reflux, while an intensive bowel regimen of psyllium hydrophilic mucilloid, docusate sodium, occasional prescribed enemas, high fiber diet, moderate amount of liquids, and a bowel retraining schedule finally allowed her to have normal bowel movements for the week before discharge after her 4-month admission. Correction of hypothyroidism led to increased energy and decreased symptoms of hypothermia. Her severe osteoporosis was treated with hormone replacement and calcium supplementation. Even at the time of discharge she had a sense of helplessness and ineffectiveness in living a life as an adult and looked forward to going home to be taken care of by her mother who had already announced that she could not take care of the patient any longer.

Comments.   Patients with anorexia nervosa, bulimic subtype, bear the twin burdens of lowered weight as well as the effects of binges, self-induced vomiting, and laxative or diuretic abuse. They have little pride or comfort from their illness yet often hesitate to give it up.

An Approach to Medical Evaluation

Medical evaluation may be best approached by outlining a series of principles to guide the clinician and a number of practice implications.

Principles for Evaluation

There are three primary principles guiding the medical evaluation of eating-disordered patients:

1. Avoid a "rule-out" approach to diagnosis. Eating disorders are positively diagnosed by psychiatric history and mental status examination. Although seldom done this way in the psychiatric community, medical colleagues may still use an extensive series of tests to rule out all possible medical causes of symptomatology before considering referral for possible anorexia nervosa or bulimia nervosa.
2. In place of the rule-out approach, perform medical evaluation to document the severity and multiplicity of medical abnormalities in a patient with an eating disorder, including the degree of starvation, the medical consequences of binge-purge behavior, and possible hidden additional contributions to patient symptomatology from preexisting or incidental illness.
3. Be aware of the iatrogenic potential of both medical evaluation and treatment.

Practice Guideline for Evaluation

There are three important practice implications of the medical evaluation for eating-disordered patients that grow out of the principles above:

1. Obtain a complete psychiatric and medical history of the present illness, and past illnesses, with an emphasis on understanding the medical symptomatology in relationship to the course and development of the eating disorders.
2. Perform the mental status examination to confirm the pathognomonic features of the eating disorders; to evaluate cognitive consequences of the illness, such as mental confusion and altered attention or concentration; and to identify comorbid psychiatric conditions.
3. On physical examination note especially alterations in vital signs, the overall degree of emaciation, clues to unsuspected purging, degree of dehydration, physical strength, signs of nutritionally based impairment of the nervous system, dental hygiene, cardiac size and functioning, abdominal tenderness, presence of lanugo hair, and signs of hypercarotenemia and hypercholesterolemia. Furthermore, the occult signs and symptoms of bulimic behavior mentioned above may also be noted.

Some suggested laboratory studies are outlined in Table 5–6. These of course need to be individualized according to patient history and medical symptomatology. Dual photon absorptiometry is appropriate, for example, for female patients with more than 6 months of amenorrhea or chronic emaciation, but would not be necessary for a bulimic patient without a previous anorexic episode or amenorrhea. Likewise, GI tests may be indicated if there is preexisting GI disease or symptoms that are unresponsive to refeeding programs, such as continued reflux with esophagitis.

Medical Aspects of Treatment

The twin pillars of treatment are the ancient guideline of "above all do no harm," and the Food and Drug Administration requirement for safety and efficacy. Here again, some balance between principles and practice implications may be of use.

Table 5–6 . Laboratory studies for evaluation of eating disorders

Routine
  Complete blood count
  Electrolytes, glucose, and renal function tests
  Chemistry panel
    Liver function tests
    Total protein and albumin
    Calcium
    Amylase
  Hormones
    Thyroid function tests
    A.M. plasma cortisol
    Luteinizing hormone
    Follicle stimulating hormone
    Estrogen (females)
    Testosterone (males)
  Chest X ray
  Electrocardiogram
  Dual photon absorptiometry (if amenorrheic or emaciated)

Selected
  Magnetic resonance imaging for brain atrophy
  Abdominal X rays for severe bloating
  Lower esophageal sphincter pressure studies for reflux
  Lactose deficiency tests for dairy intolerance
  Total bowel transit time for severe constipation

Principles

The principles of treatment for eating-disordered patients are essentially the answers to six questions:

1. *Where should the patient be treated?*   For inpatients this depends on the hospital. In most university hospitals, treatment takes place on specialized eating disorder units, usually in the department of psychiatry. Many times in community hospitals, treatment of younger patients will take place on a pediatric unit in conjunction with psychiatric consultants. The important thing is that there be a standard evaluation routine and a thorough approach to detection of medical complications of illness and prevention of problems in refeeding.

2. *Who should treat the patient?* The medical aspects of treatment can be routinely done by a qualified psychiatrist or psychiatric resident using medical consultation as appropriate for more difficult patients. Even the fairly emaciated, classically starved anorexic patient can do well with no substantial medical complications when treatment is accomplished thoughtfully and the patient adapts well to it. In other contexts, where treatment is by psychologists, for example, or when the psychiatrist works in a pediatric unit as a consultant, medical specialists in internal medical or pediatrics will deal with the majority of medical aspects of treatment. For outpatients, most eating-disordered patients will be referred to a pediatrician, internist, or family practitioner for medical evaluation and care.

3. *How fast should treatment proceed?* In this day of tremendous pressure from third-party payers, not all of it ethical or humanely based, there may be a sense of urgency to speed of treatment beyond prudence or there may be a total lack of insurance coverage. An older, leisurely approach, in which uncovering, psychodynamic psychotherapy took place before nutritional rehabilitation is certainly not appropriate, but neither is the other extreme. Progress can only be made as fast as it can reasonably be accomplished within the physiological state of and with concern for the safety of the patient. At The Johns Hopkins Hospital, we restore weight at a rate of 2.5–3.5 lb/week, averaging approximately 3 lb. Hyperalimentation presents a temptation to accomplish weight restoration quickly but the result is usually metabolic imbalance and an excess of water weight, with a "false" weight increase from water gain.

4. *Which is better for the patient, packaged treatment programs or essential understanding?* The medical aspects of care and treatment of eating-disordered patients should come out of a deep and thorough appreciation of the altered physiology and psychology of starvation, binge-purge behavior, and other causes of the existing medical symptomatology. Although a certain degree of routine can be developed, an appreciation for individual differences needs to be kept in mind. Most medical problems can be anticipated and prevented rather than dealt with on an emergent basis. "Packaged" approaches in "franchised" eating disorders programs are not always adequate.

5. *What physical complications might a patient develop?* A prudent and preventive approach is to maintain a high index of suspicion for the development of certain serious problems such as gastric dilatation or

pulmonary edema (Mitchell et al. 1982; Saul et al. 1981) or common, less serious problems such as pedal edema.

6. *How long should treatment take?*   Although acute inpatient treatment of anorexia nevorsa requires 6–12 weeks (3–6 weeks for bulimia nervosa), it should be remembered that on average normal functioning of organs may not take place until 3–6 months after normal weight has been attained. There is a pseudonormality that results from restoration of healthy body weight that should not be confused with return to normal functioning of body systems.

Practice

Finally, there are four important practice guidelines to the treatment of eating-disordered patients:

1. Bear in mind that the goals and methods of weight restoration are not uniformly agreed on. Differences exist about how to restore weight and to what point weight should be restored. No existing studies have strictly compared programs that use nutritional supplements, for example, versus "normal food" eaten normally. The essentials of nutritional rehabilitation are to use nutritional methods appropriate to the very starved patient or the patient with metabolic problems from bulimia nervosa. Excessively rapid changes in any physiological parameter may lead to iatrogenic medical symptomatology. For example, very rapid correction of hyponatremia may lead to central pontine myelinosis (Copeland 1989). Varying guidelines exist for the weight range to which patients who are underweight should be restored. Reasonable guidelines to setting a goal range include the patient's pre-illness weight, if it was not in an abnormal range; the Metropolitan Height and Weight Tables (Metropolitan Life Insurance Company 1983) with appropriate corrections for age; and the point on nomograms by Frisch and McArthur (1974) where a patient would have an approximately 50% chance of restoring menstrual periods if female and return to normal testosterone levels if male (Andersen et al. 1982).

2. Interrupt and correct medical complications of purging behavior. This usually involves obtaining values for serum electrolytes and correcting deficiencies with potassium supplements. Because body potassium stores may be depleted, there should be sufficient time for equilibration such that true total body potassium levels are restored to normal.

Dehydration from purging may present with false-normal lab values that diminish to a subnormal range with rehydration.
3. Have a plan to deal with the subjective but generally not as serious GI complications and with the less obvious and long-range problem of osteoporosis. GI symptoms as noted above generally respond to support, reassurance, and symptomatic relief. Although osteoporosis in theory can be treated in younger people with return of hormones or replacement plus calcium supplementation, this practice is not as easily accomplished as it may appear. Starved patients may not be willing to have their weight restored to the point where they have natural return of menses. In addition, some patients object if hormone replacement is done pharmacologically, and others may be avoidant about sexual and menstrual issues in general and wish not to have periods at all.
4. When in doubt, work closely with a medical consultant.

Common Complications of Treatment and Some Suggested Approaches

Edema: Peripheral and Central

Peripheral edema is generally a common and easily treated problem both in the starvation process and secondary to the refeeding of anorexia nervosa. Central edema is, in contrast, a serious problem to be avoided as much as possible with prudent refeeding and attention to cardiac overload. Peripheral edema generally responds to elevation of feet, moderation of calorie intake, and decrease in salt in the diet. In my experience, diuretics are rarely helpful or necessary for peripheral edema and may set up the patient for a round of rebound edema after excessive weight loss.

Gastric Dilatation

Gastric dilatation has been reported as a serious and potentially fatal problem of refeeding patients. At Johns Hopkins we have seen only one case of gastric dilatation among our 650 eating-disordered inpatients. When it happens, the stomach needs to be evacuated, and the patient should be maintained on intravenous fluids with gradual restoration of oral feedings.

Case examples.   The following case reports illustrate the course of medical symptomatology during inpatient treatment.

Case 7: The 47-pound patient who did well

Ms. G was a 37-year-old woman who weighed only 10 lb more than her age when she was admitted for treatment of anorexia nervosa of 20 years duration. She had no family history of psychiatric disorder. Her parents had noted that since childhood she had been an extremist, exercising excessively and being self-critical. At age 16 (at 105 lb, 5'3") she began dieting after a romantic disappointment, and her weight decreased to 46 lb. She was entirely food restricting without binge-purge behavior or abuse of medications to lose weight. Despite her low weight she kept a generally cheerful attitude, going to work and dressing herself in many layers of clothing.

On mental status examination, Ms. G had an exuberant, brisk, lively mood with normal speech saying "I'm going to die within 2 weeks, but I don't want to gain weight." She could not imagine life without anorexia nervosa but did consent to treatment. No bed was available when she came for consultation, but she was asked not to leave the hospital and instead was admitted to the medical service until a place could be found on the eating disorders service. Her initial care was focused on medical stabilization. Following the century-old advice of Sir William Gull (1874), she was given frequent small meals and kept warm. She frightened other starved, classically ill anorexic patients with her extreme degree of emaciation.

Many of her lab studies were normal, but her 8 A.M. cortisol level was elevated at 27 µg/dl (normal = 6–16), her estradiol level was low at 16 pg/ml, and her bone mineral density was extremely lowered. No hyperalimentation was needed. Initial food intake was low in fats, milk products, and salt. She was kept on 24-hour nursing observation. She was able to be increased gradually to 3,500 calories a day of food intake and approximately doubled her admitting weight without developing any significant medical crises. Hormone replacement was started for her osteoporosis. Weight restoration took place at a rate of 3 lb a week.

Case 8: The tall blond woman with a shrinking brain and swelling legs and medical complications of refeeding

Ms. H was a joyless 32-year-old white woman admitted for treatment of 14 years of food restriction with resulting severe emaciation. During her illness, she lost approximately 100 lb, remaining for several years at 80 lb (at 5'10"). She had several brief hospitalizations but refused definitive treatment on the eating disorders service until her family confronted her and insisted on treatment. She had prominent acrocyanosis. In addition to emaciation, Ms. H suffered severe osteoporosis with numerous rib fractures. She showed diffuse cerebral atrophy on a magnetic resonance imaging (MRI) scan, as well as atrophy of the left temporal lobe tip. On MRI she had prominent ventricles, sulci, and cisterns, with prominent cerebrospinal fluid space over the left temporal lobe tip but without abnormal masses or signals.

Ms. H adopted her refeeding program as enthusiastically as she had practiced her regimen of self-starvation. Although the staff was initially pleased with her weight restoration, she began to take in large quantities of extra water and gained 12 lb in a week. She developed severe edema in her feet, legs, and thighs, which responded to conservative management of no added salt, restriction of fluid intake, decrease of calories to 3,000 a day instead of 4,000, and elevation of her feet whenever she was not walking to prescribed activities. Her case was managed without use of diuretics. Ms. H left the hospital at 120 lb, still short of her full goal range, but approximately 35 lb heavier than on admission.

Comments. The effects of anorexia-related brain shrinkage on long-term outcome have not been assessed. Documentation of return to normal structure and function of the brain after weight restoration would be helpful but is lacking at present.

Summary

Eating disorders in their acute state may be as much a medical problem as a psychiatric problem. As medical issues are brought under control, the psychiatrist is free to focus on the essential and central psychopathology leading to these medical complications: the twin motifs of pursuit of thinness and fear of fatness, along with the perceptual distortion and overvalued ideas concerning the putative benefits of weight loss.

In his long-term follow-up, Theander found (1983) that anorexic patients have an approximately 18% earlier than expected death rate, half of it from medical complications and about half from suicide. For the anorexic patient, death is usually by starvation, whereas for the bulimic patient, it may occur from some combination of electrolyte abnormality and abnormal weight, when not from suicide.

Not much has been said about the bulimic patient who is overweight before treatment and has an actual, not only a feared, tendency to weight gain. Kaye et al. (1986) noted that bulimic patients may take many fewer calories to gain a pound or to maintain their weight then anorexic patients. Overweight bulimic patients may need treatment for any aspect of actual obesity, and their target weight probably should be in the upper part of the normal range rather then the lower part of the normal range, as might be appropriate with anorexic patients.

Eating-disordered patients present with extremes in human physiology that researchers would not be allowed to induce on an experimental basis. Each case of an eating disorder presents an illustration of the body's enormous capacity to defend itself against decreased caloric availability or alteration of fluid and electrolytes. Although the body's efforts are heroic and often do sustain the patient through their abusive behaviors, there are limits that can be exceeded.

An appreciation of the medical aspects of eating disorders is vital to the care and treatment of these patients. When effective methods are developed to evaluate the kind and degree of medical consequences and when complications for treatment are avoided as much as possible and treated where inevitably present, then the psychiatrist and psychologist can get to work on the central issues of these disorders and persuade patients to think and act in a healthier way in a society preoccupied with weight loss as a dubious means to an often poorly defined end. The respect of a patient for the clinician may depend on effective management of medical symptoms.

Keeping up-to-date with clinical and research studies on the medical aspects of the eating disorders and their treatment will allow the clinician to give the best overall care, whether delivered by the psychiatrist alone or in conjunction with a medically sophisticated consultant team, as is more often the case today. Until a more fundamental understanding of the etiology and mechanism of the eating disorders is achieved, treatment remains essentially pragmatic, but potentially lifesaving, based on experience with large numbers of patients. Mortality appears to have been substantially decreased in recent decades. Good medical care is a vital means to achieving psychiatric and behavioral stability in a weight-preoccupied society.

References

American Psychiatric Association: Diagnostic and Statistical Manual of Mental Disorders, 3rd Edition, Revised. Washington, DC, American Psychiatric Association, 1987

Andersen AE, Wirth JB, Strahlman ER: Reversible weight-related increase in plasma testosterone during treatment of male and female patients with anorexia nervosa. International Journal of Eating Disorders 1:74–83, 1982

Biller BMK, Saxe V, Herzog DB, et al: Mechanisms of osteoporosis in adult and adolescent women with anorexia nervosa. J Clin Endocrinol Metab 68:548–554, 1989

Bruch H: The Golden Cage: The Enigma of Anorexia Nervosa. Cambridge, MA, Harvard University Press, 1978

Copeland PM: Diuretic abuse and central pontine myelinolysis. Psychother Psychosom 52:101–105, 1989

Domstad PA, Shih WJ, Humphries L, et al: Radionuclide gastric emptying studies in patients with anorexia nervosa. J Nucl Med 28:816–819, 1987

Evans PS: Acute dilatation and spontaneous rupture of the stomach. Br J Surg 55:940–942, 1968

Frisch RE, McArthur JW: Menstrual cycles: fatness as a determinant of minimum weight for height necessary for their maintenance or onset. Science 185:949–951, 1974

Gross M (ed): Anorexia Nervosa. Lexington, MA, Collamore Press, 1982

Gull WW: Anorexia nervosa. Transactions of the Clinical Society of London 7:22–28, 1874

Kaye WH, Gwirtsman HE, Obarzanek E, et al: Caloric intake necessary for weight maintenance in anorexia nervosa: nonbulimics require greater caloric intake than bulimics. Am J Clin Nutr 44:435–443, 1986

Keys A, Brozek J, Henschel A, et al: The Biology of Human Starvation, Vol II. Minneapolis, MN, University of Minnesota Press, 1950

Lasègue C: L'anorexia hystérique. Archives Générales de Médicine 2:367, 1873

Metropolitan Life Insurance Company: Metropolitan Height and Weight Tables. New York, Metropolitan Life Insurance Company, 1983

Mickalide AD, Andersen AE: Subgroups of anorexia nervosa and bulimia: validity and utility. J Psychiatr Res 19:121–128, 1985

Mitchell JE: Medical complications of anorexia nervosa and bulimia. Psychiatr Med 1:229–255, 1984

Mitchell JE, Pyle RL, Miner RA: Gastric dilatation as a complication of bulimia. Psychosomatics 23:96–97, 1982

Mitchell JE, Seim HC, Colon E, et al: Medical complications and medical management of bulimia. Ann Intern Med 107:71–77, 1987

Morton R: Phthisiologica: Or a Treatise of Consumptions. London, Smith & Walford, 1694

Pertschuk MJ, Forster J, Buzby G, et al: The treatment of anorexia nervosa with total parenteral nutrition. Biol Psychiatry 16:539–550, 1981

Rigotti NA, Nussbaum SR, Herzog PS, et al: Osteoporosis in women with anorexia nervosa. N Engl J Med 311:1601–1606, 1984

Russell GFM: Bulimia nervosa: an ominous variant of anorexia nervosa. Psychol Med 9:429–448, 1979

Saul SH, Dekker A, Watson CG: Acute gastric dilatation with infarction and perforation. Gut 22:978–983, 1981

Silverman JA: Anorexia nervosa: clinical and metabolic observations. International Journal of Eating Disorders 2:159–167, 1983

Theander S: Research on outcome and prognosis of anorexia nervosa, and some results from a Swedish long-term study. International Journal of Eating Disorders 2:167–174, 1983

Waldholtz BD, Andersen AE: Gastrointestinal symptoms in anorexia nervosa: a prospective study. Gastroenterology 98:1415–1419, 1990

Chapter 6

Laxative and Emetic Abuse in Bulimia Nervosa

Harry E. Gwirtsman, M.D.

*C*athartics have had a long tradition as an established treatment for the relief of mental and physical illnesses. Purgation calendars figure amongst the earliest medical literature, dating back to Maimonides in the 12th century. Although the ritual of purgation has largely disappeared, guilt concerning irregular bowel habits tends to persist (Cooke 1981). The refined, fiber-depleted diet of the Western world is, as Morris and Turnberg (1979) stated, "a prime factor in leaving civilized man with his hard, infrequent, and puny stool" (p. 780). This chapter provides a general discussion of laxative abuse, with a focus on this syndrome among eating-disordered patients, and the ensuing complications, as well as some proposed therapies. Abuse of emetics, especially syrup of ipecac, is also discussed.

Demographics

The use and abuse of laxatives is extremely common in the general population. It is estimated that 15–20% of Americans use laxatives sporadically or chronically (Binder 1988), and among persons aged 60 years and older, approximately one-third consume laxatives regularly (Shaffer and Turnberg 1983). A 1985 survey (Moriarty and Silk 1988) estimated that 400–500 million dollars is spent on laxatives yearly. Looked at another way, 1–2% of all prescriptions are written for laxatives. (This, of course, does not include the purchase of over-the-counter drugs, which probably represents a much higher expenditure.) Furthermore, an estimated one-fourth of all patients presenting in general practice offices use laxatives (Moriarty and Silk 1988), and laxative abuse may be part of the underlying problem for nearly one-fourth of all patients referred to gastroenterologists for chronic diarrhea (Binder 1988).

Among teenagers, the frequency of purging behaviors and diet pill use has been estimated to be between 5% and 7%. In a survey of 1,728 15-year-olds, 0.5%–2% used laxatives at least weekly (Killen et al. 1986). Additionally, the researchers found that the prevalence rates among males and females were approximately equal, in contradistinction to the prevalence rates seen for the abuse of diuretics, diet pills, or purgation by vomiting, where females outnumbered males by more than 2 to 1. The reported prevalence rates of laxative use and abuse among surveyed high school students range from 3.5 to 7% (Crowther et al. 1985; Killen et al. 1986; Lachenmeyer et al. 1988), with approximately equal rates for males and females. However, one study (Lachenmeyer et al. 1988) reported that teenagers of upper-middle class socioeconomic status had laxative use and abuse rates double those of teenagers in lower socioeconomic strata.

The prevalence of laxative use and abuse among patients with bulimia nervosa is higher than that seen in the general population. In a study by Mitchell et al. (1985), it was estimated that 61% of 275 bulimic women had abused laxatives at some time during the course of their illness. Furthermore, 10% admitted to using laxatives once daily, and another 10% were using them several times a day. Altogether, 40% of the patients in this sample were using laxatives at least several times a week, an extraordinarily high percentage. In a follow-up of a cohort of these patients, Mitchell estimated that the prevalence of laxative abuse was even higher (J. E. Mitchell, December 1989, personal communication).

The reported prevalence rates of laxative use and abuse among patients with bulimia nervosa varies from 38 to 75%, with 20–45% of bulimic patients admitting to daily abuse and approximately 15% abusing laxatives several times daily (Fairburn and Cooper 1984; Mitchell and Boutacoff 1986; Mitchell et al. 1985, 1988).

In general, bulimic patients who abuse laxatives tend to be older and to have had a greater chronicity of binge eating. One study (Fairburn and Cooper 1984) that compared patients who vomited only with laxative-abusing bulimic patients found no increased incidence of anorexia nervosa among the laxative-abusing patients. However, Mitchell et al. (1990) noted that, among bulimic patients, those with a history of anorexia nervosa were much more likely to purge by means of laxative abuse than by vomiting.

It should be noted that, although there are estimates that more than half of the patients who abuse laxatives have some other type of eating disorder, approximately 45% have no other coexisting eating disorder (Lachenmeyer et al. 1988). Thus many laxative-abusing patients never come to the attention of psychiatrists, and numerous studies in the gastroenterology literature have been published relating to this subgroup of patients.

Classification of Laxative Agents

It is useful to review the various types of laxatives and their mechanisms of action. Many of these are listed in Table 6–1.

Bulk agents. The so-called bulk agents act by causing an increased fecal mass, either due to their intrinsic fiber content, or via a hydrophilic action, which promotes fluid retention in the lumen of the gut. This increased fecal mass promotes peristalsis and increases motility (Pietrusko 1977). Examples of bulk agents include dietary fiber, wheat bran, and psyllium seed, which is the principal ingredient in agents such as Metamucil and Konsyl.

Stimulant agents. The stimulant agents consist of compounds containing phenolphthalein, the principle ingredient of Correctol and Ex-Lax; bisacodyl, which is found in Dulcolax; and the anthraquinones, which include senna (contained in Senokot) and cascara sagrada. It is less well known that aloe is an anthraquinone and is the principle ingredient found in Carter's Little Pills (Cooke 1981; Pietrusko 1977). Laxative-abusing inpatients have been known to ingest aloe-containing shampoos, if commercial laxatives were not available, to take advantage of their colonic-stimulating properties.

It was originally thought that the stimulant agents had a direct action on the intestinal musculature, and this may in fact be one of their mechanisms of action. However, it is now well accepted that the common mode of action of these laxatives is to cause secretion of water and electrolytes by the colonic mucosa. This, in turn, stimulates peristalsis, and creates a large-volume watery diarrhea (Pietrusko 1977). It should be noted that many so-called stool softeners, such as dioctyl sodium sulfosuccinate (DOSS), also act by the same mechanism as the stimulant agents and may have the same side effects when abused in large quanti-

Table 6–1. Classification of laxatives

Bulk agents
  Dietary fiber
  Wheat bran
  Methylcellulose (Celevac, Serutan)
  Mucilaginous seeds, such as psyllium seeds, (Metamucil, Konsyl)
  Mechanism: Increased fecal mass due to fiber or to fluid retention.

Stimulant agents (most commonly abused)
  Diphenylmethane derivatives
    Phenolphthalein (Correctol, Ex-Lax, Feen-A-Mint)
    Bisacodyl (Dulcolax)
  Anthraquinones
    Senna (Senokot, x-prep)
    Cascara sagrada
    Danthron (Dorbane, Doxidan, Modane)
    Aloe (Carter's Little Pills, aloe-containing shampoo)
  Dioctyl sodium sulfosuccinate (Colace, Peri-Colace, Doxinate)
  Mechanisms: Stimulate water and electrolyte secretion from colonic
                  mucosa.
                  May cause stimulation of intestinal musculature.

Osmotic agents (most commonly used)
  Magnesium salts (Haley's M-O, Milk of Magnesia, Magnesium Citrate)
  Phosphate salts (Vacuetts, Fleet Enema, Fleet Phospho-Soda)
  Lactulose (Chronulac)
  Mechanisms: Hypertonic salts absorb isotonic fluid into gut lumen,
                  stimulating peristalsis.
                  Stimulate cholecystokinin (CCK) release, which increases
                  motility and inhibits fluid and electrolyte reabsorption
                  from small bowel.
                  Gut bacteria metabolize undigestible sugar→ decreased
                  colonic pH. Increased colonic osmolality due to short
                  chain fatty acid production by gut bacteria.

---

ties (Cooke 1981). All stimulant agents are absorbed through the colonic mucosa and can be detected in the blood and urine as well as in the stool. These agents are discussed in more detail later in this chapter.

As mentioned, the stimulant agents are the most commonly abused laxatives. In a study by Mitchell et al. (1988) it was estimated that Correctol was the most frequently abused laxative among bulimic patients, followed closely by Ex-Lax, Feen-A-Mint, and Nature's Remedy, a preparation containing cascara and aloe. In my experience and that of Russell (1979), Senokot is also a frequently abused laxative.

Osmotic agents. The osmotic agents are usually hypertonic salts, which act by absorbing isotonic fluid into the lumen of the gut and thereby stimulating peristalsis. There is some speculation that these agents also induce the release of cholecystokinin (CCK). This gut peptide itself may be responsible for increasing gastrointestinal motility and inhibiting fluid and electrolyte reabsorption from the small bowel. The osmotic agents are the most commonly used laxatives in clinical medicine. Examples include the magnesium salts, contained in such preparations as Haley's M-O, Milk of Magnesia, or Magnesium Citrate, and the phosphate salts, with trade names such as Fleet Enema and Fleet Phospho-Soda. (Cooke 1981; Pietrusko 1977).

Lactulose. Lactulose (contained in Chronulac and Cephulac) consists largely of a disaccharide that is apparently not absorbable and not digestible by human enzymes. However, it is metabolized by gut bacteria, which causes a marked decrease in colonic pH and an increase in colonic osmolality because of the production of short-chain fatty acids. This creates hypertonicity within the gut lumen, which absorbs fluid and electrolytes, and motility is enhanced (Moriarty and Silk 1988; Rutter and Maxwell 1976).

Physiological and Psychological Aspects

In general, laxative abuse is not an efficient manner of promoting long-term weight loss. In a study by Bo-Linn et al. (1983), laxative-abusing patients and volunteers were recruited to take large numbers of Correctol tablets to test their effect on intestinal absorption. After a test meal, four volunteers took 10–12 tablets, and two laxative-abusing patients ingested between 35 and 50 tablets. This produced a mean of 2.7 liters of diarrheal stool and as much as 6.1 liters in one patient who had taken 50 Correctol tablets. Nevertheless, caloric absorption of the test meal was only decreased by 6% on average, and the maximum caloric absorption prevented by laxative abuse was only an estimated 12%. The subjects did lose weight, but this was mostly temporary fluid loss.

When the weights of pure vomiting bulimic patients are compared with laxative-abusing bulimic patients, the latter tend to be heavier, despite the fact that pure vomiting patients tend to consume two to three times as much in their binges as laxative-abusing patients (Lacey and Gibson 1985; Mitchell and Boutacoff 1986). The logical conclusion is that laxative abuse is a relatively ineffective means of weight control. Nevertheless, patients continue to use these medications, probably for the following reasons: 1) laxatives tend to decrease the time of abdominal distention after a binge, and this brings relief to the patient; 2) the large amounts of watery diarrhea that follow laxative abuse do result in a transient decrease in weight (this gives the abusers the feeling that they are in control of their weight, and leads to a temporary uplift in mood [Lacey and Gibson 1985]); and 3) there is a false belief that rapid purgation after laxatives will diminish caloric absorption. In my experience, this belief tends to persist despite the physician's and caretakers' arguing the contrary with the patient.

Side Effects and Toxicity

Stimulant laxatives are probably absorbed and concentrated in the colon, where they exert a neurotoxic effect on the myenteric plexus (Cooke 1981). These nerve cells become overstimulated and either die or become markedly shrunken in appearance (Moriarty and Silk 1988), and peristalsis decreases as denervation atrophy of the intestinal smooth muscle cells occurs. Thus the individual who abuses laxatives develops constipation or obstipation, which stimulates more laxative dependency. Eventually, some laxative-abusing patients develop the life-threatening complication of cathartic colon. In this condition, the large bowel, usually beginning in the cecum, becomes dilated and takes on the appearance of an inert tube, with absent peristaltic movements. This can be a medical emergency, requiring decompression or surgery (Godding 1976; Mitchell et al. 1987b).

Other complications include steatorrhea (failure to absorb fat and malabsorption of the fat soluble vitamins A, D, E, and K); gastrointestinal bleeding, usually bright red blood from the lower intestine (Moriarty and Silk 1988); and, less commonly, rectal prolapse, caused by repetitive explosive diarrhea. Rectal prolapse may be severe enough to require surgical repair. Finally, hyperpigmentation of the skin and reversible finger clubbing have been described as complications of senna-containing laxatives (Oster et al. 1980).

Several renal and electrolyte disturbances are also associated with laxative abuse. With large-volume watery diarrhea, there is depletion of sodium and water, which results in activation of the renin-aldosterone system and an ensuing hyperaldosteronism. The kidney attempts to retain sodium and, to preserve electrical neutrality, must substitute another positive ion, usually potassium. There is also potassium ion depletion from losses into the stool. Marked decrease in total body potassium occurs, which is usually, but not invariably, accompanied by hypokalemia (Morris and Turnberg 1979). Potassium deficiency results in easy fatigability and muscular weakness, symptoms that are seen among persons who abuse laxatives. Another potential complication is kaliopenic nephropathy, which is most typically manifested as an impairment of renal concentrating ability, but interstitial renal disease, progressing to renal failure, can also occur (Cooke 1981; Mitchell and Boutacoff 1986; Oster et al. 1980; Wright and DuVal 1987).

Hypocalcemia may also accompany severe laxative abuse. This has been attributed to steatorrhea and malabsorption. However, another mechanism may be the ingestion of large doses of phosphorus-containing osmotic cathartics, or perhaps a coexisting hypomagnesemia, which has also been reported in patients with laxative abuse syndromes (Oster et al. 1980). Occasionally, hypocalcemia may result in tetany or osteomalacia, which is reversible on discontinuation of the purgatives. The risk of hypocalcemia is increased when potassium is replaced without concurrent replacement of calcium. Acute dehydration due to laxative abuse may cause a transient hypercalcemia (Mitchell et al. 1988; Oster et al. 1980). Individuals who abuse laxatives may also form ammonium urate renal calculi, partly as a result of dehydration (Dick et al. 1990).

Because of the above complications, patients who abuse laxatives are faced with alternating periods of constipation and diarrhea. Occasionally such patients will interpret the delayed stool production that occurs after a massive catharsis as constipation, secondary to laxative action. This brings on more laxative abuse, which triggers the renin alosterone system and promotes water retention. As these patients begin to gain weight, their response is further abuse of laxatives, thus beginning a spiral of repetitive abuse that is extremely difficult to interrupt (Harris 1983).

Studies of laxative-abusing patients indicate that when this behavior pattern is seen among those with anorexia or bulimia nervosa, there is a higher incidence of abuse of enemas, diuretics, and diet pills. Such patients also tend to have poor impulse control, with increased self-injurious behavior and suicide attempts (Mitchell et al. 1986). Patients who abuse laxatives are also noted to have more severe psychopathology, more extensive history of psychotherapy, and increased hospitalization for depression (Fairburn and Cooper 1984; Mitchell et al. 1986). In addition, they have a higher degree of menstrual disturbance. As one might imagine, their response to treatment is less robust, and they tend to have a poor prognosis compared with pure vomiting bulimic and restricting anorexic patients.

Diagnosis of Laxative Abuse

The diagnosis of laxative abuse is difficult because no single test is pathognomonic. It is imperative that a high index of clinical suspicion be maintained when treating eating-disordered patients. Careful inquiry into laxative abuse during history taking is essential, and repetitive denials should not be taken as incontrovertible evidence that the patient does not have an ongoing problem with laxatives (Cummings et al. 1974; Mitchell et al. 1988).

Some simple chemical tests can be done on the ward as an aid in diagnosis. The addition of dilute sodium hydroxide to either a urine or stool specimen may produce a red-purple color, indicative of phenolphthalein. However, other substances such as beet root and rhubarb can produce a similar color. The addition of barium chloride to the stool specimen will create a white barium sulfate precipitate, indicating that the patient has ingested a sulfate-containing laxative, such as sodium sulfate or magnesium sulfate (Cooke 1981; Moriarty and Silk 1988).

Broad screening methods using thin-layer chromatography are now available in many laboratories to detect phenolphthalein, bisacodyl, bisoxatin acetate, danthron, and rhein (a common metabolite of many anthraquinone laxatives such as senna, cascara, aloe, and rhubarb) in urine. All of the above, except for rhein, can also be detected in stool specimens by this chromatographic method (de Wolff et al. 1981, 1983). These methods have been used effectively to screen medical populations. For example, one study (Bytzer et al. 1989) noted that 7 of 47 patients (15%) presenting at a medical clinic with diarrhea of uncertain origin had a positive laxative screening test. These patients had all denied the use of laxatives, and no single clinical feature was able to predict the outcome of the test. The clinician should collect both urine and stool specimens, if possible, and repeated specimens should be submitted because many of these compounds are ingested sporadically rather than regularly (Cummings et al. 1974; Oster et al. 1980).

Several gastrointestinal tests are also helpful in the diagnosis and detection of laxative abuse. The barium enema may show loss of colonic haustra and pseudostrictures, which represent contractions due to neuromuscular incoordination caused by a hypertrophied muscularis mucosae (Cummings et al. 1974). These pseudostrictures tend to reappear in various parts of the colon at different times and are best visualized by fluoroscopy (Moriarty and Silk 1988). Dilatation of the colon is also seen most frequently in the ascending colon and the cecum. However, the barium enema may be completely normal in two-thirds of cases (Shaffer and Turnberg 1983) or may demonstrate alterations that are difficult to differentiate from inflammatory bowel disease (Cooke 1981).

Sigmoidoscopy may show acute and chronic inflammatory responses with disturbances of the normal mucosal pattern, including atrophic mucosae and punctate ulcers. Melanosis coli is a brown-black melaninlike pigmentation in the large bowel due to lipofuscin pigment, which is found in macrophages of the muscularis mucosae. These macrophages contain lysosomes formed by the incorporation of damaged organelles from the myenteric nerve plexus. Melanosis coli is almost always due to abuse of anthraquinones: senna, cascara, or aloe (Cooke 1981; Cummings et al. 1974). In a series of 887 patients with melanosis coli (Wittoesch et al. 1958), 850 (96%) admitted to the habitual use of laxatives. This rather pathognomonic sign is unfortunately only seen in one-third of patients who abuse laxatives, and the pigmentation may disappear within a year of stopping laxative abuse (Cooke 1981).

Rectal biopsy and microscopic examination of the mucosal tissue may demonstrate melanosis coli as well as a variety of other signs of acute and chronic inflammation. Myenteric plexus damage can also be seen, with depletion of the neurons and Schwann cell proliferation, as well as intestinal smooth muscle cell atrophy. However, these pathological signs of nerve cell degeneration appear only in 10% of laxative-abusing patients (Cooke 1981).

Electrolytes are normal in more than 50% of patients who abuse laxatives (Mitchell et al. 1983). Mitchell et al. (1987a) also found that 28% of their laxative-abusing subjects had metabolic acidosis, whereas 15% had metabolic alkalosis. Metabolic acidosis, with a diminished bicarbonate, may be a useful sign in the differential diagnosis of patients with eating disorders because it is rarely, if ever, associated with exclusive vomiting. Hypokalemia may occur in between 15 and 20% of laxative-abusing patients, and a similar proportion will have hypochloremia (Mitchell et al. 1983, 1987a). When laxative abuse becomes extremely severe, sodium losses are sufficient to produce hyponatremia (Oster et al. 1980). Such a situation again has diagnostic value because it is rarely seen among pure vomiting eating-disordered patients. Ion losses from vomit comprise mostly hydrogen and chloride found in hydrochloric acid. Hypocalcemia and hypomagnesemia are also occasionally seen among laxative-abusing patients (Oster et al. 1980).

Of all the diagnostic tests, my clinical experience, as well as comments in the literature (Cummings et al. 1974; Moriarty and Silk 1988; Oster et al. 1980; Shaffer and Turnberg 1983), attest to the value of searching patients' possessions and rooms as being fruitful and most clearly diagnostic of all available tests. This search should be conducted by experienced staff, and it is recommended that an informed and impartial witness should be present at the search (Shaffer and Turnberg 1983). It may be necessary to conduct frequent room searches, especially after community passes, because hospitalized patients have been known to bring laxatives back to the ward in ingeniously concealed caches. Although patients do have a right to privacy, this right can be superseded by a situation in which patients engage in behavior that is of imminent physical danger to themselves. At the Unit on Eating Disorders at the the the University of California, Los Angeles (UCLA), Neuropsychiatric Institute, room and locker searches are carried out by experienced nursing personnel, and the patient is always present. Notations are made in the chart concerning the type and quantity of contraband confiscated. This is not considered to be a denial of rights, but the issue is arguable (Moriarty and Silk 1988; Shaffer and Turnberg 1983).

Emetic Abuse

Emetic abuse is common among patients with bulimia nervosa. One study demonstrated that up to 28% of 100 bulimic patients had sporadic abuse, and between 3 and 4% of bulimic patients engaged in chronic, regular abuse of emetics (Pope et al. 1986). The most frequently used emetic is syrup of ipecac, an over-the-counter preparation containing emetine, which has a direct action on the gastric mucosa and on the chemoreceptor trigger zone in the central nervous system (Harris 1983).

Many individuals with bulimia nervosa will take an emetic as they are beginning to engage in the binge-vomit patterns and before they have learned to vomit spontaneously. Another group of bulimic patients begin to abuse emetics after they have lost their gag reflex and are no longer successful at inducing vomiting by mechanical means.

Syrup of ipecac is an extremely toxic substance when taken chronically. The repetitive retching can cause mucosal irritation of the esophagus and esophagitis, as well as esophageal tears and hemorrhage, known as the Mallory-Weiss syndrome. Emetine is a myotoxin that causes peripheral myopathies as well as cardiomyopathies, with symptoms of prolonged weakness and neuritis. Additionally, tachyarrhythmias and electrocardiographic changes can be seen, including ST and T wave changes and prolongation of the P-R and QRS intervals. If abuse continues, a congestive cardiomyopathy develops, which can be fatal (Harris 1983; McClung et al. 1988; Mitchell et al. 1987b). Clinicians should be alert when patients complain of palpitations, skipped beats, syncope, chest pains, or shortness of breath and should be prepared to query the patient actively concerning emetic abuse.

Management of Laxative Abuse

Most authorities agree that treatment of the laxative abuse syndrome is difficult and prolonged. In the surreptitious patient, when the diagnosis is either firmly established or strongly suspected, active confrontation is advocated by most authorities (Cooke 1981; Cummings et al. 1974; Moriarty and Silk 1988; Morris and Turnberg 1979; Oster et al. 1980), but not by all (Shaffer and Turnberg 1983). Withdrawal from laxatives can be accomplished in both inpatient and outpatient settings, although in my experience if laxative abuse has been prolonged and severe, the management of such patients outside a psychiatric unit is frequently unsuccessful. Because so little literature on the subject exists, I have set down some principles of management that we have found useful at the UCLA eating disorders program in Table 6–2.

Most inpatients can be withdrawn abruptly from stimulant agents. With outpatients, however, withdrawal needs to be done more gradually because it may be impossible for most eating-disordered individuals to tolerate the weight gain and fluid retention associated with abrupt cathartic withdrawal on their own. At UCLA we treat the withdrawal of the stimulant agent with suitable alternative promoters of gut motility, in-

Table 6–2.   Principles of management of laxative and emetic abuse

Outpatient: Gradual withdrawal. *Inpatient:* Abrupt withdrawal.

1. Substitution of absorbable laxatives with
   a. High-fiber diet
   b. Nonabsorbable bulk laxatives (Metamucil, Citrucel, bran)
   c. Magnesium sulfate (Milk of Magnesia)[a]
   d. Lactulose—nonabsorbable
   e. Suppositories—glycerin
   f. Lubricants (mineral oil)—problems with leakage and fat-soluble vitamin depletion
   g. Enemas two to three times a week as a last resort
   Treatment may take weeks or months.

2. Electrolyte disturbance
   a. Replace potassium slowly—monitor serum electrolytes
   b. Some advocate sodium bicarbonate administration (prevents decrease in bicarbonate ion when potassium is replaced)[a.]
   c. Sodium chloride restriction for fluid retention
   d. Spironolactone may be diuretic of choice—counteracts hyperaldosteronism[a]
   e. Use other diuretics (thiazides, furosemide) as a last resort—follow electrolytes carefully

3. Cathartic colon
   May require decompression or surgery

4. Confrontation (if surreptitious abuse) and periodic room searches[b]

[a]Moriarty and Silk 1988.
[b]Cummings et al. 1974; Cooke 1981.

cluding a high-fiber diet and a nonabsorbable bulk laxative, such as Metamucil or bran. Treatment with magnesium sulfate has been advocated (Moriarty and Silk 1988), but overdosage of magnesium sulfate, which is readily absorbed, can lead to toxicity (Cooke 1981; Gren and Woolf 1989; Pietrusko 1977). Glycerin suppositories can also be used for mild cases, but they have limited effectiveness.

Mineral oil is often a reasonable adjunct, although it tends to leak through an otherwise competent anal sphincter and soils the patient's clothing. Mineral oil also interferes with the absorption of vitamins A, D, E, and K (Pietrusko 1977), and these nutrients must be replaced on a special schedule, given several hours after the last dose of mineral oil. As a last resort, enemas can be given two to three times a week, or as necessary, to induce a bowel movement. Many patients may require the addition of lactulose (Chronulac), which is extremely effective in promoting reasonable bowel function with minimal toxicity (Mitchell and Boutacoff 1986). However, it should be noted that Chronulac can produce watery diarrhea and fluid and electrolyte loss. Moreover, patients have been known to abuse Chronulac after binges, and this needs to be carefully monitored, either in an inpatient or outpatient setting.

Although infrequent, severe electrolyte disturbance and dehydration can occur and must be managed with intravenous rehydration. In such a situation, potassium must be replaced slowly, usually at a rate of no more than 80–100 mEq/24 hours. Oral replacement is preferable and should be used in all but life-threatening emergencies. Serum electrolytes should be checked frequently. The administration of sodium bicarbonate has been advocated for its ability to prevent the decrease in bicarbonate ion when potassium is replaced (Moriarty and Silk 1988). Most of the time, however, sodium replacement is not necessary. In fact, within several days of the cessation of stimulant laxative abuse, patients begin to gain weight rapidly because of fluid retention (Mitchell et al. 1988; Oster et al. 1980). At UCLA, we have observed 20–30-lb weight gain, with dependent edema and periorbital edema, even approaching anasarca. This weight gain, of course, is poorly tolerated by most eating-disordered patients. Exhortations by the physician that the weight gain is due to fluid retention and only temporary are often to little avail, and therefore we have on occasion been forced to treat the condition with diuretics. Spironolactone may be the diuretic of choice, because it counteracts the hyperaldosteronism (Moriarty and Silk 1988; Oster et al. 1980). As a last resort, thiazides and furosemide may be used; however, careful observation of electrolytes, fluid balance, and consultation with an internist are necessary.

In an inpatient setting, if all sources of stimulant laxatives are blocked, it is my experience that fluid and electrolyte imbalance can be corrected within 2–3 weeks, even in the most severe cases, and substitution of stimulant agents with nonabsorbable bulk agents can be accomplished within the same span of time. However, bowel retraining and return of normal gut motility often take months, with careful management by both physician and patient to prevent relapse of laxative abuse.

Posthospital management of laxative abuse is best accomplished in an intensive outpatient setting, such as a day-treatment program, where patients can be monitored more frequently. Patients must be counseled to expect weight fluctuations, even after their peripheral edema has abated, because bowel function will continue to be erratic for some time. Patient education should include information about the laxative abuse and dependence spiral and the potential medical complications. Bulk agents such as Metamucil and lactulose may need to be continued for months or years. The clinician managing these patients must learn to expect slow progress, with occasional or frequent relapses, and must be ready to hospitalize the patient when complications develop. In general, the laxative abuse will tend to respond in concert with abatement of other symptoms of the illness, so attention must also be given to coexisting depression, psychological issues, and binge-vomiting behavior.

Follow-up of laxative-abusing patients is extremely sketchy in most reports, although many authorities opine that, in general, patients who abuse laxatives have a relatively poor prognosis; many will require chronic supplementation with potassium or repeated hospitalizations for intravenous rehydration. One follow-up study (Slugg and Carey 1984) followed 13 patients for a mean of 27 months (range 6–57 months). Six of the 13 patients were improved at follow-up, but of those 6, 1 later required further medical attention, and 1 was unable to return to work. Thus an overall improvement rate of approximately 35% was achieved, which agrees with my anecdotal observations, but is much lower than recovery rates observed for bulimia nervosa in general.

Case Examples

Case 1

Ms. L was a 37-year-old white woman who was admitted with a history of laxative abuse, bulimia nervosa, and anorexia nervosa. She initially began to lose weight by dieting (at 168 lb, 5'10.5") and using prescription appetite suppressants, such as amphetamines. This was followed quickly by vomiting and laxative abuse, which resulted in weight loss to 90 lb. Her laxative intake included 20–30 Ex-Lax tablets a day, and several bottles of Milk of Magnesia. She was hospitalized for total parental nutrition at a weight of 93 lb.

On admission, Ms. L's serum potassium was 2.9 mEq/L, and she had mild hypocalcemia. She was transferred to the psychiatric service, where she was noted to be completely obsessed with bowel function and to have multiple somatic complaints, including chest and abdominal pain. Cardiological evaluation was negative, but abdominal films demonstrated a massively dilated colon impacted with stool and a right lower quadrant mass suggestive of an appendiceal abscess. Exploratory laparotomy was negative except for large amounts of fecal stool and a free stone in the pelvis. The appendix was removed, and a feeding jejunostomy tube was inserted. Postoperative recovery was uneventful, and Ms. L was begun on a behavioral program for weight gain and a bowel retraining program, which consisted of enemas three times weekly, daily mineral oil, up to 60 cc/day of lactulose, and Metamucil. Within 10 weeks, she was having three formed stools daily, and her weight had increased by 25 lb. She signed out of the hospital against medical advice at a weight of 120 lb. At discharge, she was having normal bowel movements but was requiring daily Metamucil, and lactulose 15 cc bid.

Shortly after discharge, Ms. L began abusing laxatives again and required several subsequent hospitalizations for refeeding and rehydration. Two years later, she developed a toxic megacolon and required a subtotal colectomy, sparing the rectum. One year after the surgery, she developed intestinal volvulus and strangulation requiring exploration and removal of a section of ileum. A complication of this latter operation was chronic diarrhea, and the patient no longer had the need to abuse laxatives. When contacted 5 years later, she was no longer binge eating or vomiting and was not abusing laxatives. Her weight remained in the range of 90–95 lb.

Case 2

Ms. Z was a 28-year-old white woman who was admitted for treatment of laxative abuse, binge eating, obsessive concerns about her weight, and daily compulsive exercise. She was 5'0", weighed 92 lb on admission, gave a history of taking 4–5 Dulcolax tablets daily, and denied vomiting. She had also had episodic depressions and several suicide attempts. On physical examination, everything was normal except for decreased rectal sphincter tone. Laboratories tests, including a complete blood count, electrolytes, and liver enzymes, were normal, as was the electrocardiogram and chest and abdominal films. She was begun on a bowel retraining program, which included raw bran 15 g bid, and lactulose 15 cc bid. Her mood disorder was treated with maprotiline up to 100 mg/day, with a moderate response, and nighttime oxazepam 15 mg.

On discharge 30 days later, Ms. Z was able to have daily formed stools. She then began in outpatient supportive and insight-oriented psychotherapy. She immediately began to engage in compulsive daily swimming. Over the next 6 months, she was able to diminish her lactulose to 15 g every other day, and eventually stopped it completely, although she did complain of some abdominal distention, which was treated briefly with metoclopramide (Reglan). Her depression eventually responded more completely to fluoxetine. When contacted 5 years later, she was no longer abusing laxatives, weighed 100 lb, and was still using raw bran and occasional Colace. She also was no longer bingeing, but continued to have obsessive concerns about her weight.

Conclusions

In this chapter I have attempted to demonstrate that laxative abuse is a prevalent disorder, occurring in a high proportion of bulimic individuals, who tend to prefer stimulant laxative agents. Persons who abuse laxatives are at risk for numerous gastrointestinal and renal complications, which in turn contribute to maintaining the abuse spiral. In general, laxative-abusing patients have more serious psychopathology than eating-disordered patients who do not abuse laxatives. Emetic abuse is a particularly virulent form of purgative abuse.

Unfortunately, diagnosis and treatment are frequently prolonged, difficult, and unrewarding. Clinicians should be alert to this form of abuse in eating-disordered patients and treat it aggressively, before it becomes an ingrained behavior pattern.

References

Binder HJ: Use of laxatives in clinical medicine. Pharmacology 36:226–229, 1988

Bo-Linn GW, Santa Ana CA, Morawski SG, et al: Purging and calorie absorption in bulimic patients and normal women. Ann Intern Med 99:14–17, 1983

Bytzer P, Stokholm M, Anderson I, et al: Prevalence of surreptitious laxative abuse in patients with diarrhoea of uncertain origin: a cost benefit analysis of a screening procedure. Gut 30:1379–1384, 1989

Cooke WT: Laxative abuse. Acta Gastroenterol Belg 44:448–458, 1981

Crowther JH, Post G, Zaynor L: The prevalence of bulimia and binge eating in adolescent girls. International Journal of Eating Disorders 4:29–42, 1985

Cummings JH, Sladen GE, James OFW, et al: Laxative-induced diarrhoea: a continuing clinical problem. Br Med J 1:537–541, 1974

de Wolff FA, de Haas EM, Verweij M: A screening method for establishing laxative abuse. Clin Chem 27:914–917, 1981

de Wolff FA, Edelbroek PM, de Haas EM, et al: Experience with a screening method for laxative abuse. Hum Toxicol 2:385–389, 1983

Dick WH, Lingeman JE, Preminger GM, et al: Laxative abuse as a cause for ammonium urate renal calculi. J Urol 143:244–247, 1990

Fairburn CG, Cooper PJ: Binge-eating, self-induced vomiting and laxative abuse: a community study. Psychol Med 14:401–410, 1984

Godding EW: Therapeutics of laxative agents with special reference to the anthraguinones. Pharmacology 14 (suppl 1):78–101, 1976

Gren J, Woolf A: Hypermagnesemia associated with catharsis in a salicylate-intoxicated patient with anorexia nervosa. Ann Emerg Med 18:200–203, 1989

Harris RT: Bulimarexia and related serious eating disorders with medical complications. Ann Intern Med 99:800–807, 1983

Killen JO, Taylor CB, Telch MJ, et al: Self-induced vomiting and diuretic use among teenagers: precursors of the binge-purge syndrome? JAMA 255:1447–1449, 1986

Lacey JH, Gibson E: Does laxative abuse control body weight? a comparative study of purging and vomiting bulimics. Human Nutrition: Applied Nutrition 39A:36–42, 1985

Lachenmeyer JR, Muni-Brander P, Belford S: Laxative abuse for weight control in adolescents. International Journal of Eating Disorders 7:849–852, 1988

McClung HJ, Murray R, Braden NJ, et al: Intentional ipecac poisoning in children. Am J Dis Child 142:637–639, 1988

Mitchell JE, Boutacoff MA: Laxative abuse complicating bulimia: medical and treatment implications. International Journal of Eating Disorders 5:325–334, 1986

Mitchell JE, Pyle RL, Eckert ED, et al: Electrolyte and other psychological abnormalities in patients with bulimia. Psychol Med 13:273–278, 1983

Mitchell JE, Hatsukami D, Eckert, et al: Characteristics of 275 patients with bulimia. Am J Psychiatry 142:482–485, 1985

Mitchell JE, Boutacoff LI, Hatsukami D, et al: Laxative abuse as a variant of bulimia. J Nerv Ment Dis 174:174–176, 1986

Mitchell JE, Hatsukami D, Pyle RL, et al: Metabolic acidosis as a marker for laxative abuse in patients with bulimia. International Journal of Eating Disorders 6:557–560, 1987a

Mitchell JE, Seim HC, Colon E, et al: Medical complications and medical management of bulimia. Ann Intern Med 107:71–77, 1987b

Mitchell JE, Pomeroy C, Huber M: A clinician's guide to the eating disorders medicine cabinet. International Journal of Eating Disorders 7:211–223, 1988

Mitchell JE, Pyle RL, Eckert ED, et al: Bulimia nervosa with and without a history of anorexia nervosa. Compr Psychiatry 31:171–175, 1990

Moriarty KJ, Silk DEA: Laxative abuse. Dig Dis 6:15–29, 1988

Morris AI, Turnberg LA: Surreptitious laxative abuse. Gastroenterology 77:780–786, 1979

Oster JR, Materson BJ, Rogers AJ: Laxative abuse syndrome. Am J Gastroentol
    74:451–458, 1980

Pietrusko RG: Use and abuse of laxatives. Am J Hosp Pharm 34:291–300, 1977

Pope HG Jr, Hudson JI, Nixon RA, et al: The epidemiology of ipecac abuse (letter).
    N Engl J Med 314:245–246, 1986

Russell GM: Bulimia nervosa. Psychol Med 9:429–448, 1979

Rutter K, Maxwell D: Diseases of the alimentary system: constipation and laxative
    abuse. Br Med J 2:997–1000, 1976

Shaffer JL, Turnberg MB: Clinical clues to the detection of laxative abuse. Internal
    Medicine 4:168–174, 1983

Slugg PH, Carey WD: Clinical features and follow-up of surreptitious laxative
    users. Cleve Clin Q 51:167–171, 1984

Wittoesch JH, Jackman RJ, McDonald JR: Melanosis coli: general review and a
    study of 887 cases. Dis Colon Rectum 1:172–180, 1958

Wright LF, DuVal JW Jr: Renal injury associated with laxative abuse. South Med
    J 80:1304–1306, 1987

Chapter 7

Pregnancy and Eating Disorders

Carole K. Edelstein, M.D.
Bryan H. King, M.D.

*A*s knowledge about eating disorders continues to grow it has become clear that a sizable group of women—despite low weights, irregular menses, and disruptions in gonadotropins caused by weight loss and poor nutritional status—become pregnant, carry to term, and are faced with the task of nourishing and nurturing their infants. In this chapter we review the sparse literature on this topic and present cases from our practices and from our normal-weight bulimia group at the University of California, Los Angeles (UCLA), which over a 2-year period had several pregnant members. Based on available studies and our work with these women, we present a series of recommendations to guide clinicians faced with the evaluation and management of pregnancy occurring in patients with anorexia nervosa and bulimia nervosa.

Scattered anecdotal reports have been buttressed by the publication of three recent studies that jointly reported the experience of more than 115 patients (Brinch et al. 1988; Lacey and Smith 1987; Lemberg and Phillips 1989). Lacey and Smith (1987) retrospectively assessed the effects of pregnancy on 20 women with bulimia nervosa who delivered one or more babies before seeking treatment. In this series, as in others, advancing pregnancy was associated with remitting bulimic symptoms; by the third trimester 75% of the sample had stopped binge eating and vomiting completely—the others reduced the intensity and frequency of their bulimic behaviors. When a time line from preconception to 1 year postpartum was constructed, three patterns emerged. In the first, symptoms were greatly reduced during pregnancy only to reappear subsequently at levels higher than baseline (9 of 20 patients). In the second, 4 patients improved with pregnancy but returned to baseline. And, in the third, 7 patients maintained their improved state throughout lactation and weaning, with 5 remaining symptom free for a full year after delivery. This series was remarkable for the occurrence of midline defects (such as cleft lip and cleft palate) in 2 of 20 babies that was not associated with benzodiazepine use. Another infant who was born prematurely died at 29 weeks. All infants were breast-fed. Seven mothers were concerned that their babies were overweight, 3 put them on diets although general practitioners felt this was unjustified, and 2 mothers followed vegetarian diets. Several did not permit their children to eat carbohydrates or sweets, and more than half worried that the children would become as overweight as they judged themselves to be (incorrectly).

A Scandinavian follow-up study (Brinch et al. 1988) of 140 female patients hospitalized an average of 12.5 years earlier for anorexia nervosa found that 50 of them had gone on to bear a total of 86 children. In this group of children, prematurity occurred at twice the customary rate and perinatal mortality was six times the expected rate. Also, a girl born to one of the women died 2 years after developing anorexia nervosa at age 13. No mention of bulimic behaviors was made. Assessments of maternal functioning rated 68% as managing well, 25% as managing tolerably, and 7% as managing poorly. The authors also assessed the global functioning of the larger group of patients who were not mothers and found them to be generally more impaired. Motherhood was seen as symbolic of recovery from anorexia nervosa and was judged to be handled at a level of competency comparable with women who had never been ill.

Lemberg and Phillips (1989) retrospectively studied 43 patients who had anorexia nervosa, bulimia nervosa, or mixed symptoms at least 6 months before conception. Almost all (88.4%) doubted their ability to control weight gain while pregnant. Nevertheless, pregnancy was associated with improvement in eating disorder symptoms for 70% of the subjects; more than half said they were in full remission at some point during pregnancy. Forty percent felt more comfortable with their body image during pregnancy, and 25% continued to feel that way 1 year later. This study also focused on patients' reported interactions with their obstetricians; only 44% revealed their eating disorders to their doctors, and of these half felt the experience was not positive. All babies reported by this self-selected mail-in interview sample were healthy.

In a smaller sample of six closely followed women with anorexia nervosa, restricting subtype, Namir et al. (1986) found that although eating did improve during gestation, four of the six women were reinvested in their anorexic symptoms at follow-up 3–4 months postpartum. This study is interesting in that the authors reported how the women coped with their fear of weight gain. First they interpreted their new shapes as visible proof they were improved, better, or normal. Some experienced pleasing their husbands as beneficial, feeling they got more attention for being pregnant than for being anorexic. Several found it easier to take care of themselves than ever before. As examples of active coping they would remind themselves "this is not fat, this is baby" and keep repeating such phrases. Another switched her habitual focus from stomach to thighs, where less frightening changes were occurring.

Another retrospective study of four pregnant women with bulimia nervosa (Willis and Rand 1988) also reported that bulimic behaviors improved during pregnancy, but returned to prepregnant levels after delivery in three of the women. Only two of the women informed their obstetrician of their eating disorder. One woman equated her pregnancy with "choosing to be fat."

Our own clinical experience has included patients with eating disorders who were in one-on-one and/or group therapy before, during, and sometimes after pregnancy and delivery. In the case descriptions and discussion that follow, our goal is to distill common themes as well as practical advice for clinicians who see similar cases. Stated briefly, our hypothesis, based on the literature and our experience, is that to the extent that the eating-disordered woman is primarily driven by equating thinness with success, this rule stops with pregnancy. (We also appreciate other factors relating to the onset of eating disorders, particularly dietary restraint, neurobiologic correlates of affective state, and other cultural and psychological influences.) However, we would posit that such factors must combine with the social equation of thinness with success for an eating order to develop.

Accordingly, as the studies show, many eating-disordered patients experience remission of their symptoms when pregnant and gain recommended amounts of weight. The cruel joke is that immediately postpartum the equation is once more applied (thinness equals success) and suddenly women panic over the inevitable residual weight that has accumulated. This sets the stage for the return of the eating disorder as renewed pressures to lose weight reinitiate the starving and deprivation that precede bingeing. At this critical time therapists must somehow intervene so that the *gains* of pregnancy are not quickly and tragically dissipated. In the case examples that follow six women are presented. We illustrate and highlight some of the conclusions present in the literature and use these cases and their outcomes as the basis for recommendations for clinicians and researchable questions for further study.

Case Examples

Four of the six patients were identified through their membership in our insight-oriented therapy group for patients with bulimia nervosa. During the group's tenure, two members became pregnant, the third, a symptom-free recent "graduate" of the group notified us of her pregnancy, and the fourth, a woman with one child who introduced to the group the idea that pregnancy was possible for them, attended briefly at an earlier stage in the group's existence. The case vignettes illustrate some of the psychological and treatment issues that arose in response to these pregnancies.

Case 1

Ms. A was a 5'5" tall, 27-year-old married teacher whose eating disorder began at age 23 with the perception of being overweight and the attendant need to diet. From her then lifetime high of 118 lb, Ms. A dropped to 95 lb with a regimen of excessive exercise, laxative abuse, and the onset of self-induced vomiting. Early in the course of her eating disorder, the frequency of binge-purge behavior was described as continuous, but through intensive individual psychotherapy in the 4 years before her enrollment in group therapy the frequency of bingeing and purging stabilized at once daily. She used laxatives every other day and drank 4–8 cups of coffee and smoked one pack of cigarettes a day. Her daily caloric intake was estimated at less then 500 kcal. Her past medical history was significant for a thyroidectomy at age 18, and her family history was noteworthy for symptoms consistent with anorexia nervosa in the mother. In addition, Ms. A's father and half of her siblings had histories of significant alcohol abuse, and two of her siblings had received diagnoses of "hysteria" during brief psychiatric hospitalizations.

On entry into the group, Ms. A shared material that highlighted her struggles with low self-esteem, compensatory perfectionism, and overachievement. The group helped her to focus increasing attention on her eating behaviors and binge precipitants, initially without tangible change. But as she worked with the group Ms. A was able to increase her "allowable foods" and even to string together 5- and 7-day periods of bulimia-free eating. She developed progressively greater insight into her eating symptoms, articulating the important function that bulimia-mediated thinness served as a shield against vulnerability, as a measure of her competence, and even as part of her identity. "Can I believe my husband's assurance that he will still love me?" "Will I become susceptible to my family's craziness?" "Will I continue as a competent teacher?"

At this point in the group, another member (Ms. B, below) announced her pregnancy, and weeks later it was Ms. A who was able to give voice to the growing ambivalence in the group regarding pregnancy in bulimia, while at the same time acknowledging envy. The group looked to the leaders to admonish Ms. B for her evident lack of commitment both to the group, evidenced by sporadic attendance, and to her unborn child, evidenced by unremittent bulimia. In time, Ms. A became the banner carrier for the need for unwavering commitment to the group and became more openly critical of both Ms. B's bulimic pregnancy and of the group leaders for what she perceived as lack of intervention. Shortly thereafter Ms. A announced her own pregnancy.

The principal themes that dominated subsequent sessions included excitement with changes in her bodily sensations and perceptions and anticipated pleasures of mothering, tempered by fears of inadequacy, responsibility, and loss of control. Some members saw Ms. A's success in reducing the symptoms of bulimia, attributed it to pregnancy, and wished for similar external events that would wrest bulimia from them as well. Ms. A often shared concerns that her child would be damaged because of her bulimic history. She became increasingly anxious as the pregnancy progressed, particularly in the light of relatively slow fetal growth, which eventually mandated a fetal stress test. After her child was born healthy, Ms. A was able to articulate her anger at the group leaders for what she had perceived as a lack of appreciation for the difficult battle she had won by stopping her bulimic behavior before pregnancy (in contrast to Ms. B), and by maintaining those gains thereafter. In her view Ms. A earned the privilege of motherhood, whereas Ms. B got away with cheating.

Case 2

Ms. B was a 5'4" 26-year-old, recently married obstetric nurse whose eating disorder began at age 14 when she repeatedly witnessed her mother binge eat and induce vomiting. From her then lifetime high of 145 lb, Ms. B dropped to 100 lb over the next 3 years by purging after every meal, sometimes up to five times a day. On entry into the group, she worked long hours, jogged 3 miles daily, and attended a weekly dance class. She purged after every meal, drank 10 cups of coffee a day, and occasionally experimented with cocaine.

Ms. B's family history was noteworthy for her mother's eating disorder, chronic depression with several drug overdoses, and alcoholism. Ms. B's parents had divorced when she was 5 years old, and her mother was involved in several abusive relationships over the ensuing years. Indeed, in the year before Ms. B's presentation for therapy, her mother sustained head injuries in a domestic fight and was subsequently confined to nursing home care.

On entry into the group Ms. B initially shared feelings of helplessness about her eating disorder, but in subsequent sessions she tended to remain quiet. Because one of the other group members had a 15-month-old child, the exploration of difficulties surrounding pregnancy in bulimia was an early topic of discussion, one in which Ms. B was keenly interested. Later, Ms. B disclosed that part of her motivation for treatment derived from her husband's desire to start a family; she also expressed concern that her bulimia was harming her husband both emotionally and financially. Shortly thereafter, Ms. B again raised the issue of eating disorders and pregnancy by speculating that she herself might be pregnant. Though this first announcement proved to be a false alarm, Ms. B continued to struggle with the issue of pregnancy and childbirth by sharing vignettes from work about incompetent mothers, incompetent physicians and nurses, and poor postnatal outcomes. Declarations of helplessness about her eating disorder often gave way to expressions of guilt about her lack of attention to her own mother, her own shortcomings on the job, and concerns about her marriage.

Ms. B's attendance became increasingly sporadic as she struggled with competing commitments to work and family. She also battled the fact that since her own enrollment in the group, a number of members had significantly improved and even "graduated" from the group. Ms. B was able to articulate her ambivalence about becoming pregnant and considered the possibility that her unremittent bulimia served an ongoing need to defend her from fears of responsibility and feelings of inadequacy.

Two months later, nearly 2 years after her enrollment in the group, Ms. B announced her pregnancy with mixed feelings. The following week, with the reality of heart sounds present, Ms. B began to reveal fears of having a defective child. Later, she several times posed the question: "Does it really hurt others if I'm bulimic?" Her attendance became increasingly sporadic, and sentiment in the group became divided into expressions of support, in the form of describing experiences with friends who had given birth to beautiful babies in the face of drug abuse or severe dietary restrictions during pregnancy, and expressions of concern about Ms. B's evident lack of commitment to her own recovery and to the health of her unborn child. When Ms. B was not present, other members would speculate about what could happen to a fetus repeatedly exposed to binge-purge behavior. They revealed surprising ignorance and naivete about anatomical relationships: "Does the fetus share a common stomach with the mother?" "How is the fetus nourished?"

Over the ensuing months, Ms. B was generally absent. Letters were sent, and she was contacted by telephone. Pregroup meetings were set up on two occasions to articulate the leaders' concerns about Ms. B's bulimic pregnancy and to forecast potential problems in the postnatal period when Ms. B would be faced with ever increasing demands. She seemed trapped by increasing denial and isolation. She did not tell her husband, concerned coworkers, or her obstetrician about her bulimia. Ms. B eventually cited fatigue associated with her advancing pregnancy for being unable to attend the group and did not return after the birth of her (healthy) child.

Case 3

Ms. C was a 5'4", 35-year-old secretary student who recalled feeling as if her legs were always too fat and feeling "crippled" at times by this perceived obesity. Ms. C's frank eating disorder commenced when she was 29, after the break-up of a 3-year relationship. From her stable weight of 128 lb, Ms. C eventually dropped to a low of 85 lb through severe restriction and later laxative abuse, self-induced vomiting, and excessive exercise.

Family history revealed the presence of bulimia in two sisters and in two half-sisters. An older brother had a history of psychotic depressions and substance abuse. Ms. C's mother had a history of alcoholism and depression, and her father had abused all of the children psychologically, physically, and/or sexually. Ms. C's psychiatric history was remarkable for suicide attempts at ages 13 and 18 that were not treated.

On three occasions during her first 2 years in psychodynamically oriented individual therapy Ms. C required hospitalization for behavioral intervention aimed at weight gain as well as containment of suicidal depressions. Ms. C was poorly responsive to numerous pharmacologic interventions including tricyclic antidepressants (TCAs) with lithium augmentation, monoamine oxidase inhibitors (MAOIs), atypical antidepressants, benzodiazepines, and low-dose neuroleptic agents.

Ms. C was devoted to her psychotherapy and worked hard on recurrent issues of low self-worth, feelings of abandonment, and abuse by family members or authority figures. As she was able to tolerate increasing weight gain and the return of menstruation, she began to talk about themes of responsibility. She sometimes expressed wishes for eventual recovery, meaning a rewarding marriage and family life, but these were always ultimately dismissed as hopeless. Eventually Ms. C was able to maintain her weight at 134 lb without bingeing or purging. She worked hard toward fulfilling the requirements for acceptance to nursing school and maintained a job as a nurse's aid to support her education. She also became involved in a number of sexual relationships and on one occasion became pregnant after a "one-night stand." Ms. C recalled with exhilaration the feeling of wholeness she experienced with the knowledge of her pregnancy. Although she had actually been significantly depressed a few months before and had had a fairly good response to the addition of nortriptyline, she was now "complete" and "nurturing." During the subsequent month, however, she became increasingly concerned about the possible harm the nortriptyline might cause her child and her sense of being unable to care for a baby at this juncture of her life. She was unable to risk the chance that her child would be defective, and quickly dismissed the possibility of "abandoning" her child to adoption. Ms. C elected to terminate the pregnancy at approximately 5 weeks' gestation.

After the abortion, Ms. C continued to raise issues of marriage and subsequent motherhood with mixed feelings in psychotherapy. She feared motherhood for its potential for revealing her inadequacies or for creating a situation wherein she could perpetuate the abuses and distresses she had endured. Alternatively, motherhood could provide a chance to produce something beautiful: a tangible sign of her recovery.

Case 4

"After dinner he shows me his fat then I show him mine." Ms. D (28 years old) developed an eating disorder after marrying a formerly anorexic and still weight-obsessed young man. In an apparent folie à

---

[1]Apparent, not actual DSM-II-R induced psychotic disorder, because this copule was preoccupied with overvalued ideas, not delusions.

deux, they both examined each other for signs of fat, ate Spartanly, and exercised vigorously. In time she had full-blown bulimia nervosa. After a miscarriage, which she attributed to the eating disorder, Ms. D sought evaluation and treatment. She felt she caused the miscarriage by over-exercising (running, biking, aerobics, and lifting weights) and alternating not eating with bingeing and vomiting. Once principles of cognitive behavioral treatment were explained, a contract to eat three meals a day was obtained, and her husband was firmly labelled as eating disordered, all symptoms of bulimia nervosa disappeared within 1 week.

Several months later a pregnancy ensued, heavily overshadowed by fear of miscarriage and harm to the fetus. Ms. D became depressed, sought repeated reassurance from her obstetrician, and ultimately had seven ultrasonographic examinations during the course of gestation. No abnormalities were found, and her prenatal course was medically unremarkable. At second trimester, with robust signs of life and several normal scans for reassurance, her depression abated. At the beginning of her third trimester, therapy was tapered and discontinued. Ms. D wished to stop treatment because her bulimia had remitted early in treatment and pregnancy was going well. The therapist disagreed. Issues of relationships (with her mother, husband, barely remembered father, and mother's abusive boyfriend) deserved further psychotherapeutic exploration and would be shelved if the patient terminated. Nevertheless, she did.

At a first, accidental follow-up 1 week before delivery (the patient and therapist met on the street), Ms. D reported no problems with eating or depression; she had gained 28 lb with the pregnancy, and no signs of bulimia nervosa or urges to binge had appeared since the termination of psychotherapy. At second follow-up, 10 months after delivery of a healthy infant (7 lb, 13 oz), the patient's eating remained normal—although disciplined—but the husband had had a flare-up of weight and exercise preoccupation that paralleled the new mother's preoccupation with the infant, accompanied by some loss of intimacy in the marriage. A course of weekly individual psychotherapy and, later, couples therapy were initiated.

Case 5

Ms. E was a 32-year-old woman from South America married for several years to a nondrinker from a large American family heavily laden with alcoholism. Her panic disorder, depression, and bulimia nervosa were well controlled on imipramine 150 mg/day; she refused group and individual psychotherapy because of cost and interference with her work as a secretary. Ms. E had been followed in the UCLA Eating Disorders Program Medication Clinic and had been doing well for 3 years when she reported the wish to become pregnant. Previous attempts to wean her from the imipramine resulted in prompt reemergence of symptoms, so a genetics consultation was obtained. Because available data supported the lack of teratogenicity of TCAs at doses of less than 150 mg (Mortola 1989), she was treated with 125 mg of imipramine. At this dose, she ultimately conceived, had a healthy pregnancy without eating disorder or other psychiatric complications, and delivered a healthy infant.

Unfortunately, Ms. E was advised to discontinue imipramine so that she could breast-feed her baby. Shortly after doing so a severe postpartum depression of delusional proportions set in (she believed God was punishing her by sending her this devil child that would not stop crying). Reinstitution of imipramine at doses formerly effective produced only partial resolution of her symptoms, and she was subsequently given augmentation with lithium in an attempt to obtain better control of the mood disorder. In occasional psychotherapy—again because of financial constraints—she was attempting to sort through a sudden flood of memories concerning childhood sexual and physical abuse. She considered but was reluctant to attend an incest survivors' group. At 6 months postpartum, vomiting was very occasional (once or twice monthly), and affective symptoms were her most prominent and worrisome complaints.

Case 6

Ms. F was referred by her parents, who feared she was maintaining her low weight by vomiting. She was 28 years old, married for several years, 5'8", 110 lb, and struggling to separate from an aloof, demanding, and ungiving mother. Her parents did not, for example, consult with her husband before insisting she be evaluated. Ms. F denied vomiting and told, shyly, of having once reached 120 lb only to be informed by her mother that she was fat. Of note, friends wondered if the mother, quite thin, did not have an eating disorder herself. Although reassured she was not frankly anorexic (she still menstruated), Ms. F nevertheless felt and worried that she was not normal. After a year of a supportive therapy, her highly restricted eating pattern improved slightly and she gained 2–3 lb. However, her wish to be "normal" began to find expression in the desire for pregnancy—a way for her to be like her mother, yet also to prove her superiority to her mother (in the ideal relationship she imagined she would have with her child).

When Ms. F. conceived, her pleasure was brief, quickly overshadowed by twin fears that she would have a miscarriage and that she would deliver a girl. She feared having as much trouble relating to her daughter as her own mother had with her. Reassurance was only transiently helpful, and logic was unavailing. Her wish for normality was so at odds with the notion of being a psychiatric patient that she was unable to commit to a longer-term, more exploratory therapy. As the pregnancy progressed unremarkably her anxiety subsided slowly, although panicky phone calls to one of us or the obstetrician were frequent, especially when she noticed a small brownish discharge at about 9 weeks. Ultrasonography proved calming. Once the baby's heartbeat and movement appeared, Ms. F felt calm enough to work, until term, in once weekly therapy on her feared relationship with a daughter. Although she had an amniocentesis and fantasied being the mother of sons, she refused to know her child's sex before delivery. After delivery of a healthy girl she decided to terminate treatment, citing the logistics of newborn care and saying that she had already dealt with all potential problems "in advance."

Her ambivalence was apparent throughout the pregnancy. For example, although she wished to be unconditionally maternal and receptive, she was humiliated to be "showing." A famous story in her family was that her mother's pregnancy with her was undetectable until late in the seventh month because of her mother's restricted eating and girdling.

Discussion

Several points from the cases and the literature deserve emphasis. It seems apparent that

- During pregnancy abnormal eating behaviors did remit for most women we followed.
- This remission was often anticipated; in fact a common hope was that wellness could be achieved through pregnancy.
- Once the patients were pregnant, fears of producing a damaged infant were common, highly distressing, unrelated to whether eating symptoms continued or not, and affected both self-esteem (Ms. A) as well as frequent use (Ms. D) or avoidance of the obstetric team (Ms. B).

- Psychotropic medication can and in some cases should be recommended during pregnancy.
- Remaining in therapy can become a problem for patients. Unrealistic expectations (magical thinking) about pregnancy effortlessly conferring psychological well-being are confronted in treatment.
- Certain psychotherapeutic interventions—clarification, support, and role modeling—seem particularly useful for these patients and are recommended as part of an overall approach that ideally uses group and individual modalities and is coordinated with the patient's obstetrician.

Symptoms Recede

Table 7–1 illustrates how eating behaviors were affected by the anticipation of pregnancy (several women recovered before conception), or by the pregnancy itself. Of the five pregnant patients reported here who carried to term, all except one had total remission of eating disorder symptoms. Table 7–1 also documents the outcome of each pregnancy and the mother's use of psychotherapy.

Common Hope: Wellness Through Pregnancy

The group witnessed Ms. A's triumph over bulimia and attributed it to the pregnancy even though temporally her eating symptoms had almost ceased before she conceived and despite the fact that they knew pregnancy had not cured Ms. B. Other patients have reported that pregnancy was desirable because it signified wellness to others, even if it did not guarantee recovery. The women described by Namir et al. (1986) felt that their husbands responded to them as if they were more normal; Ms. F was eager to demonstrate to her mother that she was normal (and worthy of her love and attention).

Common Fears: A Damaged Infant

The fear of producing damaged children was a frequent theme in both the clinical literature and among our patients. Our patients were afraid that the fetus would be damaged while in utero; this fear was expressed even by those women whose eating disorders were greatly improved (Ms. A and Ms. F) or had remitted before conception (Ms. D and Ms. E). The fear represented concerns that if a woman had ever been eating disor-

Table 7–1. Effect of pregnancy on eating disorder symptoms

Patient	Diagnosis	Term or abort	Psycho-therapy	ED symptoms during pregnancy	Fully remit	ED symptoms 6 weeks after pregnancy	Healthy infant	Terminated therapy prematurely
A	Bulimia nervosa	Term	Individual and group	Improved	Yes	Improved	Yes	No
B	Bulimia nervosa	Term	Group	Ongoing	No	Ongoing	Yes	Yes
C	Anorexia nervosa and bulimia nervosa	Abort	Individual	Recovered	NA	NA	NA	NA
D	Bulimia nervosa	Term	Individual	Recovered	Yes	Recovered	Yes	Yes[a]
E	Bulimia nervosa	Term	Medication visits only	Recovered	Yes	Recovered	Yes	Yes[a]
F	Subdiagnostic anorexia nervosa[b]	Term	Individual	Improved	Yes	Unknown	Yes	Yes

Note. ED = Eating disorder.
[a]Patients later returned to therapy (D began individual and couples work, and E began group and medication support visits.)
[b]Highly restrained with menses, but low weight.

dered she would be physically incapable of undergoing a healthy pregnancy. For Ms. D, who had had a previous miscarriage while bulimic,
pregnancy represented an ongoing threat. For Ms. F, who lived in the
shadow of her mother's criticism, even the possibility of miscarrying
because of an eating disorder represented proof that her mother was right
(that there was something wrong with her). However, for these two
patients, fears diminished remarkably once second trimester was
reached. This time course had no parallel that we could determine with
waxing and waning eating disorder symptoms, per se, because both
patients had improved significantly before becoming pregnant. Although
the fear of producing a damaged child was discussed often by patients in
the therapy group, Ms. B, who continued to be symptomatic, attempted
to minimize confronting and acknowledging this possibility. Her increasing absences from the group were paralleled by progressively explicit
discussions of the possible negative effects of continuing eating disorder
on the fetus by the remaining group members as they struggled with
apparent guilt by association. One patient (Ms. A) openly anticipated the
guilt she would feel if she produced a defective child, an outcome she felt
was perhaps deserved and attributable to her years of self-abuse through
bingeing and purging.

In addition to fearing congenital malformations, most patients worried that they would damage their children emotionally by their incompetence at nurturing. Pregnancy raises, in powerful and disconcerting ways,
the issues of adequacy and competence, and these concerns do not seem
to be misplaced. Recently, Raskin et al. (1990) assessed physically
healthy adult couples experiencing their first pregnancies and found
depressive symptoms in 59% of the couples during the transition to
parenthood. Stein and Fairburn (1989) described the interactions of five
bulimic women and their children (all younger than age 6). They concluded that the mother's eating disorder—through obsessive food preoccupation, self-absorption, depression, and behaviors associated with
them—disrupted parenting. While they were busy eating and vomiting,
women reportedly ignored their children. Mothers were also aware of
difficulties coping with their children even when they were not explicitly
binge eating and purging, especially in the aftermath of binge-purge
cycles that left them irritable and dysphoric. Problems also surfaced in
feeding the children, as Lacey and Smith (1987) noted. Some of Stein
and Fairburn's patients restricted the amount of food in the house in
attempts to control their own food intake, whereas others restricted their

children's intakes (Stein and Fairburn 1989). One was preoccupied with the "large size" of her baby's buttocks and stomach and could not be reassured that they were normal.

Use of Medication

Two of our patients greatly feared the potential teratogenic effects of their psychotropic medications on their fetuses. Ms. C ultimately aborted because of this (and other fears); Ms. E had an extensive genetics work-up at UCLA about 6 months before conception, at which time she had been asymptomatic on medication for more than 2 years. With encouragement from the genetics team and the support of her psychiatrist, Ms. E continued to take imipramine with little anxiety during gestation. In fact, contrary to assumptions held by many psychiatrists, the use of TCAs is neither absolutely contraindicated during pregnancy nor during lactation (Cohen et al. 1989; Goldberg and DiMascio 1978; Mortola 1989). However, the use of MAOIs during pregnancy is contraindicated because of animal data demonstrating fetal growth retardation, the possibility of exacerbating pregnancy-induced hypertension, and compromising placental perfusion, and because pharmacological treatment of premature labor with beta-mimetics would be curtailed by the presence of a MAOI (Mortola 1989). It should also be noted that the use of benzodiazepines during pregnancy has been associated with dysmorphic offspring resembling fetal alcohol children (Laegreid et al. 1989).

Mortola (1989) made the following recommendations for the use of TCAs during pregnancy and lactation:

1. In the first trimester, depression should be treated by supportive measures without medication if possible. In cases where hospitalization alone fails to attenuate severe vegetative symptoms, suicidality, or psychosis, TCAs should be used.
2. In the second or third trimester, TCAs should be used in the treatment of vegetative symptoms refractory to supportive treatment. There is no advantage to withdrawal of TCAs before delivery.
3. When TCAs are used in the third trimester, the pediatrician should be informed so as to anticipate possible withdrawal symptoms in the infant (cyanosis, difficult feeding, urinary retention, and seizures). In the event of a significant change in maternal blood pressure, obstetric assessment of uteroplacental integrity is indicated.

4. In the postpartum period, failing effective supportive therapy, TCAs or MAOIs should be given with the recommendation to discontinue breast-feeding.

In retrospect, Ms. E may have been much better off had her imipramine been continued postpartum, because she developed a severe postpartum depression associated with resurgent bulimia. Ms. E's combined eating and mood symptoms had always responded promptly and jointly to TCAs; however, after delivery only partial resolution of the depression was seen for several months even with TCA treatment, during which time bonding with her daughter was disrupted.

Patients' Use of Treatment and the Issue of Discontinuation

Two patients who were doing well and one who did poorly left treatment before we thought it prudent to do so. This outcome suggests several possibilities. First, some patients used psychotherapy even before conceiving as a vehicle to prepare for healthy childbearing. Accomplishing this goal may have been sufficient for them. We can only hope that those who have a positive experience will return for further therapy if and when difficulties reoccur, as patient Ms. D did when marital problems developed. With this perspective in mind, patients should be prepared to view psychotherapy as a tool they can use intermittently at appropriate times. They should not be pressed unduly into remaining in treatment simply because they have not yet delivered or demonstrated their ability to deal with inconsolable infants without fragmenting themselves.

Second, patients who held inappropriate or idealistic expectations of how pregnancy might impact their eating disorders not uncommonly dropped out of treatment as their fantasies went unfulfilled as pregnancy advanced. Ms. B's dropping out appeared to occur when her indifference to the health consequences for herself and her unborn child because of her unremittent bulimic behavior continued despite advancing pregnancy. At the same time, the prevailing sentiment in the group was switching from envy and anticipatory excitement to concern for the safety of Ms. B's fetus in the absence of any observable changes in her behavior. Furthermore, Ms. B was confronted by Ms. A's apparent triumph over her eating disorder. In retrospect, it may have been prudent to have warned Ms. B early in pregnancy against premature termination of therapy in an effort to forestall her departure. Clearly, it is at the very moment when denial becomes untenable (for Ms. B, when her false belief that her behavior would not harm her child was challenged by others) that patients stand to gain the most from psychotherapeutic support; yet this is also the moment that dropping out of treatment seems most likely.

Third, among patients for whom pregnancy serves as a signal to others that they are well, a continuing need for psychotherapy is at variance with the image they are trying to project and to feel themselves. Ms. F exemplified this phenomenon. Her termination, therefore, was also a move that, on reflection, we would have liked to prevent. Although pregnancy may afford a unique window for intervention in women with bulimia nervosa, it is less clear that the gains made during pregnancy can always be extended into the postpartum period and beyond when women are confronted with residual weight, demanding infants, and families or self-images that overvalue thinness. In our small sample, it was not always possible to keep patients we knew well in treatment, even when they generally valued their treatment.

Psychotherapeutic Interventions

Psychotherapeutic interventions took a variety of forms, particularly in the group therapy setting. Based on our experience, a clinician will be called on to carry out the following functions.

Provide education and clarification. Both pregnant and nonpregnant group members raised very elementary questions about the biology of both pregnancy and bulimia. Many of the members in the group, for example, were surprised to learn that vomiting did not simultaneously evacuate both the mother's and child's stomach contents. The therapists conveyed the notion that although the fetus was dependent on its mother for good nutrition, the two did not share a common digestive system. The therapists were also able to speak directly to concerns of the bulimic mother, for example, to define the range of appropriate weight gain with pregnancy.

Interpret dynamic themes, family dynamics, and group process. All group members expressed feelings of loss, emptiness, and fragmentation that often were linked by the therapists to the patients' experiences of inadequate parental responses to their own dependency needs. Many experienced severe underparenting in their own large sibships, for example, and all had unempathic if not abusive parents and siblings. Clearly, the theme of having to compete for limited attention was raised by the introduction of "new members" to the group through pregnancy. However, as these experiences were also viewed by the therapists as pathogenic factors in the development of eating disorders (e.g., vomiting sometimes occurred for attention), conception merely highlighted issues already under scrutiny.

Provide supportive reassurance to minimize distortions.   Parenthood is anxiogenic. The bulimic mother is not immune from the fears that any parent-to-be might experience, and the group leaders often functioned to normalize such fears by highlighting their universality.

Redirect questions to obstetricians.   Our patients periodically described visits with their obstetricians, and these encounters were often experienced as if the patients were taking exams rather than being examined. Often patients asked questions in the group that were "too silly" or "too frightening" for them to ask their obstetricians. The group leaders could validate the legitimacy of these patients' concerns and encourage them to take these and other questions directly to their obstetricians. Clearly the obstetricians were being underutilized. Because we were not in direct contact with these obstetricians or pediatricians, we cannot know with certainty why this underutilization occurred. In the case of Ms. D, where seven ultrasonograms were obtained, an obstetric-psychiatric coalition might well have addressed the patient's fears effectively— without a single procedure. In the other cases, a well-informed treatment team, as exemplified by the case report by Feingold et al. (1988), should probably be the gold standard of optimal care.

A goal of therapy would be to let the patient know that the psychiatrist is available to facilitate proper utilization of the obstetric team. We now believe that patients' permission should routinely be obtained by the psychiatrist to contact their obstetricians. In this role the psychiatrist can call the obstetrician to bring up the concerns that the patient cannot raise on her own. Thus, the psychiatrist helps the obstetrician understand the role of bulimia in the expression of the patient's behavior and also helps the patient get the most out of the medical professional team. With the patient, the psychiatrist can demonstrate the advantages to this approach.

The psychiatrist can role-play questions and answers the patient can raise with her obstetrician, helping her to become comfortable with discussing her concerns. Finally, the psychiatrist can help the obstetrician understand the unique profile of the individual patient's eating disorder and develop a nonjudgmental, educative approach to the discussion of the patient's major concerns.

Role model the examination of affectively laden issues. In addition to modeling help-seeking behavior, the clinicians, in both group and one-on-one settings, approached highly charged issues in a measured, logical, and unruffled manner. Patients were thus able to explore issues of competence, identity, and self-worth, and also to see and experience the therapists' cognitive and analytic "observing egos" at work.

Recommendations

Several general guidelines for psychotherapy strategies may help improve outcome in the eating-disordered patient who becomes pregnant:

1. Assess how realistic the patient's expectations are, compared with her reliance on magical thinking, and reinforce the healthier world view that often accompanies pregnancy.
2. Reinforce the benefits for both mother and fetus of whatever normal eating is taking place.
3. Inoculate the patient against the temptation to terminate therapy late in pregnancy and during the postpartum period. To discourage premature drop-outs, encourage patients to view psychotherapy as a tool to achieve enhanced autonomy, self-understanding, and competence and point out the benefits of these ego-enhancing aspects of treatment during the initial stresses and strains of mothering. Ms. D returned to psychotherapy when her son was 10 months old, at a point where difficulties erupted in her marriage because her obsessive preoccupation with her infant was alienating her husband. Based on our experience and the report by Stein and Fairburn (1989), the postpartum period should be identified early as one of high risk for the resurgence of abnormal eating behaviors and of disordered relating as women are challenged by the need for a whole new repertoire of coping skills despite limited internal resources. The external support system of the

clinician and/or the therapeutic group should be utilized to facilitate and model the acquisition of nurturance skills.

4. Forewarn the patient that internal pressures to overvalue thinness are likely to return.

5. Where possible and appropriate, help patients work toward the goal of being maximally recovered before becoming pregnant. Some patients may deny their illness so thoroughly that they minimize the likely effects on the fetus as well as on the infant of a mother engaged in behaviors that preoccupy both physically and psychologically.

Although psychotherapy proceeds along these lines, there are several other concurrent interventions that should be pursued by the clinician treating the eating-disordered woman who is pregnant:

1. Attend to the affective state. Do not discontinue effective TCA therapy without due consideration. Specific recommendations regarding the use of antidepressant medication in pregnancy have been put forward by Mortola (1989).

2. If possible, refer the patient to a predelivery women's group where she can share concerns and appreciate the universality of many of her anticipatory fears.

3. Create a multidisciplinary treatment team with good communication between psychiatrist, obstetrician, and pediatrician. We agree with Lemberg and Phillips (1989) that encouraging frankness with the obstetrician is helpful, but we stop short of endorsing his recommendation to limit weigh-ins because we believe this colludes with the patient's denial, appears to support the patient's magical thinking regarding numbers, and undermines the cognitive behavioral stance we like to take with patients in which information (e.g., from their journals and from their scales) facilitates and enables appropriate decision making and course corrections. As an acute temporizing event, the patient may be directed not to view the scale during a weighing, but the patient's reluctance in this regard is always a matter for discussion in treatment.

4. Engage the spouse as a therapeutic ally. Although couples therapy was not described in the literature we cited earlier and was not used by us, one can imagine that benefits could accrue if the couple were treated jointly in a format emphasizing preparation for parenting. Specifically, marital deficits in communication and cooperation could be identified

and improved. In addition, including the husband destigmatizes the wife's ongoing treatment, allowing her to benefit from a wider support network as the demands of actual mothering are encountered.

5. Use recovered patients. Our more successful recovered mothers have usually offered to visit with and address current eating disorder groups on issues related to their illness, their recovery, and their pregnancies, as well as their lives as mothers. Seeing a peer negotiate these obstacles can be therapeutic in ways that cannot be obtained from a therapist.

Conclusions

The patient with an eating disorder who becomes pregnant poses unique and difficult therapeutic challenges. We have reviewed the relevant literature and added some of our experience in this area, hoping that the guidelines we present may prove useful to clinicians.

Research-based efforts are also needed to validate and refine these approaches. Areas in which research is needed include prospective studies on the frequency and nature of perinatal complications and birth defects in pregnancies in eating-disordered women; on parenting skills of women with and without eating disorders matched for age, parity, and education; and on changes in family dynamics associated with the marked changes in eating disorder symptoms that occasionally occur both during and after pregnancy. Findings in these areas will help us plan more rational preventive interventions to improve the likelihood of good outcomes for the mother, child, and couple.

References

Brinch M, Isager T, Tolstrup K: Anorexia nervosa and motherhood: reproduction pattern and mothering behavior of 50 women. Acta Psychiatr Scand 77:611–617, 1988

Cohen LS, Heller VL, Rosenbaum JF: Treatment guidelines for psychotropic drug use in pregnancy. Psychosomatics 30:25–33, 1989

Feingold M, Kaminer Y, Lyons K, et al: Bulimia nervosa in pregnancy: a case report. Obstet Gynecol 71:1025–1027, 1988

Goldberg HL, DiMascio A: Psychotropic drugs in pregnancy, in Psychopharmacology: A Generation of Progress. Edited by Lipton MA, DiMascio A, Killam KF. New York, Raven Press, 1978, pp 1047–1055

Lacey JH, Smith G: Bulimia nervosa: the impact of pregnancy on mother and baby. Br J Psychiatry 150:777–781, 1987

Laegreid L, Olegard R, Walstrom J, et al: Teratogenic effects of benzodiazepine use during pregnancy. J Pediatr 114:126–131, 1989

Lemberg R, Phillips J: The impact of pregnancy on anorexia nervosa and bulimia. International Journal of Eating Disorders 8:285–295, 1989

Mortola JF: The use of psychotropic agents in pregnancy and lactation. Psychiatr Clin North Amer 12:69–87, 1989

Namir S, Melman K, Yager J: Pregnancy in restricter-type anorexia nervosa: a study of six women. International Journal of Eating Disorders 5:837–845, 1986

Raskin VD, Richman JA, Gaines C: Patterns of depressive symptoms in expectant and new parents. Am J Psychiatry 147:658–660, 1990

Stein A, Fairburn CG: Children of mothers with bulimia nervosa. British Medical Journal 299:777–778, 1989

Willis DC, Rand CS: Pregnancy in bulimic women. Obstet Gynecol 71:708–710, 1988

Chapter 8

Eating Disorders and Diabetes Mellitus

Joel Yager, M.D.
Roy T. Young, M.D.

*I*n the 1980s numerous case reports appeared describing the co-occurrence of insulin-dependent diabetes mellitus (IDDM) and anorexia nervosa and/or bulimia nervosa among young women (e.g., Garner 1980; JI Hudson et al. 1983; MS Hudson et al. 1983). These reports suggested that the association between eating disorders and IDDM was more than chance (Powers et al. 1983), that the prevalence of eating disorders among young women with IDDM was higher than that in comparable populations (Nielsen et al. 1987), and that the interplay of diabetes and eating disorders might have several interwoven strands. The fact that IDDM often imposes conflicts about autonomy, lowers self-esteem, increases feelings of being different from peers, intensifies self-consciousness, produces family distress, and requires young diabetic women to think about their nutrition and food all the time may increase their vulnerability to develop eating disorders (Rodin et al. 1986–1987; Steel et al. 1987).

Women with diabetes mellitus might rebel against the strong dietary restrictions under which they are confined and "act out" by binge eating and purging. They might be able to "get away" with eating more than their usual diets permit by neglecting to take their insulin or reducing the dosage and thereby inducing glycosuria as a novel method of purging (Hillard et al. 1983; JI Hudson et al. 1983; Powers et al. 1983; Szmukler and Russell 1983). They might become weight phobic or carbohydrate phobic as a result of the unavoidable and constant attention to weight and diet from the onset of their illness and thereby be made prone to anorexia nervosa (Powers et al. 1983). Or they might use their diabetes in a purposeful way to pursue their desire to lose weight (Szmukler and Russell 1983) or to otherwise manipulate their environments (Brooks

1984). With anorexia nervosa, some women neglect to eat after taking insulin, provoking episodes of hypoglycemia and seizures (JI Hudson et al. 1983; Power et al. 1983; Szmukler and Russell 1983).

At the same time, these early observations raised the extremely troubling specter that these patients might be particularly difficult to treat both medically and psychiatrically and that they were possibly more prone to develop the debilitating and often life-threatening complications of IDDM such as proliferative retinopathy, neuropathy, and renal disease earlier in their course and to a greater extent than other IDDM patients. More than simply "dual diagnosis" patients, these patients not only developed multisystem complications of diabetes mellitus but also frequently had coexistent psychiatric disorders of mood, anxiety, and personality along with their eating disorders.

In this chapter we briefly review the clinically important developments in IDDM research and the meager literature on coexisting eating disorders and IDDM. We draw some tentative conclusions about their association and the implications of their coappearance and provide some suggestions and guidelines for the management of these patients.

Recent Developments in Our Understanding of IDDM and Their Implications for Eating Disorders

IDDM, the most common form of diabetes among children and adolescents, occurs in approximately 1 of every 400 children. Remarkable strides in research during the past decade have yielded a considerable amount of new knowledge about the etiology and pathogenesis of this disorder. First, it is clear that genetic factors play a role in vulnerability to IDDM, although these factors do not account entirely for its appearance. IDDM has been linked to specific histocompatibility markers: human leukocyte antigen (HLA)-DR3 and HLA-DR4. About 90% of diabetic patients have these markers rather than others, such as HLA-DR2 and HLA-DR5, which appear to confer some protection against IDDM. Nevertheless, even among identical twins the concordance of IDDM is at most 50%, suggesting nongenetic etiological mechanisms as well. Even though some alteration of genetic material is possible after conception and cleavage (theoretically capable of accounting for differences in IDDM vulnerability between identical twins), such mechanisms are thought to be less likely than others.

The most probable nongenetic influences in the occurrence of IDDM are now thought to be viral infections and autoimmune factors that destroy insulin-secreting pancreatic β-cells, frequently starting years before the appearance of frank hyperglycemia and glycosuria. Indeed, studies have shown that 8–40% of children affected in certain epidemics of congenital rubella infection subsequently developed IDDM or impaired glucose tolerance (Ginsberg-Fellner 1990). Large numbers of anti-insulin and antipancreas antibodies have been found in IDDM vulnerable children (e.g., those who have diabetic older siblings) years before the onset of their diabetes. Such children may also have other autoimmune factors, such as antithyroid antibodies, and about 10% develop Hashimoto's thyroiditis as well.

The threats of morbidity and mortality from IDDM remain considerable. Within 20 years of onset almost all patients develop retinopathy and other serious complications, nearly 30% develop end-stage renal disease, and almost all patients have a significantly lowered life expectancy (about 15–20 years less than their peers).

For patients with both IDDM and eating disorders, there are several clinically important questions: What is the relationship between eating disorders and clinically significant episodes of hypoglycemia or hyperglycemia? What are the long-term clinical implications of an increase in hypoglycemic episodes? Particularly for patients with severe eating binges, who permit themselves to maintain higher blood glucose levels and purge via glycosuria, to what extent do chronically higher than desirable levels of blood glucose contribute to earlier and more serious retinopathy, renal disease, hypertension, neuropathy, and other diabetic complications?

Although definitive answers to all of these questions are not yet available, recent technological advances have provided some preliminary answers to some of them. Methods have become available for the easy and accurate determination of blood glucose levels, permitting serum glucose testing to be performed in the home several times a day. Such close monitoring has made more exacting and refined insulin and dietary management possible. Research has also shown that glycosylated hemoglobin (HbA$_{1c}$) measurements can provide a reasonably accurate indicator of blood glucose control for the 1–2 months before the measurement. Elevated levels indicate on the average higher blood glucose levels. Of note, HbA$_{1c}$ is *not* elevated in nondiabetic bulimic patients (Feldman et al. 1990).

In past years many diabetologists allowed their patients relatively loose control of blood glucose, particularly among difficult to manage adolescent patients, who are prone to develop episodes of hypoglycemia with the risks of mental confusion and, potentially, seizures because of excessive exercise (Cryer and Gerich 1985). Evidence now supports the value of closer and tighter control of blood glucose levels and suggests that maintaining blood glucose at near normal levels (i.e., 80–120 mg/dl) is associated with a decreased rate in the development of complications, or even in the slow reversal of complications such as neuropathy and early retinopathy. However, effects on early nephropathy have not been obvious (Ginsberg-Fellner 1990).

Bale (1973) reported that repeated episodes of hypoglycemia predisposed diabetic subjects to make more errors on a standardized new word learning test than controls. Low scores were correlated significantly with a previous history of hypoglycemic episodes but not with the duration of illness. (Of course, given that this was a cross-sectional study, rather than attributing the cognitive problems to repeated episodes of hypoglycemia, one might as easily conclude that patients with poor cognitive capacity maintain their IDDM less well and are more prone to suffer hypoglycemic episodes.) Lawson et al. (1984) failed to find evidence of cognitive impairment in a group of younger diabetic patients who were ill for a shorter period of time.

The management of the IDDM patient uncomplicated by eating disorders is complicated enough!

Psychological Problems in IDDM

Although it is beyond the scope of this chapter to fully review all the psychological and psychiatric problems encountered among patients with IDDM, a brief survey will provide perspective to the subsequent discussions of eating disorders in IDDM. Suffice it to say that this area has received a great deal of attention and interest for many years, at least since the 1940s (Dunbar 1943).

The majority of patients and families with IDDM adapt constructively to the illness, although most find the accommodation effortful and requiring considerable strength (Tattersall 1981). Variations vary from delay or denial in accepting the realistic implications of the short-term demands and longer-term course to preoccupying overconcern and rumination about the illness and its complications. The success of coping depends on a multitude of factors including the child's age and developmental stage; the intellectual, emotional, and social resources of the child and family; and the family's attitudes toward the child and toward diabetes (Cerreto and Travis 1884; Johnson 1980). The problems of control are often greater with adolescents; noncompliance with dietary and insulin regimens is a common correlate of even normal adolescent moodiness, irritability, demoralization, and rebelliousness (Belmont et al. 1981; Mazze et al. 1984).

The problems of adolescents who have to cope with balancing dietary intake with high energy physical activity are well known. A subgroup of "brittle" diabetic patients (those who develop frequent episodes of diabetic ketoacidosis [DKA], hypoglycemia, and other types of dyscontrol) have been linked to active rebellion against the perceived and real differences in life-style between diabetic adolescents and their healthy peers. In addition, control issues play an important role in the genesis of family problems in this patient group. Minuchin (1974) described a family pattern among patients with "superlabile" diabetes similar to that among patients with anorexia nervosa: one characterized by enmeshment, overprotectiveness, rigidity, and avoidance of conflict resolution. One review (Johnson 1980) noted that patients whose diabetes was well controlled described their mothers as being highly supportive at the onset of the disease but becoming less supportive over time; children whose diabetes was poorly controlled described the opposite pattern.

In uncontrolled surveys, a high prevalence of psychiatric symptoms such as depression and anxiety was found among patients who attended diabetes clinics (Surridge et al. 1984; Wilkinson et al. 1987), but this morbidity was not related to the degree of glycemic control or to diabetic complications (Wilkinson et al. 1987). Furthermore, no one has established that the prevalence of these symptoms is greater among diabetic patients than among the population at large.

Prevalence of Eating Disorders in IDDM

Several reports have described attempts to ascertain the prevalence of eating disorders among IDDM populations. Before interpreting the findings of these studies (Table 8–1), a few points should be made. First, most of these studies examined diabetes clinic populations whose patients varied in age and sociodemography. The prevalence of eating disorders would be expected to be higher among groups with younger

Table 8–1. Prevalence of eating disorders among patients with insulin-dependent diabetes mellitus

Study	Reported prevalence	Methods
Hudson et al. 1985	35% BN No AN	264 diabetic females (aged 14–25) assessed with two-page questionnaire; 30% response rate
Lloyd et al. 1987	Diabetic females had higher scores on modified EAT and EDI	147 diabetic females (aged 16–25)
Popkin et al. 1988	2.4% BN	48 diabetic females (aged 16–55) assessed with DIS
Powers et al. 1990	2.2% BN	46 diabetic females (average age 15.5) assessed with a 44-item questionnaire
Rodin et al. 1985	6.5% AN 6.5% BN	46 unselected diabetic females assessed with EAT and EDI
Rodin et al. 1986-1987	6.9% AN	58 diabetic females (aged 15–22)
Rosmark et al. 1986	9% had eating disorder	41 diabetic females (aged 16–39) assessed with EAT plus records
Steel et al. 1987	5.8% AN 1.4% BN	208 diabetic females (aged 16–25)
Surridge et al. 1984	No BN	23 selected diabetic females (average age 38)
Wing et al. 1986	No increased BN	202 adolescents (male and female; aged 12 or older) assessed with EAT and BES

Note.   AN = anorexia nervosa; BN = bulimia nervosa; EAT = Eating Attitudes Test (Garner and Garfinkel 1979); EDI = Eating Disorders Inventory (Garner et al. 1983); BES = Binge Eating Scale (Gormally et al. 1982; Marcus et al. 1988); DIS = Diagnostic Interview Schedule (Robins et al. 1981).

mean ages. For example, the 2.4% prevalence rate for bulimia nervosa (among 48 patients) found by Popkin et al. (1988) was based on a population whose average age was 31, and the complete absence of bulimia nervosa (among 23 patients) reported by Surridge et al. (1984) was based on a population whose average age was 38, both much higher than the average ages of populations surveyed in other studies examining the prevalence of eating disorders in young adults.

Second, the ascertainment methods varied considerably from study to study. The highest reported prevalence (35% of 264 patients) was based on an anonymous questionnaire study (Hudson et al. 1985) using a instrument based on DSM-III (American Psychiatric Association 1980) that yielded a response rate of only 30%. If one assumes, as the authors discussed, that none of the nonresponders had an eating disorder, it is conceivable that the true prevalence in this middle and upper-middle class young (average age 18) population may have been roughly 10%. The authors also pointed out that bulimia is often undetected by diabetes clinicians; none of the seven cases they reported had been diagnosed as having bulimia (MS Hudson et al. 1983). The physicians caring for these patients never asked about binge-eating episodes despite the fact that many had poor control over their diabetes.

Another concern is that several of the studies based their estimates on findings derived from the Eating Attitudes Test (EAT; Garner and Garfinkel 1979), the Eating Disorders Inventory (EDI; Garner et al. 1983), and the Binge Eating Scale (BES; Gormally et al. 1982; Marcus et al. 1988). These instruments have not been standardized on populations of women with IDDM. Consequently, several of the studies made allowances for those scale items that one would expect to be "abnormal" among patients with IDDM (who are always carefully attending to their diets and bodies) to prevent overinflation of the estimates of eating disorders. Lloyd et al. (1987) removed 6 of the 40 items from the EAT, as well as items from the EDI that might be answered differently by diabetic patients and, using a control group of peers and acquaintances selected by the patients, found that the diabetic patients still had higher scores on both instruments, indicating that they indeed had a higher prevalence of eating disorders. Rosmark et al. (1986) obtained similar findings in a study using only a modified (36-item) version of the EAT. In contrast, using an abbreviated (26-item) EAT and setting aside those items comprising the "dieting" factor of the scale, Wing et al. (1986) found no differences between the scores of diabetic and control adolescents. Conceivably the amended, briefer version of the EAT loses sensitivity in discriminating between these populations. On the other hand, using strict DSM-III-R criteria (American Psychiatric Association 1987), Powers et al. (1990) reported a prevalence of 2.2% of bulimia nervosa (1 of 46 females, average age 15.5 years) among patients in a university pediatric diabetes clinic.

Although in the aggregate these data support the idea that a high prevalence of eating disorders may be found among adolescent and young adult female patients with IDDM and that the prevalence may, indeed, be higher than that among their peers, not all studies concur, and the issue is clearly not settled. Looking at the question the other way around (i.e., the prevalence of IDDM among series of patients with eating disorders) yields conflicting results. Although Nielsen et al. (1987) found 25 female patients with IDDM in a consecutive series of 242 patients with eating disorders (10%), other series examining the medical complications of eating-disordered patients have reported IDDM as an occasional, but not generally prominent, finding (Garfinkel and Garner 1982; Hall and Beresford 1989; Patton et al. 1986).

Nevertheless, abnormalities in glucose metabolism, glucagon secretion, and insulin sensitivity are not uncommon in patients with anorexia nervosa, even to the point of having glucose tolerance tests that would be consistent with the impairments of glucose metabolism seen in diabetes (Casper et al. 1988; Kiriike et al. 1990). However, these abnormalities are likely to disappear with recovery from the eating disorder (Casper et al. 1988). Pancreatic secretory abnormalities sometimes seen in anorexia nervosa or bulimia nervosa, or even frank pancreatitis, are not likely to affect the endocrine function or produce diabetic syndromes (Gavish et al. 1987; Kobayashi et al. 1988; Nordgren and von Scheele 1977).

Complications of Diabetes Mellitus and Eating Disorders Comorbidity

M. S. Hudson et al. (1983) reported high total HbA1c levels in bulimic diabetic patients and found that the standard approach to diabetic control, nutritional education, and assignment of a fixed caloric diet was inadequate in managing these patients' illness.

Among the 15 diabetic patients with eating disorders described by Steel et al. (1987)—7% of 208 clinic patients in their sample—2 had normal-weight bulimia; 2 had anorexia nervosa, restricting subtype; 8 had anorexia nervosa, bulimic subtype; 2 had probable anorexia nervosa; and 1 had binge eating and glycosuric purging. Of these patients, 11 were judged to have poor control of their diabetes, as measured by HbA1c, and 4 had only moderate control. Eleven had retinopathy (proliferative in 6), 6 had nephropathy (2 with renal hypertension and 1 other requiring dialysis), 4 had painful neuropathy (which partially improved after weight gain and improvement in eating disorders symptoms), 5 had episodes of DKA, and 3 had episodes of severe hypoglycemia. In 4 of the

6 patients with proliferative retinopathy, this condition developed when the patients were suffering from anorexia nervosa—at that stage the patients had had IDDM for 12 years or less. With respect to the 4 patients with painful neuropathy, the authors noted that no other young diabetic females in their clinic developed this condition. Of these 4 patients, only those who gained weight had even a partial improvement of this symptom. Of the 4 diabetic eating-disordered patients without complications, 2 had been diabetic for too short a time for clinical complications to manifest themselves (one patient for 1 year and the other for 6 years).

Of note, in an analysis of the life-long patterns of these patients, the authors found that poor control of their diabetes was not confined to or even intensified by the duration of their eating disorders. They found hyperglycemia to be just as bad before as after the eating disorder, as judged by HbA1c levels. Seven of the 11 patients with poor control had managed to avoid episodes of severe hypoglycemia or DKA completely. Furthermore, 3 of the 4 patients with histories of recurrent DKA showed no increase in these episodes after the appearance of their eating disorders, whereas the fourth case was completely free from DKA or medical hospital admission only during the 4 years in which she had anorexia nervosa! On the basis of these observations, the authors suggested that although the course of IDDM may be more complicated in patients with eating disorders, the alternative must also be considered: that eating disorders are more likely to develop in patients with more difficult to control IDDM (Steel et al. 1987). This hypothesis, as yet unproven, contradicts conventional wisdom as well as the tentative conclusions drawn in the review by Hillard and Hillard (1984) described below.

In a subsequent study of 147 of these same women, the HbA1c levels correlated positively with the total modified EAT score and, less strongly, with the total EDI and several subscales' scores (Lloyd et al. 1987). These findings are similar to those reported by Rodin et al. (1986–1987), who found that among their diabetic patients with bulimia nervosa, HbA1c levels correlated highly with the current severity of the bulimic symptoms. In a study of "subclinical eating disorders" and glycemic control, Wing et al. (1986) found, in accord with the studies above, that self-reported bulimic behaviors as measured by the bulimia nervosa subscale of the EAT and by the BES were related to glycemic control as measured by HbA1c. Patients who scored highest on the BES had HbA1c levels of 13.1%, those scoring at the 50th percentile had levels of 11.8%, and those with low scores had levels of 10.8%. With regard to specific IDDM complications, patients with retinopathy were found to have higher scores on the EAT and several EDI subscales than those who did not (Lloyd et al. 1987).

In a series of five IDDM patients (Nielson et al. 1987), four had anorexia nervosa (of whom at least one also had bulimic symptoms), and one had normal-weight bulimia nervosa. At the time the article was written only one patient was doing well psychosocially: a 20-year-old woman, who had recovered from a brief course of anorexia nervosa, restricting subtype (begun at age 18) and remitted after a 6-month hospitalization. Subsequently she married, had a child, and had no complications of her IDDM. A second patient with anorexia nervosa, restricting subtype, age 24, had no complications of IDDM but was psychosocially impaired. She always meticulously regulated her IDDM and maintained her weight under ideal on 1,500 kcal/day.

The other two anorexic patients also had poor control of their diabetes. One, age 26, had concurrent bulimia, borderline personality disorder, and alcohol abuse and had proliferative retinopathy and nephropathy as complications of her unstable course of IDDM. The bulimic patient also had borderline personality disorder, poor glycemic control, and retinopathy. The two patients with borderline features underwent extensive psychiatric treatment including hospitalizations, psychotherapy, and medication, with little evident improvement. As a group, these cases suggest that the course of IDDM may be worse among patients whose anorexia nervosa, bulimic subtype, and bulimia nervosa are accompanied by an impulse-ridden personality disorder.

On the whole, these findings agree with those reported in an earlier review (Hillard and Hillard 1984) of 22 cases, including cases reported by Bruch (1973), Fairburn and Steel (1980), Hillard et al. (1983), MS Hudson et al. (1983), Powers et al. (1983), and Szmukler and Russell (1983). The reviewers suggested that diabetic patients with eating disorders are more likely to have complicated courses and that in general they do not have good clinical outcomes. They also suggested that bulimic patients, with or without anorexia nervosa, have more difficulty controlling their blood glucose levels. The reviewers cautioned that these findings may in part result from the fact that physicians are more likely to make the diagnosis of an eating disorder in complicated rather than uncomplicated cases. As mentioned above, the "chicken-or-the-egg" problem of eating disorders and complications in IDDM is still a matter of controversy.

At least one case report has suggested that the death of a diabetic patient with anorexia nervosa was directly attributable to a hypoglycemic episode (Gomez et al. 1980), a finding also described among nondiabetic patients with anorexia nervosa who developed hypoglycemia as a result of fulminant infection (Copeland and Herzog 1987). Some patients with anorexia nervosa increase their insulin intake in an attempt to lose more weight, trying to see just how much they can get away with, and as a result provoke serious hypoglycemic episodes (Rodin et al. 1986–1987). Researchers have also noted growth retardation in IDDM patients with anorexia nervosa, suggesting that the combination of the two disorders makes stunted growth more likely than would be the case with either condition alone (Nielsen et al. 1987; Rodin et al. 1986–1987).

Management

Although the literature regarding treatment for these patients is sparse, the difficulty of managing their disorders is repeatedly stated, and no "received wisdom" is evident, several worthwhile directions do exist. Not surprisingly, the nature and success of treatment depend on the availability, dedication, and competence of the treatment team, as well as on some specific qualities of the patient, including a sustaining desire and motivation to improve and do well, discipline, stick-to-itiveness, and an externally supportive emotional and material environment. On the other hand, patients who are not clearly dedicated to getting better (or who have given up the idea that improvement is possible); whose emotions, thoughts, and behaviors toward their illnesses and most other aspects of life are tumultuously erratic and undisciplined; whose environments not only lack emotional support but contain harshly critical family or friends; and who lack the material means to obtain food, medicine, or services are extremely trying and difficult to treat in the best of hands.

Case examples. Our experiences run the gamut of these extremes, as is briefly illustrated by the following cases:

Case 1

Ms. A, an obese, pleasant 22-year-old college student who had had diabetes since age 7, was referred by her internist because she confided in him that for the previous year she engaged in binge-eating and purging episodes several times a week. She came from a generally supportive and financially comfortable family. From the onset of her illness, her mother had taken pains to see that she received the best care, that she and the family were fully informed about diabetes, and that her life should in every way possible be normal. Consequently, she had very few episodes of any control difficulties throughout her life, and her only hospitalization for diabetes occurred when it first appeared. There were no diabetic complications present. She carefully monitored her blood glucose levels and adjusted her insulin intake accordingly. Her habitus unfortunately resembled that of her obese father rather than that of her more fashionable mother. The eating disorder began in late adolescence, at a time when Ms. A's family moved from the rural South to a much more weight-conscious Los Angeles neighborhood. She started college and joined a prestigious, but extremely fashion- and appearance-conscious sorority, in which many of the sorority sisters were known to be actively bulimic and/or recovering from anorexia nervosa.

Once Ms. A revealed her bulimic condition to her mother and internist, she received a great deal of understanding and support. Her mother, a very attentive and excellent confidant, and her sister, also a staunch ally, were kind, understanding, and supportive. The internist arranged weekly meetings with a warm, flexible nutritionist who was knowledgeable about diabetes and eating disorders, and with this program the patient's episodes of purging decreased, although she still had troubling eating binges. At this point she started in weekly cognitive behavioral psychotherapy. She also started a relationship with a warm, solicitous boyfriend who from the outset of their relationship was told about her bulimia and who made himself as helpful as possible.

During the initial stages of psychotherapy it became evident that Ms. A's eating binges were not only related to a desire to keep her weight to a realistic level for her but that they occurred at times when she felt ineffective in confronting her intimidating and sometimes overbearing father over various disagreements. Whereas the rest of the family had, more or less, acquiesced to the father's wishes, she alone would stand up to him and take him on, but often find herself frustrated and defeated. Once these conflictual issues were clarified and she learned and practiced other tactics to use in these family encounters, the extent of her binge eating diminished considerably to the point where the bulimic symptoms were of little concern. Her weight remained high.

Case 2

Ms. B, a 28-year-old thin, attractive waitress and aspiring actress, had had diabetes mellitus since age 12 and in her late teens had developed an eating disorder characterized by restrictive dieting alternating with episodes of binge eating and purging. Although she had previously been quite thin, her weight was within the normal range for the previous few years. However, her binge-eating and purging episodes, occurring several times a week, often left her lightheaded and dazed.

Ms. B came from a broken family. Her alcoholic, self-absorbed mother had divorced her ne'er-do-well, abusive father when Ms. B was in her early teens. By her late teens she had left home, in spite of the difficulties that entailed for her, and got into a series of relationships with narcissistic, often abusive boyfriends. Her relationships, like the rest of her life, were characterized by impulsivity and self-destructive behaviors.

Ms. B also intermittently experimented with drugs and sometimes used alcohol excessively in spite of her concern about alcoholism. She often missed taking her insulin and other medications, often missed scheduled appointments with her internist, and ate irregularly. Her motivation to care for herself was intermittent, and she often felt hopeless or seemingly unconcerned about her future. She made some efforts to connect with a psychiatrist provided for her through our clinic, but she often had difficulties keeping her appointments. By the time she was first seen she had already developed troubling neuropathies and retinopathy.

It's fairly safe to predict that most clinicians would find patient A relatively easy to treat, whereas patient B would be quite difficult.

Peveler and Fairburn (1989) provided an excellent example of the successful application of slightly modified cognitive behavior therapy for a patient with both anorexia nervosa and IDDM who falls into the relatively easy-to-treat category, although not as easy as the patient described above. The patient was a 5'5", 22-year-old laboratory worker, who became diabetic at age 10, gained weight to 25 lb above ideal weight, and was diagnosed as having hypothyroidism at age 14. In the course of about 3 months during which she "successfully" decreased her weight from 137 to 105 lb, she suffered repeated bouts of hypoglycemia, self-induced through manipulation of her diet and insulin. An outpatient program of weekly cognitive behavior therapy was instituted, using education, meal planning, and monitoring of eating, thoughts, insulin, blood glucose, and weight. HbA_{1c} and various self-rating scales were monitored at appropriate intervals as well.

During the first 4 weeks of treatment her weight fell to about 95 lb. Hospitalization was considered but was averted when she agreed to a weight-gain program. The successful therapy consisted of 24 weekly sessions followed by 14 sessions every other week. At 3-months follow-up after termination she was maintaining her weight near 120 lb. In addition to the well-known cognitions characteristic of garden-variety eating-disordered patients, elicited thoughts in this patient included "How dare you eat if your sugar level isn't perfect," and "This hypo [i.e., episode of hypoglycemia] serves you right for not managing your diabetes properly."

In a later paper on the treatment of a series of consecutive patients with anorexia nervosa or bulimia nervosa and IDDM using a modified form of cognitive behavior therapy, Peveler and Fairburn (1990) reported that treatment took longer and was more complex than that for nondiabetic eating-disordered patients and that "adjunctive" psychological and physical treatment interventions were sometimes needed.

Behavioral programs, at least in the initial stages of hospital management for diabetic patients with anorexia nervosa, are also strongly advocated by Powers et al. (1983). Three of the four patients they described seemed to have improved in the short run with the aid of such programs. Hillard and Hillard (1984) offered several specific guidelines for clinical management. Based in part on their suggestions, within the context of a comprehensive, holistic, biopsychosocial approach that requires constant communication among all the various members of the treatment team, the following strategies seem worthwhile:

1. Assessment should be thorough for all aspects of both the IDDM and eating disorder. Biological assessment must consider dietary management and degree of glycemic control, carefully balancing the need to avoid hypoglycemic episodes with the long-term goal of keeping the blood glucose as close to normal as possible so as to minimize the development of complications. Psychological assessment must consider conflicts regarding autonomy and dependence, the excessive focus on weight and diet, low self-esteem, depression, and denial of illness. Social assessment must consider the family and other support systems with respect to helping and potentially harmful factors.

2. Adequate initial control of diabetes may require inpatient treatment with frequent, even daily, modifications in insulin dosage. In the view of Hillard and Hillard (1984), with the eating-disordered patient it is better to at least start treatment with a less restrictive rather than more restrictive program, accepting somewhat poorer control (i.e., higher blood glucose levels) than is optimal. As the patient's clinical conditions improve, tighter controls can be established through mutually agreed to goal setting. Because of the erratic eating schedules and missed meals characteristic of bulimic anorexic patients, the use of "bolus-basal" therapy has the potential of improving these patients' control of their diabetes (Bernstein 1981; Schiffrin 1982; Skyler et al. 1981). The principle of this therapy is to administer regular insulin before each eating period (the equivalent of breakfast, lunch, and supper) plus a long-acting insulin, such as ultralente insulin added to a single dose with the morning regular insulin, that will control the fasting blood glucose level for the next morning. Because the duration of action for ultralente insulin exceeds 24 hours it provides a basal amount of insulin throughout the day and night. This basal insulin provides sufficient control over the tendency to early A.M. hyperglycemia (known as dawn phenomenon) thought to be related to increases in counterregulatory hormones. The bolus-basal approach to controlling blood glucose levels for eating-disordered patients can be modified by splitting the ultralente insulin and administering half with breakfast and half with supper. This is useful for patients who experience hypoglycemia midday because of missed meals or prolonged exercise periods unaccompanied by preexercise carbohydrate intake. In yet a third modification of this regimen, an intermediate-acting insulin, such as NPH or lente, is administered at bedtime or with the evening regular insulin. This modification may be sufficient to control the following morning's fasting blood glucose level and avoid the potential risk of midday hypoglycemia.
3. The eating disorder treatment program should utilize all the familiar components, including hospitalization as necessary; individual, family, and group psychotherapy; support groups; self-help organizations; and medications as necessary and indicated.

Finally, although not specifically addressing the eating-disordered patient with diabetes, the suggestions offered by Boehnert and Popkin (1986), who discuss the treatment of severely noncompliant diabetic patients, can be very useful to clinicians who are struggling with difficult patients, such as Ms. B. Their descriptions of the problems facing the clinician who takes on the challenge of treating the IDDM patient with severe borderline, narcissistic, and histrionic personality disorders, borrowing heavily from the guidelines provided by Groves (1978) in his classic discussion of the "hateful" patient, are important to review. The following issues apply:

1. Clinicians who take responsibility for the ongoing treatment of these difficult patients must monitor their countertransference very carefully and consider whether they are psychologically prepared and in the proper dedicated and giving frame of mind to undertake this treatment. Starting with a counterproductive attitude will be a mistake for the patient, as well as for the clinician.
2. Clinicians should be prepared to devote a considerable amount of time, especially at the outset, to establishing a working alliance. They can expect to be sorely and severely tested for integrity and limit setting, a target of anger and derision for all of life's disappointments and travails including the diabetes, alternatively idealized as someone expected to satisfy dependency needs and ragefully denigrated as not being able to satisfy them, and set up for staff "splits." Furthermore, clinicians should expect such patients to act out by omitting insulin or meals and should not expect to see rapid results. Indeed, with the initial testing of therapeutic limits patients may even regress.
3. Clinicians must plan to deal with patients directly and proactively around several very common themes: denial or at least severe minimization of illness with associated magical thinking and splitting; the need for consistency; grieving lost possibilities; vulnerabilities; demoralization, depression, and death wishes; and family issues. Even the most experienced clinician will benefit from regular, ongoing consultations with experienced colleagues in dealing with these patients. We, as well as our patients and their families, will benefit from all available assistance.

References

American Psychiatric Association: Diagnostic and Statistical Manual of Mental Disorders, 3rd Edition. Washington, DC, American Psychiatric Association, 1980

American Psychiatric Association: Diagnostic and Statistical Manual of Mental Disorders, 3rd Edition, Revised. Washington, DC, American Psychiatric Association, 1987

Bale RN: Brain damage in diabetes mellitus. Br J Psychiatry 122:337–341, 1973

Belmont MM, Gunn T, Gauthier M: The problem of "cheating" in the diabetic child and adolescent. Diabetes Care 4:116–120, 1981

Bernstein RK: Diabetes: The Glucograph Method for Normalizing Blood Sugar. New York, Crown, 1981

Brooks SA: Diabetes mellitus and anorexia nervosa: another view. Br J Psychiatry 144:640–642, 1984

Bruch H: Eating Disorders: Obesity, Anorexia and the Person Within. New York, Basic Books, 1973

Boehnert CE, Popkin MK: Psychological issues in treatment of severely non-compliant diabetics. Psychosomatics 27:11–20, 1986

Casper RC, Pandey G, Jaspan JB, et al: Eating attitudes and glucose tolerance in anorexia nervosa patients at 8 year follow-up compared to control subjects. Psychiatry Res 25:283–299, 1988

Cerreto MC, Travis LB: Implications of psychological and family factors in the treatment of diabetes mellitus. Pediatr Clin North Am 31:689–710, 1984

Copeland PM, Herzog DB: Hypoglycemia and death in anorexia nervosa. Psychother Psychosom 48:146–150, 1987

Cryer PE, Gerich JE: Glucose counterregulation, hypoglycemia, and intensive insulin therapy in diabetes mellitus. N Engl J Med 313:232–240, 1985

Dunbar F: Psychosomatic Diagnosis. New York, Hoeber, 1943

Fairburn CG, Steel JM: Anorexia nervosa in diabetes mellitus. Br Med J 1:1167–1168, 1980

Feldman J, Robinson P, Smith B, et al: Glycosylated hemoglobin in bulimia nervosa. International Journal of Eating Disorders 9:209–210, 1990

Garfinkel PE, Garner DM: Anorexia Nervosa: A Multidimensional Perspective. New York, Brunner/Mazel, 1982

Garner DM, Garfinkel PE: The Eating Attitudes Test: an index of the symptoms of anorexia nervosa. Psychol Med 9:273–279, 1979

Garner DM, Olmsted MP, Polivy J: Development and validation of a multidimensional eating disorder inventory for anorexia nervosa and bulimia. International Journal of Eating Disorders 2:15–34, 1983

Garner S: Anorexia nervosa in diabetes mellitus. Br Med J 2:1144, 1980

Gavish D, Eisenberg S, Berry H, et al: Bulimia: an underlying behavioral disorder in hyperlipidemic pancreatitis: a prospective multidisciplinary approach. Arch Intern Med 147:705–708, 1987

Ginsberg-Fellner F: Insulin-dependent diabetes mellitus. Pediatr Rev 11:239–247, 1990

Gomez J, Dally P, Isaacs AJ: Anorexia in diabetes mellitus. Br Med J 2:61–62, 1980

Gormally J, Black S, Daston S, et al: The assessment of binge eating severity among obese persons. Addict Behav 7:47–55, 1982

Groves JE: Taking care of the hateful patient. N Engl J Med 298:883–887, 1978

Hall RCW, Beresford TP: Medical complications of anorexia and bulimia. Psychiatr Med 7:165–192, 1989

Hillard JR, Hillard PJA: Bulimia, anorexia nervosa and diabetes: deadly combinations. Psychiatr Clin North Am 7:367–379, 1984

Hillard JR, Lobo MC, Keeling RP: Bulimia and diabetes: a potentially life-threatening combination. Psychosomatics 24:292–295, 1983

Hudson JI, Hudson MS, Wentworth SM: Self-induced glycosuria: a novel method of purging in bulimia (ltr). JAMA 249:2501, 1983

Hudson JR, Wentworth SM, Hudson MS, et al: Prevalence of anorexia nervosa and bulimia among young diabetic women. J Clin Psychiatry 46:88–89, 1985

Hudson MS, Wentworth SM, Hudson JI: Bulimia and diabetes. N Engl J Med 309:431–432, 1983

Johnson J: Psychosocial factors in juvenile diabetes: a review. J Behav Med 3:95–116, 1980

Kiriike N, Nishiwaki S, Nagata T, et al: Insulin sensitivity in patients with anorexia nervosa and bulimia. Acta Psychiatr Scand 81:236–239, 1990

Kobayashi N, Tamain H, Uehata S, et al: Pancreatic abnormalities in patients with eating disorders. Psychosomatic Med 50:607–614, 1988

Lawson JS, Williams Erdahl DL, Monga TN, et al: Neuropsychological function in diabetic patients with neuropathy. Br J Psychiatry 145:263–268, 1984

Lloyd GG, Steel JM, Young RJ: Eating disorders and psychiatric morbidity in patients with diabetes mellitus. Psychother Psychosom 48:189–195, 1987

Marcus MD, Wing RR, Hopkins J: Obese binge eaters: affect, cognition and response to behavioral weight control. J Consult Clin Psychol 56:433–439, 1988

Mazze RS, Lucido D, Shamoom H: Psychological and social correlates of glycemic control. Diabetes Care 7:360–366, 1984

Minuchin S: Families and Family Therapy. Cambridge, MA, Harvard University Press, 1974

Nielsen S, Berner H, Kabel M: Anorexia nervosa/bulimia in diabetes mellitus: a review and a presentation of five cases. Acta Psychiatr Scand 75:464–473, 1987

Nordgren L, von Scheele C: Hepatic and pancreatic dysfunction in anorexia nervosa: a report of two cases. Biol Psychiatry 12:681–686, 1977

Patton GC, Wood K, Johnson-Sabine E: Physical illness: a risk factor in anorexia nervosa. Br J Psychiatry 149:756–759, 1986

Peveler RC, Fairburn CG: Anorexia nervosa in association with diabetes mellitus:

a cognitive-behavioral approach to treatment. Behav Res Ther 27:95–99, 1989

Peveler RC, Fairburn CG: Treatment of eating disorders in patients with diabetes mellitus. Paper presented at the Fourth International Conference on Eating Disorders, New York, April 1990

Popkin MK, Callies AI, Lentz RD, et al: Prevalence of major depression, simple phobia and other psychiatric disorders in patients with long-standing type I diabetes mellitus. Arch Gen Psychiatry 45:64–68, 1988

Powers PS, Malone JI, Duncan JA: Anorexia nervosa and diabetes mellitus. J Clin Psychiatry 44:133–135, 1983

Powers PS, Malone JI, Coovert DL, et al: Insulin-dependent diabetes mellitus and eating disorders: a prevalence study. Compr Psychiatry 31:205–210, 1990

Robins LN, Helzer JE, Coughan J, et al: National Institute of Mental Health Diagnostic Interview Schedule: its history, characteristics, and validity. Arch Gen Psychiatry 38:381–389, 1981

Rodin GM, Daneman D, Johnson LE, et al: Anorexia nervosa and bulimia in female adolescents with insulin-dependent diabetes mellitus: a systematic study. J Psychiatr Res 19:381–384, 1985

Rodin GM, Johnson LE, Garfinkel PE, et al: Eating disorders in female adolescents with insulin-dependent diabetes mellitus. Int J Psychiatry Med 16:49–57, 1986–1987

Rosmark B, Berne C, Holmgren S, et al: Eating disorders in patients with insulin-dependent diabetes mellitus. J Clin Psychiatry 47:547–550, 1986

Schiffrin A: Treatment of insulin-dependent diabetes with multiple subcutaneous insulin injections. Med Clin North Am 66:1251–1267, 1982

Skyler JS, Skyler DL, Seigler DE, et al: Algorithms for adjustment of insulin dosage by patients who monitor blood glucose. Diabetes Care 4:311–318, 1981

Steel JM, Young RJ, Lloyd GG, et al: Clinically apparent eating disorders in young diabetic women: association with painful neuropathy and other complications. Br Med J 294:859–862, 1987

Surridge DHC, Williams Erdahl DL, Lawson JS, et al: Psychiatric aspects of diabetes mellitus. Br J Psychiatry 145:269–276, 1984

Szmukler GI, Russell GFM: Diabetes mellitus, anorexia nervosa and bulimia. Br J Psychiatry 142:305–308, 1983

Tattersall RB: Psychiatric aspects of diabetes: a physician's view. Br J Psychiatry 139:485–493, 1981

Wilkinson G, Borsey DQ, Leslie P, et al: Psychiatric disorder in patients with insulin-dependent diabetes mellitus attending a general hospital clinic i) two stage screening and ii) detection by physicians. Psychol Med 17:515–517, 1987

Wing RR, Nowalk MP, Marcus MD, et al: Subclinical eating disorders and glycemic control in adolescents with type I diabetes. Diabetes Care 9:162–167, 1986

Chapter 9

Patients With Chronic, Recalcitrant Eating Disorders

Joel Yager, M.D.

*D*espite considerable research in the treatment of eating disorders recently, large numbers of patients with these conditions do not improve and have seemingly intractable courses (Garfinkel and Garner 1982; Hsu 1980, 1988; Schwartz and Thompson 1981; Steinhausen and Glanville 1983). Indeed, both short-term and longer-term follow-up studies of patients with anorexia nervosa indicate that full recovery occurs in fewer than half of the patients studied, and in well-conducted studies an average of about 20% of the survivors have poor outcomes. Many patients remain chronically symptomatic and disabled. In two follow-up studies of 20 years or more (Ratnasuriya et al. 1989; Theander 1985) the death rate was between 15 and 20%. Representative longer-term follow-up studies for anorexia nervosa and the percentages of poor outcome patients reported are illustrated in Table 9–1.

Comparable studies have not yet been conducted for bulimia nervosa. However, poor outcome in bulimia nervosa is also known to be common, especially among patients requiring hospitalization—up to 80% have been reported to have poor outcome (Swift et al. 1987). Moreover, among patients who have both bulimia nervosa and anorexia nervosa poor outcomes are notorious (Russell 1979). At least among bulimic patients seeking help, we can also infer that chronicity is often the rule, rather than the exception, from the common observation that patients initially presenting at various well-known university clinics have, on the average, had bulimia nervosa for 6–7 years (Hamburg et al. 1989; Mitchell et al. 1986a).

Supported in part by the Karen Carpenter Memorial Foundation.

Table 9–1. Chronicity in anorexia nervosa: representative studies

Study	Sample size	Average age at onset	Average age at contact	Treatment	Length of follow-up (years)	Percent with chronic illness or poor outcome	% dead
Burns and Crisp 1984	27[a]	18	22	20 hospitalized	2–20 post-assessment (average 8)	30[b]	
Hall et al. 1984	50	16	20	36 hospitalized	4–12 post-assessment (average 8)	26[b]	2
Hsu et al. 1979	105	17	21	Most hospitalized	4–8 post-assessment (average 6)	20[b]	2
Morgan and Russell 1975	38	15.5	< 31	All hospitalized	4–10 post-treatment (average NA)	29[b]	5
Morgan et al. 1983	73	17	< 31	Few hospitalized	4–8 post-evaluation (average NA)	18[b]	1

Study	n					Outcome	Mortality (%)
Ratnasuriya et al. 1989	41	18	21	All hospitalized	> 17 post-admission (average 20)	25[b]	15
Theander 1970	94	NA	NA	All hospitalized	≥ 8 post-treatment (average NA)	15–20[c]	13
Theander 1985 (same series)	94	NA	NA	All hospitalized	20–30 (average NA)	15–20[c]	20
Tolstrup et al. 1985	151	16.6	19	97 hospitalized	4–22 post-assessment (average 12)	19[b]	6

[a] All male patients.
[b] Outcome measure based on Morgan-Russell Outcome Scale (Morgan and Russell 1975).
[c] Estimate based on other data in study.

Recalcitrance in the face of therapeutic effort may or may not have a seemingly volitional component: some patients may be extremely compliant in many respects but not be able to improve in spite of their best efforts and the best therapeutic efforts of the staff (Hamburg et al. 1989). Other patients may be very reluctant and oppositional toward treatment, refusing to engage in or adhere to it for reasons that may appear quirky or capricious. Some patients, perhaps sensing that they are incapable of mastering and changing the overriding obsessional and compulsive aspects of the eating disorders, may try to gain some shred of mastery over their symptoms by convincing themselves that they *want* the symptoms. In other words, because they are powerless to change the symptoms, they may attempt to reduce their internal cognitive dissonance by bringing themselves to believe that the symptoms are a function of their own will and desires. Such beliefs may provide patients with a greater sense of self-efficacy than might otherwise be attainable.

Patients or their families may be so embarrassed by the disorder that they refuse to consider treatment for extended periods of time (Hamburg et al. 1989). Patients' treatment reluctance may be abetted by feelings of humiliation over being sick; by pessimistic views about themselves and their conditions (essentially enduring negative cognitive distortions); by fears that they will lose whatever pleasures or self-esteem they achieve by maintaining certain symptoms; by fears that they will lose self-determination through surrendering decision making to caregivers; and by fears that they will be vulnerable to the unwanted "objective" appraisals of medical authorities (Goldner 1989). On the other hand, the patient or family's reasons for avoiding treatment may, on reflection, seem to be a judicious decision based on repeated bad experiences with professionals or treatment programs.

Whatever the causes, chronicity and recalcitrance in eating-disordered patients can generate frustration and burnout among treating clinicians not too different from reactions described by professionals working with patients with other chronic psychiatric disorders (Ludwig 1971).

In this chapter, I address several clinical questions about the population of patients with chronic, recalcitrant eating disorders:

1. What clinical dimensions are most relevant to chronicity, and what subtypes of patients with chronic eating disorders exist?
2. What do we know about the factors contributing to chronicity and prognosis?

3. How can therapeutic goals be set, and which goals may be countertherapeutic?
4. What unusual treatment approaches are available?
5. What humanistic principles of care should be followed in the treatment of nonresponding patients?
6. What legal means are available for emergency intervention?
7. What countertransference issues emerge, and how can they be approached?
8. How should the family be advised?

Patient Characteristics

For many psychiatric conditions described in DSM-III-R (American Psychiatric Association 1987), chronicity is defined as existing after a disorder has been present for 2 years or more. However, authorities writing about eating disorders have offered differing opinions. For example, based on a study of 140 patients, Dally (Dally 1969; Dally et al. 1979) suggested that after 7 years of illness patients with anorexia nervosa are unlikely to improve. Assessments of this type have not yet been suggested for normal-weight patients with bulimia nervosa. The important empirical question is the extent to which these cutoff points may seem to define different outcomes or have different prognostic implications.

Within the population of patients with chronic eating disorders, several distinctions must be made. First is the distinction between anorexia nervosa and bulimia nervosa. As implied above, sufficient study has shown that patients with chronic low weight and marked anorexic thinking may be considered, at least probabilistically, as unlikely to improve. Such information has not yet been developed for normal-weight bulimia nervosa. Patients with combination syndromes, in which both anorexia nervosa and bulimia nervosa coexist, are thought to be particularly unlikely to improve (Russell 1979).

The second distinction is that between stable and unstable clinical course. Some patients remain at a chronically low weight and keep the same compulsive and obsessional rituals day after day, year after year. Several patients seen in our programs (at the Neuropsychiatric Institute and Hospital at the University of California, Los Angeles [UCLA]), who maintain their body weights at 60–70% of recommended weight, have rarely missed work over a period of decades. Some of them live socially isolated, whereas others enjoy seemingly successful marriages and families. Other patients have a more volatile and unpredictable course, with surges in self-destructive behaviors and emotions and roller coaster weight patterns. These patterns are not mutually exclusive. For reasons that are hard to discern, after a period of chronically low weight and invariable compulsive rituals that have endured for years, some patients may suddenly alter their patterns for the better or worse, showing real improvement or substituting certain new self-damaging behaviors for others (e.g., starting binge-purge cycles or laxative abuse after many years of pure restriction). Some patients alternate between periods of successful restriction, binge eating with purging, and binge eating without purging. As with other complex phenomena throughout nature, more or less predictable patterns of behavior may suddenly and inexplicably (at least to current science) become chaotic, and even though the chaotic elements in such behavior may be governed by deeper rules we seem far from adequately comprehending them (Glieck 1987).

Third, the various psychological, behavioral, social, and physiological dimensions of function and impairment that often contribute to our definitions of "chronicity" are to a considerable extent distinct from one another. Whereas in one patient with a chronic condition the physical and behavioral impairment may be far greater than the psychological and social impairment, in another the exact opposite may be true. One patient may be able to carry out a professional career in spite of low weight and daily episodes of binge eating and purging, whereas another may have disabling degrees of obsessional thinking and compulsive behavior around food and self-image in spite of relative normal weight and infrequent episodes of binge eating or purging.

For the first type of patient, the eating disorder behaviors and mentation are loculated away from the rest of life, which may be productive. Examples of the first type among female patients seen in our programs include a successful stockbroker, a psychiatric social worker who has functioned continuously, a physician, an attorney, and a successfully married mother who maintained a successful business and also completed several graduate degrees after the development of her anorexia nervosa. All of these patients have had anorexia nervosa for 10–20 years, are now in their 40s, have chronically weighed about 60–70% of their expected weight, and have been continuously high functioning professionally. The second type includes a large number of patients whose concurrent avoidance, timidity, anxieties, and dysphorias render them nonfunctional to a degree not easily attributable solely to their eating disorders.

Marked differences in chronic disturbances may occur within a given dimension, such as physical complications. The particular idiosyncratic vulnerabilities that account for why some chronically ill patients develop osteoporosis, severe dental deterioration, or marked pancreatic and salivary gland inflammation and the like, whereas others with comparable levels of eating disorders behavior escape from these complications, remain mysterious.

Of course, many chronically ill patients have total impairment and are unable to function independently or without supervision. Representative patients seen in our program include a 48-year-old woman, who has been ill since her teens and has never been employable and who often takes hundreds of laxative tablets each week, requiring constant observation and frequent hospitalization for medical complications; a 35-year-old nurse, who for the past 15 years has had intermittent periods of relative wellness with sporadic employment alternating with debilitating periods of severe weight loss; a 28-year-old woman, who has been ill since age 16, unable to finish school or work, and living in halfway houses on handouts from her parents; and a 35-year-old intensely avoidant and neophobic woman, who has been ill since age 15, in continuous treatment, in and out of hospitals and day hospitals for repeated episodes of weight loss and marked anxiety, and in a fragile, childless marriage with a timid, fearful man.

Clinically important dimensions of chronicity include the nature and intensity of the specific eating disorders symptoms, personality factors, affective state, and social supports. Eating disorders symptoms vary from simple weight restriction to some of the following patterns occurring in chronically ill patients in our program:

- Bizarre eating rituals marked most dramatically by limiting intake to foods obtained preferentially from certain garbage cans on our campus or behind favorite restaurants in the nearby neighborhood.
- Unyielding cycles of massive binging and purging averaging 8 to 10 times a day that literally consume the entire day and night and persist in spite of frequent episodes of documented hypoglycemia with mental confusion and severe back pain due to pancreatic inflammation (with accompanying serum amylase values chronically in the range of 600–1400 IU/L).

- Acts of severe self-punishment for minor dietary transgressions (e.g., taking a hundred laxative tablets in anticipation of suffering severe cramps and diarrhea for several days for permitting oneself to have eaten more than 300 calories a day).
- Routine consumption of from 50 to 100 laxative tablets a day resulting in chronically severe hypokalemia, fatigue, and frequent mental confusion.

That patients doing such things to themselves go on living for as long as they do is a testimony to the adaptive resilience of the human body.

Personality dimensions differ significantly among patients with chronic eating disorders. Although in general personality features such as rigidity, avoidance, shyness, and fear of novelty are widespread (Casper 1990), the course of illness appears to be strongly influenced by the extent to which any one of these features are present and commingle with qualities such as motivation to get better (Crisp 1980), diligent persistence, achievement orientation, striving for autonomy, affiliative needs, insight, self-awareness, optimism, self-acceptance, self-confidence, and a sense of self-efficacy on the one hand versus self-deception, denial, catastrophizing, pessimistic thinking, poor self-esteem (Fairburn et al. 1987), impulsivity (Sohlberg et al. 1989), and obsessional or histrionic thinking styles on the other.

Not entirely unrelated to these personality traits are the concurrent dimensions of mood disturbance, such as dysphoria, depression, anxiety, and panic, which may be pervasive or intermittent.

As for social supports, the presence of involved family and friends who are accepting and nurturing and can provide emotional support as well as instrumental support, such as the economic means of survival, will make a difference (if not in good versus bad outcome, per se, at least in the quality and extent of a bad outcome). At least with regard to the day-to-day conveniences of life and access to medical care, the amount of money available makes a real difference.

Prognostic Factors Contributing to Chronicity

It should be clear that although many of the factors mentioned below have been statistically related to prognosis for eating-disordered patients, the presence or absence of any one or of even a few factors cannot offer any foolproof guide to a patient's prognosis. If only negative prognostic features are present, probabilities are that the patient is not likely to have a good outcome, but exceptional cases are always encountered.

The literature suggests many different features that appear to be related to poor prognosis in anorexia nervosa, although many are still not entirely settled. Those most strongly suggested by available studies include older age of onset, long duration of illness (chronicity of more than 7 years according to Dally [1969]), lower minimum weight, being married (which may correlate with age), vomiting, personality or social difficulties, and disturbed relationship with family and previous treatment (Hsu 1987b). Other highly suggestive negative prognostic features include bulimic features, laxative abuse, lower socioeconomic status, older maternal age, obsessive-compulsive character traits (Steinhausen and Glanville 1983), persistent soft neuropsychological deficits after weight gain (Hamsher et al. 1981), high negative expressed emotion in families (Szmukler et al. 1985), and parental psychopathology (Crisp et al. 1974). In contrast, M. Strober (October 1990, personal communication) found no characteristic that could predict prognosis in his series of young anorexia nervosa patients hospitalized at UCLA.

Few studies have attempted to calculate the variance accounted for by these variables. In such studies the amount of variance has been modest (Norring 1989; Sohlberg et al. 1989). Even long-standing chronicity in anorexia nervosa does not predict an inevitably poor outcome, as demonstrated by a small group of patients with good outcome at 20 years who had previously been categorized as showing poor outcome after 4 years (Ratnasuriya et al. 1989). Exactly what accounted for the surprising turnarounds in these patients is uncertain, but the implications for clinicians are clear: at least with chronic anorexia nervosa, we still don't know enough to justify complete certainty when we offer dismal prognoses.

Much less is known about long-term outcomes for bulimia nervosa in the absence of anorexia nervosa. However, at least for patients whose illness has been sufficiently severe to require hospitalization, available data suggest that many have unfavorable outcomes (Fallon et al. 1990; H. E. Gwirtsman, R. Apple, J. Yager, May 1991, unpublished observations; Swift et al. 1987). Other studies point to the likelihood that many untreated patients with normal-weight bulimia suffer from chronic conditions (Yager et al. 1987a, 1987b), but persistent treatment approaches may help patients with bulimia nervosa who have been ill for prolonged periods of time (Mitchell et al. 1986b; Pope et al. 1989).

Therapeutic Goals

Patients who have been chronically ill and treatment resistant for many years present several familiar problems for treatment planning. Initial treatment goals are relatively easy to establish for episodes of acute deterioration such as a sudden precipitous weight loss or medical problem in an habitually marginal patient. In such instances the short-term goals will include life-saving interventions, with or without the patient's cooperation. Here the clinician does whatever is necessary to get the patient hospitalized and to provide nutritional support. For longer-term, chronic difficulties, the problems are less simple: the clinician must establish therapeutic goals that neither grossly overestimate what can realistically be achieved nor underestimate the patient's potential.

As with other chronic psychiatric disorders, for any patient with a chronic eating disorder treatment goals are multifaceted and should be specified along discrete dimensions concerning specific symptoms, social and vocational functioning, and utilization of health care services. Specific targets may include increasing weight; reducing specific psychopathological features such as obsessional thinking, ritualistic behaviors, depression, anxiety, and panic attacks; reducing specified physical symptomatology such as gastrointestinal complaints; improving social functioning with family and friends; improving vocational functioning; and reducing the likelihood of rehospitalization. Each of these dimensions warrants independent contemplation and the formulation of separate strategies. Although improvement along one dimension may increase the likelihood of improvement in certain others, even when some of the seemingly central problems such as malnutrition and anorexic attitudes toward food abate, there are no assurances that across-the-board improvements will occur.

Clinicians may be crudely stereotyped and subdivided into those who become very therapeutically aggressive and those who become unduly passive, when faced with intractable problems. The therapeutic stances that clinicians adopt are often closely tied to the clinicians' central personality features rather than to anything "objective" called for by the situation. Clinicians must, therefore, monitor their own therapeutic biases to assess their propensities toward undue therapeutic zeal or toward undue therapeutic helplessness.

In my observations, aggressive clinicians who work with patients suffering from truly chronic syndromes are prey to three common pitfalls: 1) prematurely attributing the patient's poor course to previously inept treatment; 2) cavalierly assuming that one can do better than previous attempts; and 3) setting therapeutic goals too high. The problems that can be created by these errors are considerable.

First, as with chronic schizophrenic patients, if the clinician sets unrealistically high expectations for the patient, the patient may feel even greater internal pressures for doing the impossible than already exist. Such performance pressures generally lead patients to feel even more guilty and disappointed with themselves, shamed in relation to the clinician and family (for failure to perform), and resentful of the clinician and others for establishing, or even hinting at, these expectative demands in the first place. The resulting sense of failure, added to the considerable burden of demoralization already carried by these patients, may lead a patient to give up and occasionally contributes to a suicide.

Second, the clinician whose patient fails to meet expectations may self-critically and nihilistically feel that he or she is a professional failure and may develop angry, resentful feelings toward the patient. These feelings and attitudes may result in nontherapeutic remarks in treatment sessions that blame the victim (e.g., accusing the patient of not wanting to get better) and result in therapeutic neglect.

On the other hand, setting therapeutic expectations too low and expecting virtually no change may lead to inadequate attention given to the possibility of even minor improvements, too little emotional energy being put into the patient, and even to unconscious, often subtle attempts to squelch patient behaviors that might actually represent positive changes. The difficult task for the clinician is to steer between these two poles by steadily setting explicit but very modest goals in a step-wise fashion. Small bits of improvement can be objectified and specified, and additional improvement can be built onto previous steps. When no further improvement is achievable, efforts should be directed toward assuring that the previous small gains are retained and consolidated.

What Unusual Treatment Approaches Are Possible?

Before considering available treatment options, it is important to reemphasize the dangers of being therapeutically overzealous and setting the family's and patient's expectations too high. Even though a clinician may be temperamentally geared against leaving things as they are, some-times the wisest path is to do relatively little. Sometimes less is more.

One particularly problematic situation occurs when a patient's goals are simply to be left alone and the family isn't able to accept noninter-vention. In such cases the clinician must ask him or herself "why not leave the patient alone?" If a patient is not in danger of acutely dying and has come to accept herself at a chronic, dysfunctional, and unlikely-to-change plateau, perhaps the most humane act is to accept the patient's wishes. As in the case of cancer patients who are ready to die but whose families cannot bear the thought and want everything possible done to keep them alive, the proper intervention on the part of the clinician may be to help the family accept this sad situation without forcing the patient to be subjected to a great deal of unwanted and ultimately ineffective and punishing treatment.

On the other hand, previously untried treatments may be justified if they might help yet not harm—where the potential advantages far out-weigh the foreseeable risks. In such situations, if both the patient and family are willing to try the treatment, the intervention is probably worth trying even if the odds of making effective improvements are small.

However, because clinicians must walk where scientists fear to tread, the following therapeutic interventions may be helpful for patients with chronic disorders:

1. Establish a heartfelt connection with the patient to secure a durable and effective working alliance. An inability to make this link, which may sometimes be quite difficult to effect if the patient's personality is uninviting or frozen, may suggest that treatment cannot start. If the patient does not sense a working alliance with the clinician, any attempts at treatment will be experienced by both parties as fights for control and as coercive. Most observers believe that it is important to establish at least some areas of alliance and agreement (e.g., "At least we can both agree that you aren't very happy in your present condi-tion") and that it is generally counterproductive to argue, struggle with, or attempt to scare a resistant patient with chronically low weight (Goldner 1989; Hamburg et al. 1989).
2. Review as fully as possible the nature of previous psychological, psychosocial, and medical (including psychopharmacological) treat-ment attempts and seek both the patient's and caregivers' perceptions of what worked, what failed, and what the likely reasons were for

previous successes and failures. Base future treatment planning on this review.

3. Assess the patient's current true goals for herself. Listen carefully to statements that may include determination to maintain the status quo and try to assess the degree to which such goals are based on depressive distortions or more realistic appraisals.

4. Assess the patient's beliefs about what future treatments might work or not work and why. Plan treatment around the patient's own desires for modality specific intervention (if rationally based) as much as possible.

5. Establish a treatment team that includes a primary care physician and dietitian, in addition to mental health clinicians. The members of this team, who set up what Hamburg et al. (1989) refer to as a "safety envelope," should communicate frequently to assure that each one knows the others' observations and activities.

6. With the patient's active collaboration, attempt to develop a detailed behavioral program and contract, based on life-saving nutritional and medical needs, and/or on small steps directed to psychological, social, and vocational issues. If behavioral programs have not previously been tried, it is possible (although not common) that institution of a sophisticated, not necessarily rigid behavioral program late in the course of a chronic illness may lead to modification of the patient's symptoms and level of functioning. However, except in acutely life-threatening situations, treatment-reluctant chronic patients should not be coerced into dehumanizing, rigidly monitored control battles around eating behavior. Furthermore, in no instance should a program be inherently punitive (Goldner 1989). Such programs, if they work at all, work only for the time they are sustained and over the long run generally yield minimal symptomatic improvement with a large residue of frustration, resentment, and feelings of impotence among the patient and staff alike. Still, basic limits regarding weight and medical severity should be established, beyond which the treatment team will insist that the patient be hospitalized at least for medical stabilization (Hamburg et al. 1989).

7. Consider whether the patient has been properly assessed regarding psychotherapeutic interventions. Even if individual psychotherapy had been offered as part of a treatment program in the past, a reassessment of the potential use of a specific psychotherapeutic approach, which may differ from previously attempted "psychotherapies," is warranted.

Many varieties of psychodynamically based (Garner and Garfinkel 1985), cognitive behavior (Fairburn 1981), behavioral (Agras 1987; Wilson et al. 1986), and other forms of psychotherapy (Hornyak and Baker 1989) have been described for patients with eating disorders, and it is conceivable that a novel approach may help a given patient where others have failed.

8. Family assessment should be undertaken in every case, and family therapy should be considered as a treatment option. The specific benefits of family therapy, especially for patients with onset at a younger age who may still be living at home with their families, have been demonstrated in an elegant study in which the effects of family versus individual therapy for eating disorders were examined (Russell et al. 1987).

9. Given the patient's symptom patterns and attitudes, offer medications that have not previously been used (Garfinkel and Garner 1988; Judd et al. 1987). Patients with chronic anorexia nervosa often have only spotty denial about the existence and severity of their condition and often fully acknowledge that they feel powerless to do anything about it. In my experience, patients with chronic conditions are more likely to accept, or even seek, potentially helpful medications than are patients with disorders in earlier stages. Sometimes patients will try conventional antidepressant medications for the first time, after many years of illness. The potential contributions of medication should be presented realistically, not oversold, and in a spirit of collaboration, with phrases such as "Some people have occasionally found these to be helpful with. . . ." Patients should be given information to read about the medications they will be taking. Less frequently employed medications worth considering (with which our group at UCLA has had occasional success) include

Fluoxetine. Our group was initially reluctant to use this medication for patients with anorexia nervosa because of its association with weight loss, at least at higher doses. Nevertheless, we have now seen about half a dozen patients with chronic anorexia nervosa treated with 20 and occasionally 40 mg/day who have shown surprising improvement in their obsessional thinking, compulsive behavior, and weight (Gwirtsman et al. 1990). Fluoxetine has been shown to be beneficial for weight maintenance and in reducing obsessive-compulsive symptoms in some anorexia nervosa patients (Kaye et al. 1990; Weltzin et al. 1990). Although the obsessional and compulsive symptoms often associated with anorexia nervosa might be thought to respond to clomipramine, the only controlled study did not show this medication to be particularly effective for anorexia nervosa (Lacey and Crisp 1980).

Naltrexone. We have employed naltrexone in doses of 25–75 mg/day and have seen some improvement in some patients with chronic anorexia nervosa. (For more information see Luby et al. 1987.)

Monoamine oxidase inhibitors. Although the sparse literature dealing with the use of monoamine oxidase inhibitors (MAOIs) in anorexia nervosa is not encouraging (Kennedy and Walsh 1987), we have occasionally found patients with unremitting anorexia nervosa who have responded dramatically to tranylcypromine or phenelzine. The use of MAOIs is, of course, well studied and successful in bulimia nervosa. Cautions regarding diet and blood pressure are in order.

Other medications. Other medications that have had variable effects in our hands include cyproheptadine, for which some encouragement exists for patients with anorexia nervosa, restricting subtype, based on a double-blind placebo-controlled trial (Halmi et al. 1986), lithium (Gross et al. 1981; Hsu 1987a), benzodiazepines and other antianxiety agents (Andersen 1987), and, for patients with bulimia nervosa, anticonvulsants (Kaplan 1987), among others. Clearly, such medications should be used judiciously, only when medically safe, and under close supervision.

10. Use legal procedures or court-mandated interventions only in acutely life-threatening situations to save life and to demonstrate seriousness of intent and commitment of the treatment team to the patient.
11. Get consultation freely.
12. Avoid putting the patient through expensive and time-consuming treatment programs that are unlikely to effect any sustained improvement, and avoid instilling false hopes that are almost certain to be dashed. However, playing for time in the hope of some improvement may be justified, with different potentially helpful therapeutic trials offered serially. The point is not to fool the patient into thinking that the next intervention will work magic, but rather to keep extending to the patient in every way possible the idea that the clinician has the patient's interest and well-being at heart, is willing to try interventions

that have at least some reasonable chance of being helpful, and is not giving up all hope.

13. When all has been tried, and nothing seems to work, continue to treat the patient with compassion as a fully franchised human being, minimizing suffering and unrealistic expectations while maintaining a realistic yet not unduly pessimistic attitude.

Humanistic Principles of Care With Nonresponding Patients

Every experienced clinician will encounter some patients who, in spite of everyone's good intentions and the best currently available treatments, remain prisoners of their obsessions, compulsions, rituals, and impulses. Some are content to remain in their diminished state, not wanting to beat a dead horse but attempting to adapt and resign themselves to their conditions; others are willing to do anything including psychosurgery to alter their symptoms; and still others are so fatigued, debilitated, and demoralized that they would just as soon die. Some want everyone to simply leave them alone, even if in dire straits, because they feel that their families and caregivers are all making them feel worse, not better. Clinicians must ask themselves, morally and legally, when to agree with these patients, offering them an open door should they ever want to return and asking permission to keep in touch if only to remain informed about their conditions and courses.

Treatment guidelines for such patients parallel those for patients with any chronic, unremitting illness that may lead to premature death:

1. Primum non nocere. Clinicians should not be driven by passions of therapeutic zeal to deal with their frustrations and feelings of impotence by imposing potentially risky unorthodox (or orthodox) treatments on patients. Patients should give full informed consent for all interventions and should not be coerced into accepting half-baked treatment plans that are not likely to ultimately benefit them.

2. If the clinician and patient do plan to spend time together under these circumstances, the clinician should have a clear idea of what treatment sessions are supposed to accomplish and what they are unlikely to accomplish. For example, it may be unlikely that any pervasive characterological change or even significant behavioral change will occur. Some patients with intractable anorexia nervosa want to stay in treat-

ment to have close contact with someone who will listen to them in a compassionate way, without rejecting, taunting, or belittling them— someone to witness what they are going through and with whom to existentially share their experiences. Such a relationship may provide an important human touchstone for the patient, in which she can be brutally honest with herself and another person about what is transpiring in her life and thoughts, and through which she can feel less isolated. But no more than that. Clinicians must ask themselves if they feel personally equipped to honestly and unresentfully provide such services. Some clinicians feel that such work wastes their time or find that their negative countertransference toward such patients, whom they see as unmotivated, is so overwhelming that they cannot in good faith work constructively with them. Other clinicians approach these therapeutic tasks in the same spirit as working with dying patients who need close alliances and comforting. Certainly within the large tradition of medicine there is room and many precedents for such work.

3. If any unorthodox treatment is contemplated, extensive consultation and institutional review should be obtained as for a research protocol. Discussions and decisions should be documented in the medical record, and patients and their families should be asked to sign consents. If a physician wishes to use a novel medication for anorexia nervosa (i.e., one approved by the Food and Drug Administration but only for other indications), the physician may wish to request an IND (investigational new drug permission) for compassionate purposes from the Food and Drug Administration in Washington, D.C. Such permission is usually granted easily for compassionate purposes if there is a rationale and a treatment plan.

4. The patient should be kept comfortable without undue restriction (except that necessary to sustain life) or imposition. The basic necessities of life should always be available (i.e., food, clothing, and shelter).

5. If a patient is unable to bring herself to eat a regular diet and the clinical staff views the situation as acutely life threatening, the patient should be offered alternatives to regular food by mouth such as Ensure Plus, nasogastric feedings, or total parenteral nutrition. Several hospital programs of which I am aware routinely place nasogastric tubes in all their patients on admission, based on the rationale that the nasogastric tubes provide anorexia nervosa patients with a sense of security. The program directors' clinical observations have led them to believe that

patients become positively attached to the nasogastric tubes; indeed, many patients are described as experiencing the nasogastric tubes as transitional objects and are said to be reluctant to surrender them even after weight is regained. Although our own observations suggest that nasogastric tubes are rarely if ever indicated or needed routinely in the chronic care of the hospitalized patient with anorexia nervosa and I am unaware of any systematic studies to show the long-term benefits of such interventions, there are clearly at least some treatment programs that differ in their perceptions and experiences.

One patient with whom I'm acquainted, who is now in her 40s and has been ill for more than 10 years, has used an indwelling catheter for total parenteral nutrition (TPN) on an outpatient basis for more than 4 years, keeping the line anticoagulated and intermittently administering TPN to herself to supplement the maximum 300 kcal/day she is able to permit herself to take as food by mouth. The TPN program was the patient's own idea. After she required six admissions to general hospitals for severe malnutrition and electrolyte imbalance in the 2 years prior to having the indwelling catheter placed, her internist, a nephrologist, reluctantly agreed to the procedure. The patient actively lobbied for the indwelling catheter program and had to convince a reluctant vascular surgeon to place the catheter. The patient has not required any further hospitalizations since the catheter was inserted.

6. In the event of acute, imminently life-threatening starvation due to food refusal, the staff may institute nasogastric feedings temporarily on a good Samaritan basis while seeking legal conservatorship for ongoing treatment. In such cases, acute intervention, with treatment of both malnutrition and depression with or without conscious suicidality, may avert the threatened death and is therefore warranted and justified. Here the procedure is best thought of as a short-term bridge that will hopefully lead to a situation in which the patient is at least less death prone.

It must be stressed that without the patient's eventual cooperation plans using nasogastric tubes or TPN setups are at best usually short-lived and are ultimately likely to fail. I have been told of several patients who simply pulled out TPN lines that were placed against their will. However, I have also seen cases in which patients who absolutely refused to eat were forced to accept one or two nasogastric tube feedings after which they acquiesced to taking food by mouth.

7. From the legal and economic point of view, treatment for the patient who chronically refuses food and seems to be constantly walking on

the edge in a flirtation with death resembles the treatment for patients with other chronically suicidal psychiatric disorders. In this regard several realities intrude. First, few facilities are able to keep such patients hospitalized indefinitely, and few patients and families have the means to pay for such prolonged care. Second, aggressive and assaultive treatment for these patients may prolong life but not often improve its quality. Drawn out suicides, subintentional suicides, and dying processes can continue for years.

To begin with, clinicians should not actively assist suicidal behavior. In fact, this is rarely necessary because the truly and unambivalently suicidal patient will find the means to kill herself, even in the hospital. Of course, few clinicians want their patients to die, especially in the hospital. However, compassionate clinicians will understand that for some patients the pain of continuing life is more than the patient can bear and the ordeal of struggling against all odds is too terrible a price to pay for continuing a miserable existence. In this situation, as with patients suffering from terminal cancer or acquired immunodeficiency syndrome (AIDS), the family and treating staff are often unable to accept the "rational" nature of the patient's desires to die. In these instances, therapeutic work may entail preparing the family and staff by increasing their compassionate understanding for the possibility or even likelihood of a fatal outcome and, in the case of death, dealing with family and staff in postdeath intervention around the same issues.

Even more difficult situations are those in which suicidally ambivalent patients repetitively engage in suicidal or subsuicidal self-destructive acts—performed in such a manner that they are very visible and obvious to the family and/or staff—so the family or staff must continuously rescue the patient. To make matters worse, patients rescued in such situations are often (at least on the surface) petulant and ungrateful for having been saved. These games can lead to death—in some instances the result of a patient's miscalculations—as when staff members inadvertently fail to recognize that a patient has taken a lethal overdose right under their noses. In any event, staff are likely to become progressively infuriated at chronically suicidal patients for placing these responsibilities on them. Therapeutic strategies in such instances require understanding and labeling of the repetitive games and, in addition to attempting to help patients deal more adaptively with the underlying causes for their angry acts, attempting to construct behavioral interventions that reduce patients' secondary gains from these activities.

8. Keep the long view. For reasons as yet unexplainable, symptoms and resistances, even for very chronically ill patients, may change or evolve toward healthier states over time. If the clinician maintains a good relationship with the patient throughout, without alienating her via countertransference anger, derision, denigration, or other subtle attacks on her self-esteem, small changes may be slowly guided in a positive direction. For example, even though anorexia nervosa with concurrent bulimia nervosa is generally regarded as bad prognostically, the new appearance of some bulimic features as a patient with anorexia nervosa, restricting subtype, starts to regain weight may represent a phase that is sometimes seen on the road to improvement (Hamburg et al. 1989). Such shifts may be framed for the patient and her family as potential indicators of improvement and not necessarily as changes for the worse. Similarly, resistances to treatment may shift over time and result in greater interest and participation in specific new treatments or even in treatment in general (Goldner 1989).

Legal Tools

Legal tools available to clinicians and patients' families vary from jurisdiction to jurisdiction and from courtroom to courtroom (Dresser 1984). The basic legal interventions concerning involuntary interventions apply. First, for acute life-saving situations most states accept two physician signatures in good Samaritan actions. Second, most jurisdictions allow brief involuntary incarcerations, for example for 72 hours with subsequent extensions based on legal hearings of 14–90 days, for treatment of mental disorders in the case of patients who are acutely suicidal, acutely homicidal, or gravely disabled, the latter defined as inable to provide oneself with food, clothing, and shelter. Some judges have allowed the chronically ill anorexic patient's inability to provide herself with food as grounds for ruling continued grave disability. Longer guardianships with judgments of incompetence for such patients have been agreed to by some judges but not by others.

Most clinicians generally endorse the use of involuntary force feeding (which may require legal sanction), when the patient's life is in danger or when the effects of starvation are presumed to be so severe that they seriously distort the patient's ability to make treatment decisions.

Because patients with anorexia nervosa often persistently hold beliefs regarding their nutritional status and weight that resemble delusions seen in schizophrenia or psychotic mood disorders, they may sometimes be judged by the courts to be psychotically suicidal or gravely disabled.

However, given the propensity of most mental health courts and of much public opinion to preserve patients' liberties regardless of the presence of severe mental illness, even seriously disabled patients with anorexia nervosa may successfully contest attempts to treat them involuntarily. In one memorable case, I testified on behalf of a family and staff attempting to get permission to treat a woman who was seriously malnourished but who refused treatment. She demanded to be released and requested a jury trial on the basis of habeas corpus. She had been admitted weighing 47 pounds, and with the benefit of those legal means at the hospital's disposal—first a 72-hour and then 14-day involuntary hold—she was treated involuntarily so that by the time she reached court her weight was 56 pounds. The judge and many of the associated attorneys were quite sympathetic to the hospital's arguments, but the jury ruled that the patient should be set free. In their opinion it was within her rights to weigh whatever she wanted to weigh, even if it meant an untimely death.

Countertransference Issues and Management

Several common countertransference problems have been mentioned. Clinicians may feel narcissistically challenged by a bedeviling clinical problem, frustrated and angered by the patient's seemingly obstinate and oppositional behavior and failure to progress, blameful of the patient for not getting better, and progressively therapeutically impotent and disengaged. The snydrome resembles "chronic staffrenia"—described among clinicians working with chronic schizophrenic patients—which occurs when the clinicians' therapeutic tools are not up to the challenges and their therapeutic expectations are too high (Ludwig 1971).

Management of countertransference requires that clinicians constantly self-assess their attitudes toward these patients, that they seek frequent consultation and supervision in their care, and that hospital staffs meet regularly and air their opinions of and experiences with these difficult patients to get validation or redirection regarding their feelings and attitudes.

Talking With Patients and Their Families

The challenge of talking about prognosis and treatment with patients and their families who are struggling with chronic eating disorders requires clinicians to confront the difficult tasks of integrating a realistic assessment of likely outcome while providing some degree of hope and comfort, all based on a great deal of uncertainty. It is clinically unsound and humanistically untenable to offer either undue optimism or harsh, unfiltered pessimism. For example, as a defense against the frustrations of therapeutic impotence, clinicians may opt for a self-protective going-in position of therapeutic hopelessness and nihilism.

One self-protective strategy clinicians sometimes use in these situations has been called "hanging crepe," a reference to the black crepe hung over coffins in years gone by, essentially a strategy in which the clinician opts to tell the patient and family the worst likely scenario—that the patient will die. In this way the physician is seen as a wise prognosticator if the patient doesn't improve and as a magical healer if the patient does miraculously improve. Some clinicians have justified presenting patients and their families with bluntly described worst-case scenarios as the most likely outcome by suggesting that this presentation occasionally provokes paradoxical oppositional reactions in patients. In these instances, theoretically, the patient will refuse to do badly just to spite the physician who has predicted the patient's poor outcome. However, proof that such paradoxical approaches have ever been therapeutically successful with chronically ill eating-disordered patients is entirely lacking. There is even a dearth of good anecdotal reports. The danger of hanging crepe lies in potentially depriving the patient and her family of any shreds of hope that might facilitate improvement.

In my opinion, the best clinical approach in these situations is to provide the patient and her family with carefully presented, empirically accepted data (i.e., what has been published in reputable peer-reviewed journals), filtered through the perspective of reality-bound optimism, and further couched in statements regarding our considerable ignorance and limited prognostic abilities. Such prognostications should always contain broad statements that include the possibility for change. To support these statements, clinicians can point to cases where change for the better occurred for poorly understood reasons even after years of chronicity and poor functioning (Ratnasuriya et al. 1989), to the fact that many patients with chronic eating disorders manage to survive for years on incredibly meager intakes, and to the scientific advances that are rapidly producing more effective treatments not only for eating disorders but for associated symptoms such as depression, anxiety, obsessions, and compulsions. Families in particular also have to know that it may not be the worst thing in the world for a patient not to be in treatment, at least for a while.

However, when the patient, or more likely the family, appears to be hoping against hope for unrealistic improvements, the clinician should—without abandoning hope—gently educate them to the facts as we know them over whatever period of time is necessary for them to assimilate and incorporate the information. They may benefit from meeting with other patients and families who have been struggling with chronic eating disorders, through family-involved local and national eating disorder self-help organizations such as those listed in Table 9–2, and through association with family-oriented self-help organizations such as the Alliance for the Mentally Ill that deal with all types of chronic and severe mental illnesses. By resetting their expectations, patients and their families may be able to establish more realistic plans and accommodations, and perhaps live together with less tension and bitterness than would otherwise be the case. In the face of severe, chronic disabling symptoms, we as clinicians should do whatever we can under the circumstances to sustain the highest quality of life possible.

Table 9–2. Self-help organizations for eating disorders

1. American Anorexia/Bulimia Association, Inc.
   418 East 76th Street
   New York, NY 10021
2. Anorexia Nervosa and Related Eating Disorders (ANRED)
   PO Box 5102
   Eugene, OR 97405
3. Anorexia Nervosa and Associated Disorders (ANAD)
   PO Box 271
   Highland Park, IL 60035
4. Bulimia Anorexia Self-Help (BASH)
   PO Box 39903
   St. Louis, MO 63139-8903
5. National Anorexic Aid Society (NAAS)
   PO Box 29651
   Columbus, Ohio 43229

References

Agras WE: Eating Disorders: Management of Obesity, Bulimia and Anorexia Nervosa. Oxford, England, Pergamon, 1987

American Psychiatric Association: Diagnostic and Statistical Manual of Mental Disorders, 3rd Edition, Revised. Washington, DC, American Psychiatric Association, 1987

Andersen AE: Uses and potential misuses of antianxiety agents in the treatment of anorexia nervosa and bulimia nervosa, in The Role of Drug Treatments for Eating Disorders. Edited by Garfinkel PE, Garner DM. New York, Brunner/Mazel, 1987

Burns T, Crisp AH: Outcome of anorexia nervosa in males. Br J Psychiatry 145:319–325, 1984

Casper R: Personality features of women with good outcome from restricting anorexia nervosa. Psychsom Med 52:156–170, 1990

Crisp AH: Anorexia Nervosa Let Me Be. New York, Grune & Stratton, 1980

Crisp AH, Harding B, McGuinness B: Anorexia nervosa: psychoneurotic characteristics of parents: relationship to prognosis. J Psychosom Res 18:167–173, 1974

Dally P: Anorexia Nervosa. New York, Grune & Stratton, 1969

Dally P, Gomez J, Isaacs AJ: Anorexia Nervosa. London, Heinemann, 1979

Dresser R: Legal and policy considerations in treatment of anorexia nervosa patients. International Journal of Eating Disorders 3:43–51, 1984

Fairburn CG: A cognitive behavioral approach to the treatment of bulimia. Psychol Med 11:707–711, 1981

Fairburn CG, Kirk J, O'Connor M, et al: Prognostic factors in bulimia nervosa. Br J Clin Psychol 26:223–224, 1987

Fallon BA, Walsh BT, Sadik C, et al: A 4.5-year follow-up study of inpatient bulimics. Paper presented at the Fourth International Conference on Eating Disorders, New York, April 1990

Garfinkel PE, Garner DM: Anorexia Nervosa: A Multidimensional Perspective. New York, Brunner/Mazel, 1982

Garfinkel PE, Garner DM (eds): The Role of Drug Treatment for Eating Disorders. New York, Brunner/Mazel, 1988

Garner DM, Garfinkel PE (eds): Handbook of Psychotherapy for Anorexia Nervosa and Bulimia. New York, Guilford, 1985

Glieck J: Chaos: The Making of a New Science. New York, Penguin, 1987

Goldner E: Treatment refusal in anorexia nervosa. International Journal of Eating Disorders 8:297–306, 1989

Gross HA, Ebert M, Faden V, et al: A double-blind controlled trial of lithium carbonate in primary anorexia nervosa. J Clin Psychopharmacol 1:376–381, 1981

Gwirtsman HE, Guze BH, Yager J, et al: Treatment of anorexia nervosa with fluoxetine: an open clinical trial. J Clin Psychiatry 51:378–382, 1990

Hall A, Slim E, Hawker F, et al: Anorexia nervosa: long-term outcome in 50 female patients. Br J Psychiatry 145:407–413, 1984

Halmi KA, Eckert E, LaDu TJ, et al: Anorexia nervosa: treatment efficacy of cyproheptadine and amitriptyline. Arch Gen Psychiatry 43:177–181, 1986

Hamburg P, Herzog DB, Brotman AW, et al: The treatment resistant eating disordered patient. Psychiatric Annals 19:494–499, 1989

Hamsher K de S, Halmi KA, Benton AL: Prediction of outcome in anorexia nervosa from neuropsychological status. Psychiatry Res 4:79–88, 1981

Hornyak LM, Baker EK (eds): Experiential Therapies for Eating Disorders. New York, Guilford, 1989

Hsu LKG: Outcome of anorexia nervosa: a review of the literature 1954–1978. Arch Gen Psychiatry 37:1040–1046, 1980

Hsu LKG: Lithium in the treatment of eating disorders, in The Role of Drug Treatments for Eating Disorders. Edited by Garfinkel PE, Garner DM. New York, Brunner/Mazel, 1987a, pp 90–95

Hsu LKG: Outcome and treatment effects, in Handbook of Eating Disorders: Part 1: Anorexia and Bulimia Nervosa. Edited by Beumont PJV, Burrows GD, Casper RC. New York, Elsevier, 1987b, pp 371–378

Hsu LKG: The outcome of anorexia nervosa: a reappraisal. Psychological Medicine 18:807–812, 1988

Hsu LKG, Crisp AH, Harding B: Outcome of anorexia nervosa. Lancet 1:61–65, 1979

Judd FK, Norman TR, Burrows GD: Pharmacotherapy in the treatment of anorexia nervosa and bulimia nervosa, in Handbook of Eating Disorders: Part 1: Anorexia and Bulimia Nervosa. Edited by Beumont PJV, Burrows GD, Casper RC. New York, Elsevier, 1987, pp 361–370

Kaplan AS: Anticonvulsant treatment of eating disorders, in The Role of Drug Treatments for Eating Disorders. Edited by Garfinkel PE, Garner DM. New York, Brunner/Mazel, 1987, pp 96–123

Kaye WH, Weltzin TE, Hsu LKG, et al: New evidence suggesting that anorexia nervosa is related to obsessive compulsive disorder. Paper presented at the Fourth International Conference on Eating Disorders, New York, April 1990

Kennedy S, Walsh BT: Drug therapy for eating disorders: monoamine oxidase inhibitors, in The Role of Drug Treatments for Eating Disorders. Edited by Garfinkel PE, Garner DM. New York, Brunner/Mazel, 1987, pp 3–35

Lacey JH, Crisp AH: Hunger, food intake and weight: the impact of clomipramine on a refeeding anorexia nervosa. Postgrad Med J 56:79–85, 1980

Luby ED, Marrazzi MA, Kinsie J: Case reports: treatment of chronic anorexia nervosa with opiate blockade. J Clin Psychopharmacol 7:52–53, 1987

Ludwig AM: Treating the Treatment Failures: The Challenge of Chronic Schizophrenia. New York, Grune & Stratton, 1971

Mitchell JE, Hatsukami D, Pyle RL, et al: The bulimia syndrome: course of the illness and associated problems. Compr Psychiatry 27:165–170, 1986a

Mitchell JE, Davis L, Goff G, et al: A follow-up study of patients with bulimia. International Journal of Eating Disorders 5:441–450, 1986b

Morgan HG, Russell GFM: Value of family background and clinical features as predictors of long-term outcome in anorexia nervosa: four year follow-up study of 41 patients. Psychol Med 5:355–371, 1975

Morgan HG, Purgold J, Wolbourne J: Management and outcome in anorexia nervoas: a standardized prognosis study. Br J Psychiatry 143:282–287, 1983

Norring C: Psychological diagnosis and prognosis in eating disorders: ego functioning and the eating disorders inventory (doctoral thesis, Department of Psychiatry, Uppsala, Sweden). Acta Universitatis Upsaliensis 207:1–56, 1989

Pope HG Jr, McElroy SL, Keck PE, et al: Long-term pharmacotherapy of bulimia nervosa. J Clin Psychopharmacol 9:385–386, 1989

Ratnasuriya RH, Eisler I, Szmukler GI, et al: Outcome and prognostic factors after 20 years of anorexia nervosa, in The Psychology of Human Eating Disorders. Edited by Schneider L, Cooper S, Halmi K. New York, New York Academy of Sciences, 1989, pp 567–568

Russell GFM: Bulimia nervosa: an ominous variant of anorexia nervosa. Psychol Med 9:429–448, 1979

Russell GFM, Szmukler GI, Dare C, et al: An evaluation of family therapy in anorexia nervosa and bulimia nervosa. Arch Gen Psychiatry 44:1047–1056, 1987

Schwartz DM, Thompson MG: Do anorectics get well? current research and future needs. Am J Psychiatry 138:319–323, 1981

Sohlberg S, Norring C, Holmgren S, et al: Impulsivity and long-term prognosis of psychiatric patients with anorexia nervosa/bulimia nervosa. J Nerv Ment Dis 177:249–258, 1989

Steinhausen HC, Glanville K: Follow-up studies of anorexia nervosa: a review of research findings. Psychol Med 13:239–249, 1983

Swift WJ, Ritholz M, Kalin NH, et al: A follow-up study of thirty hospitalized bulimics. Psychosom Med 49:45–55, 1987

Szmukler G, Eisler I, Russell GFM, et al: Anorexia nervosa, parental "expressed emotion" and dropping out of treatment. Br J Psychiatry 147:265–271, 1985

Theander S: Anorexia nervosa: a psychiatirc investigations of 94 female patients. Acta Psychiatr Scand 21:1–194, 1970

Theander S: Outcome and prognosis in anorexia nervosa and bulimia: some results of previous investigations, compared with those of a Swedish long-term study. J Psychiatr Res 19:493–508, 1985

Tolstrup K, Brinch M, Isagen T, et al: Long-term outcome of 151 cases of anorexia nervosa. Acta Psychol Scand 71:380–387, 1985

Weltzin TE, Hsu LKG, Kaye WH: An open trial of fluoxetine in anorexia nervosa: maintenance of body weight and reduction of obsessional symptoms. Paper presented at the Fourth International Conference on Eating Disorders, New York, April 1990

Wilson GT, Rossiter E, Lindholm L, et al: Cognitive-behavioral treatment of bulimia nervosa: a controlled evaluation. Behav Res Ther 24:227–288, 1986

Yager J, Landsverk J, Edelstein CK: A 20-month follow-up study of 628 women with eating disorders, I: course and severity. Am J Psychiatry 144:1172–1177, 1987a

Yager J, Landsverk J, Edelstein CK, et al: A 20-month follow-up study of 628 women with eating disorders, II: course of associated symptoms and associated clinical features. International Journal of Eating Disorders 7:503–513, 1987b

Afterword

*T*he material presented in this book undoubtedly strikes a familiar chord with clinicians who work closely with eating-disordered patients. Open acknowledgement that a large number, if not the majority, of patients with eating disorders suffer from complicated multifaceted (rather than easy to manage unidimensional) conditions; that their co-morbid substance use, mood, personality, and medical conditions test the inventiveness and skill of even the most experienced clinicians; and that many of these conditions simply don't respond to quick fixes may be useful for clinicians who are new to the field, to patients and their families, and, perhaps, to third-party payers.

This information may help clinicians engage in more thorough and comprehensive treatment planning, taking into account the "total patient." Patients and families dealing with complicated conditions and armed with this knowledge may better prepare themselves for the likelihood that many eating disorder conditions will not go away with brief treatment. And, if they are serious about wanting to foster the levels of clinical improvement achievable even with today's limited knowledge, third-party payers also need to realize that adequate reimbursement for the types and durations of treatment necessary for these complex cases will be required. Otherwise, patients will simply be discharged prematurely and partially treated, guaranteed to result in their returning with additional episodes in a revolving door of psychiatric care.

There is much yet to be learned of the etiology, pathogenesis, and treatment of eating disorders and of the frequent concurrent conditions described in this book. As with many other psychiatric and medical problems, it is likely that having the additional burden of concurrent psychiatric and medical problems increases an individual's vulnerability to a new disorder, so that the adolescent with additional loading of mood, personality, substance abuse, and certain physical health problems may well be more susceptible in the right social and family environment to developing an eating disorder. At the same time, advances in our understanding of all the concurrent problems may be brought to bear in alleviating our patients' burdens. We may hope to see the day when not only better specific treatments for eating disorders will be available, but also when better treatment for many of the prominent concurrent disorders, such as mood and personality disorders, help reduce patients' overall disability and thereby improve their chances of recovering from the eating disorders as well.

Eating Disorders Clinic Medication Visit Progress Note

Part 1 (To be completed by patient)   Date of visit:_____/_____/_____
                                                        MO   DY   YR

In the past week, how often have you been:

	More than once a day	Once a day	Several times this week	Once this week	Not at all
a. binge eating?	5	4	3	2	1
b. vomiting?	5	4	3	2	1
c. using laxatives?	5	4	3	2	1
d. having sleep problems?	5	4	3	2	1
e. exercising?	5	4	3	2	1
average hours/day	_____				
f. fasting or eating 600 calories or less per day?	N/A	4	3	2	1

On average, during the past week:

	Seriously	Moderately	Mildly	Not At All
a. How depressed have you been?	4	3	2	1
b. How anxious have you been?	4	3	2	1

	No Change	Gained	Lost	Didn't Weight
Has your weight changed?	4	3	2	1

If you know, write in your current weight. _____
                                                    1

How many nights of medication have you missed this past week? _____
                                                                          1

If you take your medication more than once a day, how many doses have you missed this past week?

_____

Please write in the name of the medication you are taking. _____
How many tablets do you take? _____ When? _____
What side effects, if any, are you experiencing (please list)?

_____

_____

Over the past month, how much would you say your symptoms have interfered with your life in the following areas? (Please check all that apply.)

	Family	Social	Work	School
a. Doesn't apply to me	_____	_____	_____	_____
b. A tremendous amount	_____	_____	_____	_____
c. A substantial amount	_____	_____	_____	_____
d. Moderate amount	_____	_____	_____	_____
e. Minimal amount	_____	_____	_____	_____
f. Not at all	_____	_____	_____	_____

This week, what are your most important concerns? _____

_____

_____

Part 2 (To be completed by clinician)

The Beck score is: _____

Mental status examination abnormalities:
(Cite problems only with dress/hygiene/relating; speech/psychomotor activity; mood/affect; suicidality; thought process; thought content; altered perceptions.)

_____

_____

_____

Other abnormalities:

_____

_____

Assessment:

1. Assess severity of associated alcohol/drug abuse:

   _____

   _____

2. Assess affective state:

   _____

   _____

3. Assess severity of bulimia: frequency of binge eating _____

                               Vomiting _____

                               Using laxatives _____

   _____

   _____

4. Other assessment:

   _____

   _____

   _____

Medications:

	Medication 1	Medication 2	Medication 3	Medication 4
Current drug name:				
Dosage:				
Signature:				
New plan name:				
Dosage:				
Signature:				
Prescription today:				

Other notes:

_____

_____

_____

_____

Date of next appointment: ____/____/____   Physician's Name: _____, M.D.

Physician's Signature: _____   Date: ____/____/____
                                                 MO   DY   YR

Index